THE ANTARCTICA OF LOVE

SARA STRIDSBERG

THE ANTARCTICA
OF LOVE

Translated from the Swedish by
Deborah Bragan-Turner

MACLEHOSE PRESS
QUERCUS · LONDON

First published as *Kärlekens Antarktis*
by Albert Bonniers Förlag, 2018
First published in Great Britain in 2021 by

MacLehose Press
An imprint of Quercus Publishing Ltd
Carmelite House
50 Victoria Embankment
London EC4Y 0DZ
An Hachette UK company

The cost of this translation was defrayed by a subsidy from
the Swedish Arts Council, gratefully acknowledged.

ISBN (HB) 978 1 52940 237 7
ISBN (TPB) 978 1 52941 588 9
ISBN (Ebook) 978 1 52940 238 4

Designed and typeset in Minion by Libanus Press Ltd
Printed and bound in Great Britain by Clays Ltd, Elcograf S.p.A.

Papers used by MacLehose Press are from well-managed forests and
other responsible sources.

CREATION

We were in the forest at this point. In a kind of twilight, but with no sun, a brownish rainy gloom settling over the scene. Could I have rung someone? No, I couldn't, because even if there had been someone to ring, time would have run out. Now there was just the fading, submerged light and the huge trees and giant raindrops falling from the branches like the tears of grotesquely large beings and the two of us, he and I, and the feeling so intense of being the only ones left in the world, a feeling no reality could have changed, no cars we encountered on the roads, no lit-up telephone boxes we drove past, no voice on the radio gently purring, preaching, intoning like a devotional chant. The sound brought little scrapbook pictures to my mind. Of the Virgin Mary with the great menacing angel. Of Mary with the chubby little baby that was wheeling around at her breast in every painting, without wings but still beyond gravity's pull. And finally of Mary alone, without her child, when he was gone from the earth.

I lay on the forest floor looking at the dark tree roots steadily pushing down into the lakewater. Everything was so still even the most gradual of movements showed, the treetops swaying in slow motion high above, the insects crawling on the underside of every flower and the drops of water falling from the branches and breaking in a slowed-down splash against the earth, miniature pearls of reflection travelling through the air in an infinitely slow-moving arc. And now it was cold, and urine and blood and faeces ran down my legs. I was thinking that the trees must be suspended between man and God, stretching their crowns up to the heavens, their roots like dragons' talons clawing into the earth where the dead reside and where soon I would be.

It was too late to ask for help now, too late for praying, time was irretrievably up. He said: "Get on your knees." And I knelt in the black grass. He said: "I'm going to blindfold you now. It'll be easier that way," he said. "That's good," I said, wondering which of us it would be easier for. "Now I'm going to strangle you and you won't be able to say anything else."

"Do it," I said. "I have nothing to say in any case."

And now he cuts what is left of my body into seven pieces and stuffs the rest into two white suitcases. He throws my head into a slurry pit that has a surface the same pink colour as vomit. It is not very far from the lake, down a little path through the wood; he has worked everything out on an old orienteering map. He stands for a while staring out over the thick bubbling mass before he drops it carefully into the sludge. Green and black flies and shimmering dragonflies zigzag across the surface as my head sinks slowly to the bottom, not very deep, just a few metres. My dark hair spreads out like a black parachute above me until my head comes to rest where no-one will ever find it, for it will soon be eaten away by chemicals. That picture keeps coming back to me, my hair in the water, reaching upwards as my head strikes the bottom, before settling.

*

And then? He walks back along the path. The sun is on its way down on the far side of the lake. A gentle rain falls on the forest. I have always loved rain. Always – how brief that was. How brief life was.

I mean to let your world be, but suddenly I find myself looking in again. It has such beauty from a distance, the fragile, iridescent blue of the atmosphere surrounding your planet, slightly impaired but still there. Beneath it there are clouds drifting slowly over the sky that is yours and bare autumn trees reaching out for sunlight, and further down still the black water streaming into Stockholm from the sea, glistening dark and oily between the islands, just the odd fallen leaf dotted on the surface. A world as motionless as an old oil painting at the National Museum. Only when you come close do you see there is movement down there, the aeroplanes and birds in their sky, human beings on their earth, worms crawling through the flowers and the eyes of the dead.

I try to concentrate on things that don't hurt. A child walking down the street, holding on to a balloon, unable to stop looking up all the time at its wondrousness. I watch rabbits playing in the grass at night outside the major hospitals. I often watch the light, at it constantly changing like refractions in a kaleidoscope. It affords me a kind of solace. Sometimes I watch two people making love; it is bad manners, there is no doubt, but nobody notices I am there and I think there is something beautiful in the way they cling to one another. I often look into hospital wards when a child comes flying in from eternity and alights at her mother's breast. I always love that moment when everything is still perfectly intact between a mother and her child. The other day, at first light, I saw a youth stop to help an old woman who had collapsed in a drunken stupor in the park at Björns Trädgård. When he lifted her up from the ground, she draped her arms around his neck like a child who had fallen asleep. Before he left her, they shared a cigarette and laughed about something I couldn't hear. But I saw the fear in her lacklustre blue eyes gradually give way to a faint glow; I saw her worn-out old soul light up in the first rays of sun. I avoid looking at evil wherever possible. I have already seen evil.

Someday I too will be indifferent to what happens on earth, like everyone else. But that takes time, and there are so many voices not yet hushed. A distant hubbub from professors and criminologists and private investigators and journalists. They say you die three times. The first time for me was when my heart stopped beating beneath his hands by the lake, and the second was when what was left of me was lowered into the ground in front of Ivan and Raksha at Solna Church. The third time will be the last time my name is spoken on earth. And so I am waiting for it to happen. I wish all the voices would hush soon. I don't like hearing my name. It crawls like insects in the place where my heart once was.

If I were to say who did it, would the voices be silent then? I don't think they would, and no-one would believe me anyway. And it is so difficult to distinguish the light from the dark, and even harder when you are alone and time has ceased to exist, and space too. So I make some attempt to understand the difference. I have always confused love with insanity, heaven with death. I believed for a long time that the drugs came from the powers on high as compensation for my little brother. I don't believe that anymore. My little brother and I were blind alleys. Eskil walked into the river when we were children and didn't come back and, much later, I walked out into the immensity of the night to find him. Although sometimes I think I only entered the darkness because I had nowhere else to go. Maybe I knew I would never find Eskil there, in those endless labyrinthine nights, but it didn't matter, the other world was already closed to me. In any event, our family line stops here. That last part isn't really true, our family carries on with Valle and Solveig, even though they don't know where they come from. Sometimes I see Raksha's features in them both, appearing in their faces like a fleeting ripple in the water.

It is strange that I fantasise so much about Solveig. I don't know her and I never have. All I have is those two hours on the maternity ward when she was a tiny bundle of warmth in my arms. But it is easier to think about her than to think about Valle, because I never did her any harm. I kept her safe by making sure she would never need to be with me. For Solveig I did the only thing I could have done, even if Shane could never forgive me for it.

We were in the forest. The sky above was criss-crossed with black branches and I told myself they were lightning cracks leading into another world, and this was the world I was travelling towards now. "Here I am, God," I whispered. "Help me God, whoever you are."

In the forest, where we were now, the only sound was of flowing water, water running everywhere, out of the lake, the sky, the treetops. I had that vague reeling sensation of watching everything from above, as if I were suspended up there like a fluttering angel. All the laws of vision had collapsed, only fragments of broken images through which I viewed the world: his back in a light-coloured anorak, the back of a large head, pale freckles covering hands that squeezed a girl's neck on the grass. I saw the girl resting there against the earth's dark membrane, and it looked as though the ground would swallow up both him and her as he clung on to her like a giant beetle. "I only want to be close to you," he whispered to her, and I heard it even though I was floating some distance above. I wasn't dead yet, but I was already floating. And then my hearing slipped away. I was glad, now we were moving within a sphere of complete silence. Without the sense of hearing, it was easier to see, as if the world became clearer and the colours more intense. I thought maybe the world had been filled with water because everything was happening so slowly now, time slackened its pace, the gods held their breath.

*

Out of the treetops and flowers flew demonic images, all of them featuring me. I didn't want them. Grimy frames of film, momentarily lit up and immediately extinguished, they dropped from the trees like blazing flypapers and I shut my eyes, but the images seemed to be projected inside me and the whole of me was alight with these pictures. There I was, sitting with Valle at my breast, looking down at him. There was Nanna cycling through the first snowfall, before the filmstrip snapped and the forest came back. And now the man forced his way into the girl lying on the ground, me, into the dark opening between her legs, his fingers interlaced like a corset around her throat. A storm howled inside me and maybe that was why it was so silent outside. I saw a single butterfly teetering in the black grass beside the girl and the man. It must have been a snow butterfly because it was white. Were there such things as snow butterflies? Did butterflies exist? Did the world still exist?

Yes, it did exist. A string of vertebrae existed, large square pearls that formed a backbone that had once been mine and now was broken. There were sinews that had severed. There was my windpipe, through which air still passed back and forth, used air pushed up out of his lungs and down into mine, a mixture of carbon dioxide and fire and hunger for blood. And these lungs that had been mine were filled with black blood. A body existed, on top of mine, and it was so heavy it didn't feel human; but human it was, this was what humans did, and this body crushed me against the earth and soon I would be earth myself, dark and cold and full of writhing worms. I had wished for something that would pin me down to the earth, a weight, a rope pulled tight across my wrists and ankles, something that eventually would hold me down and stop me. But this was not what I had wished for. Not this forest, not this hunter. Or maybe this was exactly what I had been waiting for all the time. Perhaps I had always hoped for a way out of the world, the black hole suddenly opening to devour me.

I saw a cloud collide with the crown of a tree and be rent apart. I saw the pupil in an eye quiver like a compass needle. I saw the little tree that Raksha had planted by the river when I was born and it must have been uprooted in a winter storm, for now it was hanging upside down between heaven and earth. I saw its branches growing downwards to the black soil while its roots reached up for the light of the sky. The branches made me think of veins in a placenta or arteries filled with a deadly black liquid as they grasped for the depths of the earth. I saw Valle in front of me. He was crawling around by himself at Sergels Torg wearing only a little nappy and high above hovered a bird of prey, waiting for the square to empty of people. And I saw myself, sitting at a table at Burger King, waiting for a dealer, as the huge bird dived out of the sky and took off again with my child in its claws.

And when the air abruptly returned, I dropped back down to earth, to the perspective of the slithering ground. I saw the world from below, I saw the sky skating from one fixed point to another and the light falling in golden shafts through the treetops. He had loosened his grip for a second and the world had come back with its choppy, broken light, the butterflies and the drooping dandelions, and then he took out a knife and it gleamed like a little mirror in his hand. A butcher's knife or a hunting knife and I am sure only the Devil would have answered me if I had knelt in prayer. Just before death, when fear and pain are overwhelming, the quarry is stunned. As it is for animals, so it is for human beings. When it is too late to defend yourself and futile to try in any case, the terror and despair transmute into a gentle anaesthetic fluid that unfurls like a vapour through the bloodstream.

Once, in the beginning, it had been like that with the drugs as well. When the bubbling brown liquid shot through my veins, something happened, something akin to this last moment of my fate at his hands, when everything suddenly stilled and I stopped fighting back. As the bewitching fluid swept through me, so vanished the feeling of being inferior and unworthy, of being nothing more than a piece of vermin to be eliminated. Because when this world holds no hope, your body goes numb and fear vanishes, as if the fear that has preyed upon you, day and night, was never there, and you float in the moment before death, like a patch of sky.

Even though I was so young and at the very start of something, I had always had the powerful sense of being at an end, standing right by a precipice I was about to slide off. Rubbish, feeble, weak and useless, a Friday-afternoon dud amidst that mass of fifties' girls the world didn't need, who would disappear one day without trace, missed by no-one.

We were on our way through the trees and the last stretch of the path was narrow and stony before the forest finally opened out to a lake lying before us like a shining mirror. Did I think it was my grave, that I would die in the water?

The rain was falling on the trees and the trees had stood there for a hundred years or more, their realm a slow and silent one. And they saw everything happening in the human world but couldn't intervene. If I had begged to stay and make one last call in that telephone box just before we reached the silver lake, I would have stood inside the misty panes of glass, a large black receiver in my hand, with choking, rattling breaths, and snot and saliva and tears dribbling from my nose and mouth, and fear like an icy claw around my spine. And if the rings had suddenly been interrupted by Raksha picking up in Svartviksvägen – according to the map still no more than a few kilometres away, in reality separated from me by a whole universe – I would probably just have dropped the receiver and left it dangling at my feet with her voice calling out. For what would I say? "Mamma, Mamma, I don't know where I am."

A long time ago, when I was still a child and was making a call to Raksha from a telephone box outside the church by the river, my hand clamped around the large black receiver as if it were life itself, it seemed as though I would never breathe again if I didn't hear her voice. Raksha's heartbeat was in that telephone receiver and nowhere else. She had left and gone to Stockholm and Ivan was sinking deeper into his loneliness on the kitchen sofa. And all I had was her voice living in the telegraph wires running under the ground all the way down from Stockholm, where she was clattering along in a metro carriage far below the city in which she and I would later live without Ivan. But this time it was too late. This time there was no way out. The raindrops running down the windows were as large as globs of spittle sliding down the streaked glass with unnatural restraint until they hit the ground and disintegrated.

In the summertime this formidable, fusty space was so vast and monstrous, and these trees so primeval where they stood, their crowns heavy with water. In the car he sat absolutely still, as though he was listening to a voice within him that drowned out the radio music, and he had no thought that I might dash into the forest and flee. The headlights illuminated the world of rain around us and everything apart from the two of us was swallowed up by the creeping mist: the city, the people and the future that no longer concerned me. He switched the radio off and all that could be heard was the slow sweep of the windscreen wipers and the warm sound of the engine and in some places the sky was so low the trees seemed to disappear into the clouds. Long ago I had tried to stretch my hands up to touch Eskil in heaven.

And I could still have run away, *run, run, my heart,* into the forest like an animal. A faint sun glimmered through the rain-laden trees and it was still possible. He opened the car door and looked at me and when he turned to the forest his gaze was impenetrable. I could have disappeared into the trees if I had run now. But the thing is, even now I had nowhere to go. The forest would have come to an end and I would be standing at the side of the road and he would come driving past again and pick me up and drive me back here, to the banks of the silver lake and the slurry pit. So I remained sitting in the car, which was gleaming white against the faint brownish light settling on the landscape in the heavy summer rain.

"Come on," he said.

And even if time hadn't run out and even if there had been someone to call, Raksha or Shane or an angel, I still wouldn't have had anything to say. For what could I have said now that I hadn't managed to say before? Perhaps the reason I was already at the end, too soon, far too soon, on this muddy road at the edge of an unknown forest, was because I had no words for who I was and what I had come from. Inside me was voiceless silence, above me only a bare, defenceless sky and beneath me the earth's unrelenting gravity, pulling me down.

"Mamma, Mamma, I don't know where I am."

"Is that you?"

"Yes, I think it's me."

"Whereabouts are you?"

"In the forest."

"You have to tell me where you are so I can help you."

"I can't."

"Why not?"

"I don't know where I am, I told you."

"What can you see around you?"

"Rain and huge black trees. Ancient trees. A lake a bit further away. And birds screeching. No signs . . ."

"You mustn't hang up now."

"I only wanted to hear your voice. That was all I wanted."

A few weeks later they found me. It was a woman out with her dog at daybreak. On the shore below Haga Palace there was a white suitcase containing parts of me. Later that summer they found another suitcase by a cliff at Hägersten right beside the motorway. They transferred the contents to a room of death, and that was all there was of me. A pelvis with genitals and uterus cut out. Two arms, a femur, a calf and two breasts, but no head. And since the head was missing, cause of death could not be ascertained; in other words, they couldn't rule out the possibility that, like Snow White, I had been poisoned by an apple or had choked on my own collar.

Nobody missed me at first. Valle and Solveig were too young and too far away, placed somewhere along the length of Sweden. Shane had disappeared and that I didn't turn up at the local authority office when I should have done was nothing unusual. That was how it used to be. I came and went, and sometimes I went to ground and would be gone for months. For a long time, Ivan thought that was it, I was somewhere under the city, in the metro system or the culverts beneath one of the big mental hospitals. Ivan always had his theories and at the end of that first summer he began to search for me. He never believed it was me in those suitcases.

I could have told the police right from the start how it would end. I could have said straightaway that there was no point in bringing anyone in for questioning, the perpetrator would deny everything, that is what they do. I could have told them he would say that he had never met me, that he had never been to the desolate street that runs like a gaping wound over the Brunkeberg ridge. The guilty deny death with such force they end up believing themselves. And my life is no longer a legal concern; the statute of limitation expired ages ago. What sort of concern am I then? No concern whatsoever, presumably. I died, that was all.

We were at the edge of a primordial forest somewhere beyond the city. I had gone with him in the way I always went with people. Because I needed the money, because I had a mission that went on day and night and there was nothing outside that mission. "To be free," as Nanna would say. "To punish myself," as people who thought they knew a thing or two would say. What should I be punished for? They never said. I had followed him like a dog.

In some other time, something about him might have caused me to back off when we were on Herkulesgatan, to shut the car door and walk away. In some other time I might have said to Nanna and the rest of them that they should beware of him, but that time was as distant as Nanna was now. Of course, you learn to pick up the signs on the street, it is pure instinct, but in the end you can't even bother about signals any more. Signs such as the sky suddenly opening over the Brunkeberg ridge, letting unbridled light flood in, violet-yellow and ominous. Or the harsh strident squawks of the white bird screeching from the roof of the bank headquarters. Or the cloven-hoofed beat of the music streaming out of the car radio. He said it was Mozart, but it sounded like death. The silence hung over him like a cold smoke, the Arctic sea smoke that rises out of the water at dawn, and now I know the same silence enshrouds a grave.

I had arranged to meet him on Herkulesgatan. I was still

wearing the wristband and joggers they had given me in the hospital and I had on my fox-fur boa and a pair of red shoes. I was clearly of this world, but it felt as though I was dead. I had brushed with death so many times, I had stopped being afraid and for some reason I had been flung back into the world of the living once again. He stepped out of the shadows.

"Come on," he said.

We drove out of the city. When I turned and looked out of the back window, the road we left behind us was a sinking nothingness of mire and decay and the buildings were toppling into the abyss.

The forest we were in was inundated with brown water; I remember thinking the lake must have burst its banks because all around was the sound of running water. No, it wasn't nature weeping. Not even I was weeping. And the ground had a strange undertow, as if invisible hands were snatching at me from the underworld and globs of dank saliva dripped out of his mouth onto my face.

The mellow sunshine that had lingered in the air made every movement restrained and slow, almost suspended.

"I only want to be close to you," he whispered, and I laughed, because it was so unexpected, such a childish thing to say, almost comical, and I wasn't afraid anymore and all the pain from the hurt before was gone now. I laughed, and I heard the hard, metallic noise I made, and I wanted to say something, but when I tried, earth dribbled out of my mouth, a turbid, greyish fluid, a mixture of sludge and slime and decaying leaves. And there was no sound, no words, just those lumps of graveyard soil and something white, a grainy, rancid liquid with the stench of truffle. He gave my head a quick, hard twist and from the side a sliver of sky reflected in my eyes. Sky, against my will. But what was my will, in truth? I had wanted to be free, light as a gossamer, but it didn't work. I had one hand reaching for the firmament and one hand scrabbling in the mud. And in the heavens, night was falling now. Pink clouds, slightly frayed and fuzzy, clung to planet earth's great membrane. How could there be such beauty in heaven and such horror on earth? Where do you run to when you have nowhere to go?

"I only want to be close to you," he whispered, over and over. It sounded like a sermon and I laughed again, louder this time, and I don't think he liked people laughing, especially not girls, because then darkness came, as if someone had thrown a blanket over the sun, a dreadful howling blackness, and I was falling through an immense void. In the passage of an instant and a thousand years. I prayed for an angel to come, but there was no angel. I hoped this wasn't the end, but it was.

One day nothing about my story will matter anymore, not even to me. One day all of us will be part of the thin black layer of earth that covers this planet, amongst all those who died in bygone times. The human body is so easily damaged, its substance mere fluids and chemical compounds. Our bodies give us a place in time, and time is a form for evil, a vessel for dark encounters. Though sometimes I think brightness is worse; there were instants entirely without shadow and yet Shane and I couldn't sustain them. Like the moment Valle soars into the sky in his baby swing and Shane and I watch him whizzing away and hurtling back towards us. And now I have so much time, I see that all along he looks at me with eyes full of openness and trust, and those eyes still have faith in me.

Raksha's birthday came and went in June, soon after I turned twenty-four. Even though I didn't keep in touch at any other time, I always rang Raksha on her birthday, so she began to count the days. Two days passed, then ten, and suddenly it was three weeks. It was a time when nights were never more than twilight, when daylight lingered all night long, summer nights when dawn was just a breath on the horizon, a softly glimmering veil. Did Raksha realise I was dead, that I was no longer anywhere in this world? Was she aware that what had once been part of her was swimming in liquefied remains? Did she feel relief when they discovered the suitcases, a kind of wild release, something forbidden that went through her head like a flake of ash from a night-time fire? *At last it's over, there's nothing left to grieve. Not Eskil, not her.*

When I was seven I was given a baby brother. It was the best thing I ever had from Raksha and Ivan. We used to keep him in a laundry basket and transfer him from room to room, like a tiny candle that we had to keep alight. But a few days before my twelfth birthday he drowned in the river.

Raksha and I are in the same situation. We should all have the chance to understand one another, and yet we never do. Then again, perhaps we did understand one another, but we didn't like what we understood. If I turned up at her house now, she might ask, like she used to ask, "Surely you've missed me a teeny bit, my silly little girl?" And she would be right, because I always longed to be with Raksha, even though I was hurt by her every time I came close. Later she would whisper, in her stifled, guilty little voice:

"You know I'm always so clumsy. I lose everything and forget what's important."

"Yes, I know."

"I even lost my beautiful babies."

"That makes two of us, Raksha," I could say at that point, since it was true, even if nobody cared about the truth anymore; but there is a certain kind of misery you cannot share, at least not with the one who bore you.

It is an archaic landscape swept by cold, harsh winds; it looks modern but it is ancient. A cluster of islands surrounded by motionless seawater beneath a naked sky. A patchwork of faded facades in yellow and pink with modern buildings made of black steel and glass. Bank headquarters, shopping malls and multi-storey car parks have a futuristic look, but age-old thoughts fill people's minds, ponderous, inalterable; there are victims, there are perpetrators, there are witnesses, and they all peer down at the ground. The well-heeled live in the centre, as they always have. And the lifeblood of this city circulates along Herkulesgatan and from there to the banks, the money moves in and out of the state, and the architecture framing all of this is raw and cold. Some are doomed to failure, others destined to advance, a certain few will rise above the rest; and you can see the early signs, children defined from the start. A secret watermark or a caste mark glowing under the skin on a child's brow. And in this city there is also someone who has been stalking me for quite some time, or chasing someone like me, a girl who no longer cares what happens to her. Let us call him the huntsman.

Imagine this scenario, and a city on the go, cars and people and the pulse of the future beating in everything; the future is all around us for now, sweeping like a mighty motorway or river through the landscape. We believe it will take us with it, but to think about the future is to yearn for death, and there will always be someone left behind on the riverbank, abandoned in the mud and mire. Now imagine a chequered public square in the middle of the city and a few metres from this chessboard I stand and wait.

We had met a few days earlier, on one of the many evenings I spent on Herkulesgatan, and he had said:

"I'm going to show you something. I think you'll like it."

There were very few things I liked in the world and I found it hard to imagine that this would be one of them, but I didn't say it.

"What if I don't want anything anymore?" I said.

"Well, you'll get it anyway. Sometimes you get things you never knew you wanted."

The light emitted from the streetlamp above was like electric rain, static and grey. Streetlamps had been installed here a while ago, for access to the shops; I kicked the lampposts every time I walked past them and sometimes they went out and night would descend again over the street and I could move about without feeling pursued by the glare. He had been fingering something in his coat pocket, a small silver packet that he produced. It was straight morphine, he said, it went straight to the heart. A pure sensation of fire and gemstone; and I had always thought that drugs were like being on fire without burning yourself, falling without hurting yourself. In the end, of course, you did hurt yourself, sooner or later you fell through the world before people's eyes, but the sensation is what I am trying to describe. And so it was. We fell together, Shane and I. The tragedy of falling is that it takes such a bloody long time, because you can't help resisting, even though you long for it to end. I really wanted something to defeat me, but it didn't, the will to live kept on ticking inside me like a terrible eternity clock. That is how you end up waiting for a hunter.

"I think I know what you want," he had said. "I think I can give it to you."

He was talking about death, but I didn't realise at the time, I thought we were talking about something else; I was thinking about my mission, unable to think beyond that. It is liberating to have a purpose, the only thing to fill your being, a form to inhabit, like a prayer. He was thinking about death. A secret desire forcing through him like a surge of water.

"OK," I said.

Because the hunger tore through my blood vessels. A storm raging within me, drowning out everything else. I only hoped he wasn't one who liked to talk. It was always the same story anyway, and I didn't want any more stories, I wanted reality to be an open, bleeding wound. That was why I had loved Shane; he never lied to me.

There he sat in his car with the passenger door open, waiting for me, without saying anything, not even looking at me. As if we already knew one another, as if we had an agreement. He didn't seem particularly eager; he was neither angry nor drunk. He wasn't dark either, and by that I mean the kind of darkness that encases certain people. He sat still as a statue behind the wheel and if I hadn't seen his lips move I would have thought the voice came from inside me.

"Are you coming then?"

"How did you find me?" I asked Shane once, right at the beginning.

"I was always looking for you," he said. "I just didn't believe you existed until I found you."

I didn't believe it either, that the person I became with him existed. The girl who was afraid of nothing, whose laugh made people turn in the street. It was as though life finally began when I met Shane.

Before we had Valle, I thought that if I was still going to perish, I wanted it to be with Shane; I believed that if I died it wouldn't matter, because I would die with him. I had pictured our dead bodies so many times, it was as real as if it had already happened; we were lying side by side on the floor in an empty apartment, lips black, eyes open. That, for me, was death, and the image no longer scared me. I never stopped to think we wouldn't be together when death came.

The only thing that moved inside the car was a single black-and-white photograph vibrating in the draught from the blower on the dashboard. The photo was of an old woman whose eyes were so pale it looked as though the iris and pupil had burned out. It was hot and stuffy in the car and the seats were scorching against my thighs from the sun; there was the smell of Little Trees air freshener and sheet metal. When death comes, it comes quietly. No tattooed lilies, no Devil's foot-prints. You climb into a car as you have done a thousand times before, with no thought for the past or the future, no notion that fate has prepared something special for you. And yet you know. When you sift through your memories afterwards, you understand it all, you see everything as if through cold, clear water. You see his entire soul, the solitary beast of prey resting beneath the wavering sun before it springs. You see the gods hold their breath.

"Are you coming then?"

It was just like the deadly disease that would take all my friends later on. We saw it make a grab for us like the hand of dark-ness on Herkulesgatan, but we all thought we could deal with it. No prayers could relieve that sickness; it interfered with love at the very moment two bodies became one pulsing eye. But by the time all that happened, I was long gone.

*

Nanna and I used to sit on the bridge over Kungsgatan and watch the cars speeding past below us. We always sat up high and looked down on the streets and it gave us a sense of eternity, at least for me. Up there we were untouchable, no-one could get at us while we sat like old thieves or angels watching over people's lives below us. We could face anything as long as we were able to sit there together suspended above everything else. We laughed at the old men and the young boys, we laughed at the people who were agitated, or sentimental, or furious, we laughed at the people shouting for their mother or for God as they passed.

"Being on the street is like a bloody church service," Nanna said.

Her words always set us free, like her high, brittle laughter.

I think I should say a few words about my childhood, but it feels so remote, as if it happened to someone else, and I don't know which parts of it I ought to include. A lot of what happened much later seems more relevant, such as becoming a mother myself, or dying. First of all, you are condemned to being a child, like being in prison, and then one day you come out and find you are responsible for your own life. What difference do the experiences you have had actually make? I think of Raksha's silky hands, the freckles that looked as though they were sprinkled over her skin, and her face as she lay sunbathing, half asleep, by the riverbank. I remember how the whole of her was soft as sand, the smell of her hair, the sound of her voice.

If I was going to relate anything, it would be the time I went to the hospital when I was seven and held Eskil for the first time. He still smelled strongly of the sea and ancient times and he had a little tube in his nose because it was difficult for him to breathe. I sat motionless for hours gazing at this strange being that had just come out of Raksha. I could tell you about everything else that Raksha gave me, without her knowing she had given me anything at all. How she cut everyone's hair by the river; how they came up to us with their bad, unkempt hairdos and left like new people, revitalised. They always had something to drink while they waited their turn and sometimes, when there was a crowd of people waiting, there was a party and Raksha would put her scissors away and join the party instead. But it didn't matter, because most of them were out of work and they came back the next day. The best days were when she said I could miss school and stay at home with her and we would sit at the kitchen table all morning in our nightclothes. Ivan would have left ages ago, long before we woke, and Raksha would play her first game of solitaire and smoke her first cigarette, humming along to the radio, slightly hungover, while the cigarette smoke curled gently up to the ceiling. I never thought about her not working, apart from the haircuts that came and went periodically. Sometimes the place was full of people waiting, sometimes no-one came for months.

"Blow me a smoke ring, Mamma!"

I used to ask her to make a smoke ring for me and after she had done one, I begged her to blow another into the first one. To me the whole smoke-ring thing was a miracle. When I grew up, I would smoke like her, I thought.

Here, in the wind, you can hear the voices of all those of us who disappeared against our will. I hear the echo of our loneliness, I hear shouts and prayers and children crying. I hear the ugly sound of blood spattering on walls, of locks turning in morgues. I feel thousands of hands slowly burrowing into children's bodies and staying there forever. I hear screams from the slaughterhouses, from children's bedrooms, from unmarked graves.

It sounds as though many would have wanted to stay a little longer and catch the remaining light, but the question of will is complicated, an illusion for the most part. It is so easy to confuse liberty with living out a dream, with intensity, isolation, death. You might as well get used to the idea that life is not going to be the way you want it to be, that one day you too will sell a bit of yourself. Maybe not your cunt, but most certainly your soul, at the perfume counter in Åhléns or as director of some television company or president of a youth group. So I believe it was determined from the beginning of time, or at least from the moment I emerged from Raksha's womb one night at the end of the fifties, that I would meet this hunter in the forest.

Death has its advantages as well. When you are dead it doesn't matter if you are a loser and can't pay your bills. When you are dead everyone thinks they were fond of you and they forget your bad points. They miss you and want you to come back, but nobody considers what would happen if you actually did, if, for example, you were sitting on Raksha's sofa one day when she surfaced from one of her tablet-induced dreams.

"Hello, dearest Raksha."

"Heavens! Is it you?"

"Yes, I'm here again."

"I had a horrible dream about you."

"I know, but death let me go. I fought and kicked so hard I was let loose."

"My God. It was a dreadful dream. Some pill dreams are truly awful. Well, what shall we do now?"

"I don't know. I only just arrived. Tell me what's been happening here instead."

"Um, well . . . my new doctor's absolutely fantastic, he's a bit like Jesus, he lets me have as many tablets as I like. So today, to give you an example, I had nothing but sleeping pills for lunch."

"I can see why you're happy then . . . And Ivan must have been here?"

"Ugh, that creep . . ."

"But weren't you glad he was here? I got the impression you were."

"Yeah, maybe. But now he's gone again. Just as well."

And then she would look around, puzzled and slightly embarrassed, and we would sit there, and all the difficulty between us, everything that had been temporarily erased by death, would be back: that she wasn't the mother I had needed and I wasn't the daughter she had wished for. But who gets everything they wish for?

I was so young when it began, no longer a child, but not yet a woman. I don't know if I ever did become a woman, but one day I couldn't stand normality anymore and that was when I crossed over to the other side. I stood in a rain of broken glass with my first syringe in my hand and if I could, I would tell you how beautiful it was, as if all things were suddenly illuminated from within. A glass wall that was soundlessly smashed and gave access to the world.

One day you find something that makes you free, genuinely free, like a child who is lost in the forest and brought up by wolves and never finds her way back to what there was before or can never even remember that there was something else before. You chance upon it after an eternal night in Vitabergs-parken and after that you are no longer afraid of anything, of the night, of strangers, of dying. Later the fear will return and take everything, pushing you to the ground, but for now you are just a beached mermaid, reclining on the bonnet of a car.

A girl with amber eyes and soft hair, who later will turn out to be Nanna, has helped me tighten a blood-red belt around my upper arm. Her hands are pale as her eyes, an artificial, washed-out bluishness, but her nails are a glittering apricot. Her hair makes her look like a fairy-tale creature; I find out eventually she hides behind it when she is afraid, and it is so fair it merges into grey.

*

My heart is beating as though it is perched on the outside of my body, and this is a point of no return, I know. Whatever I may say later, I know. At the hour of the star, you know. You know because this is precisely what you want, never to return to what there was before, to your old self. The last thing you want is to be yourself and it is so simple, simple as a heartbeat, a small silver packet over a flame and the smell of vinegar pervading the room, like no other smell I have ever known. A musty, lifeless sea, the inside of a coffin, of a shell. And when the needle hits a vein and the bubbly brown fluid mixes with blood, I vomit straight out into the room and my genitals contract like a jellyfish. We go out to the street, Nanna and I, and it is like walking through water or waist-high snow or pure love, and all at once I am lying on the bonnet of a car with Nanna's hand in mine, looking up at the cold, naked sky and never has it been so close, floating above me and yet inside me too. Someone kisses my neck, not Nanna, she has disappeared. Someone finds my mouth in the streetlamp's silver light, and that is where the world begins, where it opens up. I still have not made love to anyone, never been naked with anyone, never kissed anyone, but after this I am a virgin no longer. An angel, fantastic, unknown, intoxicated, has raped me and dragged my soul out into the bitter cold of space, never to give it back.

It is not that I am instantly addicted that first time, because I am not. I wake up in a room filled with sunlight after many hours of deep sleep, a strange, looping sleep, and my body is relaxed and soft and normal and the others have left, all except Nanna, who is asleep beneath the open window in her pants and vest. My Detroit sweatshirt is in a heap on the floor, covered in puke of a faintly pinkish colour. Next to me on the sofa is a white feather, which I put in my handbag when I leave. When I walk home along Drottningholmsvägen it is different, reduced somehow, narrower, greyer, despite the bright sunshine. A lifeless world. No birds, no trees; there they stand, and yet they are not there. A silent blue sky, bottomless, faceless.

It is silent in the apartment; gently quivering shafts of sunlight extend like pillars into the kitchen. I snuggle down behind Raksha and fall asleep at once. It always used to be me waiting for Raksha, and now at night Raksha waits for me. She sits at the kitchen table until dawn when she gives up and goes to bed. Days pass, and everything is as it always has been, and one morning on my way to school I take a detour past the metro, and next time I look at my watch it is too late to go to school. Because now that I know about it, I can't ignore the fact there is somewhere else, an outside, with more room, or a truer place, a paradise that can rise up inside me at any moment, and it is the place I have been looking for all this time. There is no compulsion, it is not that I am forced to return, but I want to go back and let the angel take me again, harder.

Nanna opens the door when I ring the bell, her skin white as snow, her eyes paler than ice under the sunglasses. Later, people will say we are so alike, though she is fair and I am dark.

"Hello, Boomerang. I knew you'd come back."

"Did you know I'd come today?"

"I thought it might take a bit longer. But I hoped it would be today."

*

Something dropped out of heaven for me when I met Nanna. It was made of silver and gave off the scent of ash and ammonia, and I imagined, when I sat next to her and once again she tightened the thin belt around my arm, that what was flowing into me had travelled far, perhaps for many years, to reach me, and it was given to me because I had waited so long for Eskil. The water took him, and therefore it took Raksha too, and as compensation I was entitled to this feeling, unlike anything I had ever known before. And I was given Nanna, who was so much older than I was and had no fear of anything at all. It is a state of holiness, the little blue flame and the dark liquid coursing through the blood, the heartbeats drawing me into another world. And there, in the magic spell, I finally meet Eskil. He is walking towards me out of nowhere, like a fairy tale. Wearing the same bright-red bobble hat he always wore, he is just as small and beautiful. His lips are black, but his eyes are clear and full of light, as if he were alive. He stands quite still by my side, looking up at me. And I had forgotten how little he was, just over a metre tall. His hand as dainty as a flower.

"Are you very angry, Inni?"

"Why would I be angry?"

"Because I drowned. I thought you were angry because I didn't listen to you."

You think you are always going to be angry, but then one day, you are not angry any longer. One day you are not anything.

"I'm not angry. But Raksha's missed you so much, she nearly drowned herself. But no-one's angry with you."

His eyes move from side to side, as if he is following

something in the sky behind me, a bird or a plane, though there is nothing there. When I touch him he is cold.

"I don't believe that. I think she's angry."

"Raksha's just annoyed with herself for being such a fool. I am as well."

He still smells so good, he still smells of Eskil, with a hint of sour milk, and washing powder. His eyes are darker than I remember and I daren't touch him again even though he is standing right beside me, so close I can hear his breathing. I love his tiny breaths.

"I should have come for you, but I didn't know how to find you," I say when he doesn't reply.

"It doesn't matter. I'm fine now. Everything's fine."

"Are you sure?"

"Yes, I don't need anything here."

"Not even me?"

"I wanted to stay with you, but that wasn't to be. They took me. And I don't think I'm allowed to miss anyone here."

"Who took you?"

I reach out a hand to him, but, as I do, he disappears.

People peer up at the sky and I wonder what everyone is look-ing for. Everyone except Raksha, who sits at the window, staring down at her hands. They are old now, veiny and yellow, and her nails look like claws. I love those hands so much, I want to touch them. She sits all day doing crosswords, when she is not lying in the bath, staring at the cracks in the ceiling. Out in the street she keeps her eyes firmly on the ground, terrified of meeting another human gaze. She is so lovely, sitting there alone, waiting for death, and I never tire of looking at her. A little while ago I heard her singing to herself. Sometimes I think Raksha looks exactly as she did when I was young, just a few sizes smaller; she has shrunk, as old people do over time. She still colours her hair a crazy shade of reddish orange. Although she never goes out, she is very careful the silver doesn't show, not even as an outline at her temples.

One day somebody telephoned and asked for me. It was a man, he didn't introduce himself and I assumed it could be someone from before, who still had my number.

"She can't come to the phone at the moment," Raksha said.

"Why not?"

"Because she's dead," Raksha said, and hung up.

When it rang again, she pulled the cable out of the socket.

VERTIGO

It was the summer I had disappeared. Every afternoon Raksha sat on the sofa, looking at the grey square that was the television, afraid there would be something about me in there, if she switched it on. No other news item that summer held the same fascination as the one about my body in white suitcases. The television was her closest friend, but now she felt as though the people inside the set were looking at her accusingly. They were glancing in her direction, even when they weren't talking about me, and she wanted to go up to them and explain. But what would she say? *That thing without a head in a suitcase is my child . . . Those pieces of flesh floating in liquefied corpse, that's my little mouse . . .*

I couldn't understand how this Raksha, sitting and looking out of the window with a cigarette burning in the ashtray in front of her, could be the same Raksha I had always waited for when I was a child, the person who once had filled my field of vision and embodied my entire world. They had the same name, the same face, but they weren't remotely similar. She had smoked before too, but usually she would take a few hard drags, brisk, strained, almost slapdash, before crumpling the cigarette into the ashtray. And she had always been in a hurry. Now she was sitting perfectly still, watching the smoke rise to the ceiling, where it slowly dispersed into nothing. Smoke is time getting away from her, and it can't be stopped.

Whilst the city outside Raksha's window was a river surging ahead without her, her own time stood still. The flies collected on the flypapers and the rubbish remained in the bin. She would sit for the whole day, looking at the hoarding over the front of the building on the opposite side of the street. If it hadn't been there, she would have been able to see the sky, but what she saw instead was a photograph of a view and a woman in a swimsuit running across a beach. She looked tired, but her heart was beating so violently, it was visible against her dress. I would have liked to lay my hand there, to calm it. The advertising vista on the wall opposite was all there was, now that she could no longer watch the television. And she didn't read anything from her water-damaged books the way she always had before. The type mingled with the wood pulp and slipped away from her, despite the magnifying glass at her side. Around her the world was silent, but inside her it roared.

She hadn't told anyone I had been found. But one day she sat down next to the telephone. It transmitted its electrical signals and she heard Ivan's voice, scratchy and defensive, and after so many years, it brought back a whole world from the past, of the emotional thrill on wild nights and the sound of cranes drifting around in the twilight and of deep unhappiness, and she asked him if they'd had any snow, even though it was the middle of summer. And when it went quiet, she heard the sound of a football match in the background. He won't want to be disturbed right now, she thought, and she wouldn't wish to disturb a living soul, not even herself. She wanted to drowse in the bath and let the days drain away until there were none left.

She had no idea how she would phrase it, what words she would use to describe the sky crashing down on her, cascading to the ground. Words were intangible, empty and strangely weightless, at once too forceful and too meagre. So she said:

"Are you watching football?"

He mumbled something that might have been a yes.

"That'll make you happy. But now I'm afraid I have to make you sad."

"You've always done that," Ivan said, but his voice was unsure now, slightly less rasping, as though really he knew what was coming, but hung on nevertheless to the world of before, which in a few seconds' time would be gone forever.

*

It was the first time he had heard her voice for many years and it still had the same effect on him, made him hollow with anger. He was quiet and so was she, both of them waiting for her to say something, and in the silence he was suddenly struck by the smell of her, as distinctly as if it came flowing out of the receiver into the room. She smelled acrid and intoxicating, a little like glue, a scent that had once made him drive for miles through the night, just to experience it again. Instinctively he held the receiver away from his head to avoid what was coming next, to escape the intrusive odour. In his heart of hearts, he knew what she was going to say. There was a newspaper on the table in front of him. For the last few days my body had been drowning in printers' ink on newspaper billboards and now here was Raksha's breathless voice in the receiver after all these years. The photographs of my face hadn't been published yet, and there was no name, but the articles about my mutilated body had fluttered briefly past Ivan's life, as news does, like bats in the night, scary and entertaining in equal measure. I was the sort of news that drew a circle of light around the reader and inside that circle there was warmth and sharing, where you were safe. Outside the circle was where we were, the shadows.

Raksha groped her way through the syntax of death, listening to his breathing. The syntax of death was this: if she said it was a tragedy, so painful was the understatement, she found it difficult to breathe. She found it hard to breathe all the time. And if she said she wanted to die, it just sounded like something you say when you've made a spectacle of yourself at a party. Besides, she had been saying she wanted to die for as long as she could remember. Was it only her speech that was devoid of content, or was it the whole world? Where was the language to describe what had happened? Sylvia was the only person she had seen since and she had said nothing to her.

"Why aren't you saying anything, Raksha?" I had whispered to her a few days earlier, while they were sitting on Sylvia's balcony in the sunshine, smoking. Maybe she was trying, maybe she intended to tell her, but no words would come out.

"You're going to need someone now, you stubborn old mule," I said outright, into nowhere. It sounded like a tiny gust of air passing through, that was all, and I realised the only person she wanted to speak to was Ivan, there was no-one else who could understand, despite the distance. And now she did speak.

"She always rings on my birthday," Raksha said. "She rings and asks what I'd like and I always say I just want to have her back . . . So I thought . . . So then I thought, well . . . There's so much time to think . . . Actually, for the last few years I've just been waiting . . . I really wish I could have called you about something else, now that I'm finally ringing after all this time . . ."

Ivan hadn't seen me since I was fifteen; for him I was still the skinny kid that Raksha had taken away with her on the train so long ago. At first I went down to see him, but then I stopped going. Raksha had written asking for help on all those occasions she was at her wits' end. The last time was when Shane and I lost Valle. Ivan had never answered her letters, but he had read them – they were gathered together in his bedside table, envelopes opened. I had been Raksha's child from the start and for as long as I can remember, I had reached out for her.

It wasn't that I was afraid of Ivan, it was more that he never seemed to see his children properly. We belonged to a different species, our voices on a frequency he didn't catch. All he saw was Raksha, and her very spirit made him furious. At that time, by the river, he and Raksha and their love devoured everything around them. Us as well.

When we did eventually leave, Ivan stood on the platform smoking a farewell cigarette, talking to a woman in a red coat who was also there to wave someone off. Or did he already know her? Ivan made friends with people so easily, always starting conversations with strangers; maybe we were the ones who never got to know him. He had offered her a cigarette and now they were standing there looking up at me hanging out of the window. Raksha hid in her seat in the compartment. As the train started to move, he said something.

"What did you say?" I shouted into the high-pitched whine in the overhead lines caused by the train's motion.

"Never trust anyone."

"Can't I trust you?'

"Least of all me."

Raksha twisted the telephone cord round her fingers and dried her eyes with the hem of her dress. She wasn't weeping, but water poured out of her eyes all day long now, streaming silently out of her. She wavered and started again. She was ashamed of waiting far too long before calling him. She had told the police there was only her, there was no-one else, and that was true, really, there had always only been her. And after that she couldn't bring herself to telephone. Days had passed, as she sat with the receiver in her hand, listening to the single tone. On paper they were still married, they hadn't even got around to sorting that out. But what difference did an official certificate make after such a long time? She felt as though she must be unhinged now, to be pestering him with what had happened to her daughter. I came from her, both Eskil and I came from her. The fault was hers. But be that as it may, she carried on.

"You've always said you don't have children anymore. So I was ringing . . . I was just ringing to say, I don't either now."

When he didn't say anything, she continued.

"Someone cut her up into pieces – how should I put this? Her head's gone. Maybe you read about it in the paper? And her holy of holies too."

She didn't say anything else after that, and nor did he. White and perspiring, she looked as though she had just spewed her guts onto the floor in front of her.

They sat in silence, each listening to the breathing of the other and the faint sound you used to hear in those days of voices on telephone lines from every part of the world. I imagined there might have been a woman in Poland making a similar call to a Polish man. Far away, Ivan sounded short of breath, he took a few sharp gasps, but he wasn't crying. Not that she could hear, at any rate. After a while she lit a cigarette and took a couple of draws so deep I thought I heard it crackling in her lungs. Then she said, "Ivan are you still there?" When he still said nothing, she whispered, "Goodbye then, my friend." And she gently replaced the receiver on her side of the world.

It was the blue hour, the hour when the sun and the moon met and the first tremulous night-time light and vestiges of day-light merged like magical waters and swathed the world in a quivering violet phosphorescence, when everything grew soft and nebulous and all the outlines and shadows melted away. For a while we just sat there and he didn't look at me. His hands were resting on the wheel, his eyes focussed on the world before us, and at this point he hadn't turned the engine off. What were we waiting for?

There was a smell of old leather and detergent, as if he had recently scoured the entire interior of the car. A single child seat in the back, a teddy bear lying in a ray of sunlight on the seat. A rosary of beads hanging on the rear-view mirror suspended in blue droplets in front of me. Afterwards I assumed he wanted to give me one last chance to escape. I had the feeling he could see straight into my soul, past all that had already been and beyond what was to come. And there was no way to elude those eyes, the black ink pouring out of the pupils under the ponderous vault of his eyelids. There was no way to avoid what was coming. And now with a purr the car started to move. The gentle stirring of a beast of prey.

We drove through a mellow green landscape, groves of young birch trees, derelict houses and a sky so low, it looked as though we were driving into it. On the dashboard there was a photograph of a woman; his mother, I guessed. He wanted her to watch him all the time, whatever he was doing, and now there was something he wanted to show her.

"It's beautiful here," he said.

"Do you think so?"

"Yes."

"OK."

"Don't you see it?"

"No."

The world seemed to be heavy with rain, a world of rain in which the green appeared in sharper focus, a world immersed in water. Treetops softly dappled with chlorophyll. Asphalt dark with rain. Bloodstained shadows of animals now dead. Badgers and birds. That was what I saw.

"I don't like nature," I said.

"Why not?"

"You can't hide."

"What do you want to hide from?"

"The massive glare."

"You're so cute, you don't need to hide."

It was quiet for a moment, and then he offered me a small silver packet, the packet I was hoping for, the packet I was here for, a packet that glittered in the dim light. I took it and opened the stiff foil and searched for matches. And as always when the smell of burnt metal and vinegar rose above the little flame, my groin tightened in a spasm, a showering of silver inside me and the gentle touch of an embrace from within, and the rest of the world faded away, as if it had never existed. I pushed the needle into the crook of my arm and there was no rush, it was a long time since there had been, but it worked the same spell on me every time, my heart shuddered and grew still and I fell through the layers of time until I was floating inside a womb. The sensation of the needle pressing into my blue-blotched skin, the buzz of electricity deep inside me. I closed my eyes and leaned my head backwards, and it was like following a fairy godmother into the forest, hypnotised by her dancing backwards, and suddenly realising, when she finally turns and you have no idea how to find your way out in the dark, that her back is an open wound of rotting black.

And that was the thing. I never really wanted to give up heroin. Not properly, not even for Valle and Solveig's sake. It is the kind of insight that makes you weightless, the knowledge that there is something greater than all love.

I had told him what it would cost, two hundred and fifty kronor, and we had agreed I would go with him. The price had dropped of late, and I had sunk deeper into the mire and slime that existed beneath the city, below the earth and asphalt where the filth gathered, in the underground sewers and metro bunkers where people lived like ghosts.

We drove along the motorway and I don't know if it was the rain or time running out like sand in an hourglass, but in certain places where the landscape opened out after miles of pine forest, you could actually see that the world was round, that it curved in an arc along the rim of matchstick-sized trees in the distance.

"Where are we going?"

"Wait and see."

"I can't see anything."

"Sleep for a while if you like."

He drove with his eyes on the rain-soaked road as if in a trance, concentrating on something within himself that had nothing to do with me. I don't know why, but suddenly I was telling him about Eskil. I had never told anyone else, not even Shane.

When I was a child, you could see the glint of fish like lightning silver slivers across the surface of the river, before they disappeared again to become striated shadows on the bottom. You could see beavers in broad daylight. Eskil and I used to spy on people bathing in the river. From the trees we could see the beavers swimming right next to them and they never even noticed. Small glistening heads with black peppercorn eyes watching humans at play. Only we saw the beavers, from the drooping trees on the riverbank, where we sat all day in summer. Only we two had enough time to notice them. The river had its source further upcountry and after it had passed the power station it sped on, its currents flowing like electricity, like menacing hands snatching at us. At least that was how it was in our day. It is no-one's fault if a child disappears in circumstances such as these; it is the forces of nature and the particular weight someone has in water. And if that person can't swim, she sinks like an object, like stones and shells and the black sand on the river bed.

"Poor kid," he said, sitting next to me in the car, and I didn't know if he meant me or Eskil. His gaze was wide open, no shades, no animosity, and for a moment he was my confidant, almost my friend. But it wasn't a friend I needed, it was a cure, for what I was. I needed something to believe in, I needed a miracle; but it was too late for miracles.

Perhaps he too was searching for a miracle, a release, a kind of absolution. He needed someone like me, had been looking for a girl for whom the world held no more fear; apart from fear of love and of salvation. "Poor kid," he said again. For that second, I don't believe that he had any intention of hurting me. But when I turned and looked out of the back window, there was no asphalt, no verge, no road signs, just the motorway fracturing behind us and collapsing into giant craters in the ground, as if there had never been a road that we had travelled along.

He drove slowly through the rain, as though he didn't quite know where we were heading; but he did know, he had studied the maps, he knew everything there was to know about the forests around here, he had marked the slurry pit by the thousand-year-old silver lake on his map. They existed in those days, dark holes where you could dump things you wanted to disappear, really disappear, a pool of glossy pink corrosive sludge over which the metallic green blowflies gathered in summer. Maybe they don't exist anymore, those slurry pits, maybe they belonged to a different age, I don't know for sure. Anyhow, he slowed down more and more, as if he wanted to drag out the moment as long as possible, it was so precious. It was precious for me as well, considering it was my last. I thought of Valle's hands when he had just been born, how they opened and closed like jellyfish, how he seemed to be making a grab for life with those tiny fingers, making a grab for us. And then later, when his little hand sought mine at night. I thought of Shane, of him singing to me in his cracked voice when I couldn't sleep. I thought of Solveig, of never knowing her.

I should have done the same with Valle as I did with Solveig. Not tried to soften the harsh core of coercion in the gentle voices of the social workers, the fate that had already been sealed for us, that had only to be fulfilled before my eyes. But from the start I said I wanted them to take Solveig, and so it was. I had gone to the social services office, still a few months to go, but Solveig was already moving in there in her weight-lessness, and her heart was beating, they said. As it should, they said. It would soon be a bit cramped in there, and she would come out, but for the time being she was mine alone.

"Do you understand what permanent means?" the person in charge asked. "You won't be able to get the child back if you change your mind."

"I'm not going to change my mind."

"And you won't be able to see it again."

"I don't want to see her again. She'll be better off without me."

But now the huge black trees on either side were making everything dark. Massive treetops heavy with rain bowing down as if in prayer and the landscape closing around us like a cage. It was too late for prayers. But then I've already said that, haven't I?

I have never prayed to God. "You ought to," said those people at Storsjön who had taken over the care of my child. What should I pray for? To get Valle back? In the face of their unimpeachable, ingratiating prayers, I would stand no chance of keeping him. And how do they know it isn't Satan they are invoking when they pray, those self-righteous tossers? I have nothing to say to God, and nor to anyone else for that matter.

All I know is that I got into that car on that twilit night at the beginning of June.

"I've been waiting for you," he said in a low voice, without looking at me, as we drove past the airport. It was the first thing he had said since we set off.

"Have you?"

How could he know who I was? I, just one of all the anonymous people who lived by night in this city, like a bat on the world's flip side. And no-one here knew who I was, I scarcely did myself, and I never said my name. I said I was called John Wayne or Snow White, I said I was on my way home after an awful storm. And in a way that was true. It was just that there had never been any home before the storm. I had moved out long ago to find something, and what that was I could no longer remember. Now he turned to me and his eyes were so intense, I was forced to look away.

"Maybe you've been waiting for me too?"

I hadn't, and I said so.

"What have you been waiting for then, my little friend?"

"I've been waiting for a miracle."

He smiled. It looked as though someone pulled sharply on a string at the corner of his mouth, and made his smile vanish in an instant.

"Which one?"

"Which what?"

"Which miracle have you been waiting for? Not Jesus?"

The nature of a miracle was such that you couldn't imagine it in advance. All you knew was that it would change your entire existence forever. How could he not know that?

"Why would I have been waiting for you?" I asked instead, since I didn't want to talk about miracles.

"I don't know. I just thought you might because I've been waiting for someone like you."

"Like me?"

"I've been waiting for someone who's not afraid of anything, who doesn't fear for her life anymore."

It was so long since I had felt fear, but I did then, a trickle of dry ice along my spine.

I looked out of the streaked window at the rain falling from the heavens and I saw the trees bending over the road. It was June, it was the month for disappearing, the month for being found in pieces, the month for losing your head, and your tongue and your genitals. Solveig's eyes followed me wherever I went, and whenever I closed my eyes I saw hers, quite still and clear, gazing at me from eternity. We drove through a tunnel of rain and flowers and trees and the world was now just one single room, one single chamber, a grave and a coffin, a wall of trees that would all soon be dead. But first I was the one about to die.

I told myself I had always been heading towards this moment, always travelling on this dark, muddy road leading out of the city, and when I turned and looked out of the window at the back, I saw the road cave in and disappear behind us. No road ahead of me and no road back. It was something I had thought so many times, without understanding how many roads still existed then. But now they were gone, irrevocably, and for a second I was struck by a sensation of freedom, a wave breaking over me, dazzling green and cold. It was Eskil's wave, the cold, clear river water, and I realised that what happened to me no longer mattered to anybody on earth, and it didn't matter to me either. I said, "Do with me what you will."

A solitary bird seemed to fall out of the sky, swooping over the silver lake a little further away. And I supposed death was merely being outside time, being outside a human body in which time could be measured. That was the only way to comprehend it; death, and time. But now there was nothing else to comprehend, at least not for me.

All beasts of prey leave the entrails behind, and the hunter did too. My intestines were left on the little brown mudflat in the forest. They soon disappeared, dragged away by a vixen whose young were in a den nearby. It is the natural order of things; we are brought into being in order to be given up to death. Perhaps it is our only function? To become food for the animals. The birds came back later to eat what was left of me. My last remains taken by a flock of jackdaws, pieces of smooth pink flesh ascending with the jackdaws from the shore to the firmament.

It is very fortunate birds exist, and maggots, and decay. If we corpses didn't lie in the earth and decompose, we would be piled to the sky, high-rise blocks and towers of the deceased. I often reflect on how many we are, those of us who have already taken our leave, so infinitely many more than you who are left. And yet we can't do anything to you. You can do what you want with us, say what you want, throw black earth on top of us and tell whatever stories you like. No-one can check the facts with us, that is what is so nice about the dead. A perfect friend, someone who never argues, and we never change, we stay the same as we have always been. Frozen in tableaux. A person is forgotten in two generations. That is the extent of human memory.

*

And what else did he say in the car, driving along the main road to an unknown forest? He said he was a hunter, that he had a job as a butcher, that he was an architect. Or did he say he was a judge? It doesn't matter now; this was a world I didn't want to live in anyway.

It was the summer I had disappeared. Raksha went into the bathroom, ran a bath and slid straight into the water. Why had she said, "Goodbye, my friend," to Ivan? They had never been friends. They had loved like a pair of dogs, but they had never liked one another. Raksha had never had any friends at all, she had me and Eskil when we were little and that had been enough for her; and after us she had nothing whatsoever, that at least was true. Pills were her best friends, unimaginably wonderful friends, meek and docile, never troublesome. Sylvia in the apartment below was always trying to worm her way in. She would follow Raksha's every response with another question, her prying eyes on everything, wandering the whole time, and she would spot anything left on show. Sometimes Raksha would drape a cloth over the books on the shelf, because she thought they revealed too much about her. Otherwise Sylvia would stand there, staring at the titles, as if it was a bloody library.

She looked down at her body lying in the bath, flabby and ugly, with skin sagging from her stomach in a way it hadn't before, maybe because the only things she ate now were sleeping tablets. She had done everything she could to survive in this world. And for this? Now she felt as though she had known all along what was in store for her, seen the shadows gathering in her life, and that was why she had wanted to leave for good. She had seen a great sorrow ahead of us a long time ago, but it was like a cloud that was constantly moving, and she and

Ivan were so happy tearing around, they ran straight into it. At heart, she had known from the beginning that both Eskil and I were too much of a miracle to be real, she had known she had only received us in order to lose us, in a gruesome game that entertained the gods after a night of roister. And now we had been transformed in her head into the impossible dreams we had actually always been, intangible, elusive soap-bubble versions. In her dreams we were in our winter cardigans, crying and looking at her, and when she tried to reach for us, we simply disappeared. That was what she learned from the dreams, that she mustn't touch us, or we would instantly slide away and dissolve. So she didn't touch us, she just gazed at us for as long as she could. That way she could prolong the dreams. And every time she woke, it was night-time in the world; and in the end she had got it right. She had instinctively wanted to shield herself from what was to come, and she hadn't been able to. She had been made to stay in the world, as if governed by a dictator, and there was no-one to tell that she had been right all along.

She had always been afraid of falling stars, had never wished for anything more than those children we were. She had tried to keep her demons to herself, without success. In a way, Raksha had been dead for a long time. She had lain in the bottom of a coffin and looked up at the little assembled company, which was me, standing there weeping, hoping she would rise again like a second Jesus. She dipped under the hot water in the bath, and the world was soundless and filled with warmth, like the unfailingly soft light in the realm of her pills. She had called Ivan and now she would never need to ascend to the real world again. In the apartment beyond, the telephone rang, a sharp, exhorting sound, but under the warm water she didn't hear it. It rang a few times and then it stopped.

Every time she took a bath, she stayed in the tub long after she had let the water out. The little eddy that swirled round the plughole as the last of the water poured out was her life, a tiny spiral of her life's light draining rapidly away, to no purpose. When the telephone rang again, she heard it, jumped out of the bath and answered it, naked. It was Ivan.

"You're back."

"Yes."

"I was in the bath."

"Ah."

He was silent. And so was she. She twisted the telephone cord round her finger so hard it hurt. She took it into her head that she was the one who had rung him, and he was annoyed.

"Did you have something on your mind, Ivan?"

"I wouldn't have rung if I hadn't."

He sounded angry again.

"I can talk for a bit if you like. I just need to put something on. Will you wait a second?"

"Yes."

She hurried out into the hall and pulled on a coat at random, a winter coat, and then she sat down, perspiring, the receiver in her hand, hair dripping, the ornate belt pulled tight round her waist, waiting for him to say something. And that was how it went on. He rang again that evening and early the following morning and soon she started to wait for his calls, and when he didn't ring, her stomach began to ache, but then the shrill noise suddenly filled the apartment again. And there they would sit, saying nothing. She grew accustomed to his silence; indeed she knew it well from before. They had often been at home together, in silence; they could go months without saying anything.

In the course of those telephone calls she sometimes heard birds chirping in the background, he must have opened the window, and she remembered the sky, how low it always was by the river, how it had been everywhere; whilst in the city there were just brief glimpses here and there, and she had always missed it. Sometimes she heard the television in the background and she switched hers on to see what he was watching, and they sat there, watching together. When he was with her she wasn't scared of the television, and anyway he only watched football matches. Ivan's breathing was right beside her in the receiver, and just as it had once filled her life, it was filling it again; she couldn't understand how this could happen so fast, when she had coped without it for so many years. Whenever there was a goal, he cheered. It made her happy; inside she was cheering too. And when the match was over, they quickly switched off, before the news started. Then they sat in silence once more, and nights came and went; she had stopped waiting for him to say anything, it would feel almost absurd if he suddenly began to speak. In the evenings she fell asleep with the receiver in her hand and when she woke the room was light and the sound of birdsong flowed through the receiver, such a loud sound, so close, as if the birds were singing inside her. She didn't dare think about the cost of these telephone calls.

*

Raksha no longer tore the pages out of her calendar; she hadn't done this since the day the police called. She was living outside time, perhaps she had been for a while, but now she didn't know if it was day or night, summer or winter, war or peace, if she was young and still waiting for life to begin, or if she was already lying under the earth; and it was comforting not to know. She had heard someone say on the radio, during a programme about death, that if time and space no longer existed, there could be no pain. Evil needed time and space to operate.

It was early morning and she had slept with the receiver in her hand as she had every night for the last week, and now she woke to a single tone beeping in her ear. She immediately replaced it in the cradle and waited for him to ring back. And when he did, a few minutes later, she said:

"Do you want to come and see me, Ivan?"

"No," came the quick reply, in his rasping, gravelly voice.

Then she had hung up and heard nothing more, but the next morning he was at her door with his suitcase. She had just woken up and opened the door wearing a T-shirt, bare-legged. She had slept all night because he hadn't rung, and before she fell asleep she had wept at her own stupidity, and now she thought he was Sylvia, wanting to borrow something for some stupid baking.

Ivan had taken the night train, he mumbled, standing outside Raksha's door, looking down at the fossil-streaked stone floor, to find out more and do what he could. He didn't trust the police and he couldn't afford to stay in a hotel. What he might want or could afford made no difference to her, she could see he was furious with himself for coming and furious with her. There were no words for love and none for death. So she walked into his arms and held him and listened to his old, angry heart beating inside him. After a while he shoved her away, of course he did, he brushed her aside like a clinging cat and stared at her with the ice-blue eyes that had always made her feel so dirty and disgusting. But now they had no effect on her. She had seen what she needed to see, found out what she needed to find out. They drank coffee together, maintaining their silence; he took a shower and had something to eat, and then they put the television on, the afternoon repeats. He could do what he wanted as far as she was concerned, as long as he didn't leave now. And when all the programmes were over, he came to her. They went into the bedroom together. She lowered herself cautiously onto him and they sank into the blackness together.

He couldn't do what he did before, but it didn't matter. This was something different, as if they were two very elderly people. He was shaking, and she wished she could help him be still. In the dark room it was as though they had just come into being; when she looked down at her skin it was shimmering, her clothes had slipped off her body unnoticed, the flabbiness had disappeared and the broken rawness that was usually there was also gone. Gently he stroked the scar under the elastic in her pants, and perhaps he was thinking of us, of Eskil and me. It was still red after all those years, a botched stitching job, and sometimes it still hurt, a tight, burning sensation. Raksha gasped with fear when he touched her, her breathing quick as a bird's and halting, afraid he would suddenly get up and leave and take the night train back and never be in contact again. But he stayed where he was, and she found no malice in his eyes. When he bent and kissed her on the scar, I looked away. This was not for me. This was their hour on earth.

Raksha and Ivan came flying in from nowhere and became a family, a sudden constellation which was as arbitrary and haphazard as a newborn cloud in the sky, as transient and momentary as a flock of birds rising up as one, doomed to scatter in the wind.

The years by the river when Raksha and Ivan stayed up all night and Raksha woke me with her hearty laugh, I would lie in my bed listening to their voices drifting through the apartment in gentle loops. Suddenly Eskil was there next to my bed, with his bright little halo of hair.

"May I come in with you, Inni?"

I used to carry him back to his bed after he had fallen asleep, there wasn't much room in mine, but after a while he would be back. I never understood how he could know where I was when he was asleep, but he did, and in the end I let him stay. He lay curled up in the crook of my arm, while the winter storms roared outside the window. Sometimes I would get up and follow the low voices in the room next door. A tune was playing on the gramophone in the sitting room, a violet trail.

They were often up all night, Raksha and Ivan. Then they slept for half the day. It wasn't possible for anyone else to reach inside their world; they had sealed themselves off in something that was made of the two of them alone. In this first light of day they look so young, like they did before, and when I look at them now I see how short their lives have been, how little they know. Although deep furrows are already drawn across their faces. I look at my parents, Raksha and Ivan, gently dancing in the dawn, cheek to cheek.

"Mamma?"

She turns, pulling slightly out of his embrace. She has been crying, black streaks under her eyes making her look like a raccoon. And she has been drinking; how would she survive otherwise? Then she turns away and they carry on dancing, locked into the paradise and the hell they constitute for one another. They are alone in the world, those two, no relatives, no family, at any rate none that came home to us. When I watch them now, I don't know whether it is before or after what happened by the river. But when I go back into our room, Eskil's bed is no longer over by the window, so it must already have happened. The wardrobe has been emptied of his clothes.

They knew no other way of living, Raksha and Ivan, and without alcohol they were lost. It was as if the sun rose inside them every time they brought out their bottles. A sun that turned black in the end, after a few days or weeks of drinking, but even so, they would never have coped without that black light. It was a hunger I inherited from them.

You could say we lost Eskil because of Raksha and Ivan's drinking, that they were bewitched by each other and the light they found in alcohol. But it could also be said that higher powers were out for Eskil, and they would keep on trying until they succeeded. He was always hurting himself, stumbling over stones and doorsteps from an early age and hurting himself, falling out of trees and off rocks. As though a large hand in the heavens was making a grab for him. We had warnings, premonitions, but we didn't listen.

NIGHT

I would like to have my head back, I miss it. They always dispose of the head first, to eliminate the horror of looking a dead person in the eye. It is the gaze they want to get rid of; that is why they kill, to extinguish the light in the eyes, the stranger staring out from a foreign land. The head often ends up in a rubbish chute or a skip. Not mine; mine disappears into the slurry pit with the pink surface, sinking slowly to the bottom; and as it descends, my hair opens out like a little parachute over my head. No-one ever comes to find it. The thick, frothy liquid dissolves my face first, and then the rest. I would rather have been a skeleton in a secondary school somewhere, sitting there empty-eyed, an earthly representative of the dead.

We had reached the lake now, where the road came to an end at the edge of the forest. It felt as though we had been driving forever along the muddy road that receded behind us. When the engine stopped we sat in silence, surveying the lake's silvery sheen; a solitary black bird, soaring and dipping over the inky surface, the world's last bird. As if we were both waiting for something to happen, for the sound of icy wing beats from an ageing angel who would eventually come to my aid. But I was tired of angels, tired of hoping for rescue and deliverance; no-one could help me now. This was the place for my death, this was my great window to eternity, my trapdoor out of this world. I longed for the sound of the coffin lid closing above me, for everything finally silenced. No birds, no sky, no light, no escape.

"May I smoke in here?" I asked; after all, we were only sitting and waiting. I wondered what we were waiting for; perhaps for the courage to take my life, the courage I didn't possess myself. I imagined he might be afraid too, as I was. What was I doing in this terrible forest by this awful lake?

"Of course, smoke if you need to," he said, opening a small ashtray on the dashboard.

"Would you like one?"

I wasn't in the habit of offering; I was usually asking for cigarettes, even when I already had some, to avoid ever being without.

"No," he said. "I detest cigarettes and alcohol. They're disgusting."

He was funny, he had forgotten he was talking to a junkie.

"OK," I said, and lit what I knew was to be my last cigarette. And for one last time the little flame flared in front of me, the innermost cone of blue, the smell of sulphur stinging in my nose, the smoke spreading quickly in the small car.

"Go on, smoke, babe," he said.

I smoked, and I looked at the woman's photograph on the dashboard. She was waiting too, just as we were, and I hoped Eskil was waiting for me in some place a bit like a heaven. She had an age-old look in her eyes, as though she were viewing us from the perspective of eternity, her gaze stern, introspective, her eyes so pale they seemed inhuman.

"Who's that?" I asked eventually, for something to say, and because she was staring at us. My hands were shaking as I held the cigarette, there was a twitch in my eyelid; I think my fear excited him.

"She's part of my work."

"I assumed it was your mother," I said, to win time; suddenly I wanted more time. For what? What would I do with more time? Time was up, and that was what I had wanted; that there would be no more time.

"I don't have one of those," he said, getting out of the car.

I didn't know where I was going, but I knew I couldn't take anything with me. Whatever happened, my bag would be left behind in this world. I wished I could take it with me. At least the photos of Valle. Though I do have those inside me, etched behind my eyelids. I don't have eyelids any longer, but you know what I mean. I travel light. With little baggage.

"So how did your mother die?" I asked. He flinched, as if I had hit him. Now I think he hated that word more than anything else.

"Have I said she's dead?"

"You just said you don't have a mother."

He gave me a quick look, as though checking to see who I was. Maybe there had been so many girls in his car, he couldn't be sure it was actually me. Did it matter that it was me? I keep thinking I was chosen, but it might have been pure chance, or that thing called fate.

"Just because you've lost someone doesn't mean that person's dead," he said, and we spoke no more. There was nothing left to say.

I needed to prolong time, even though I wanted it to be over quickly, but it was the end itself that frightened me. I was afraid I would suddenly start running and be caught in his hands like a rat; I was afraid that something inside me would flare up, a will, an eagerness, a pulse for survival. I knew what he meant. No-one had died, but I had lost Raksha long ago. She had continued to be there, but I was no longer her child.

"I can't be your mamma any longer."

"Why?"

"There's nothing left."

"But I'm still here."

"It's not enough, Inni."

In hindsight I thought that possibly we were alike, the hunter and I; the same inner lassitude, the same way of sitting and waiting, of not running, not trying to repress what we had inside us, the precipice, the huge destructive force within a person, unseen, but relentlessly dragging her down. But I didn't say that then. Instead I asked:

"May I smoke another cigarette?"

"No. Shall we go?"

It wasn't a question, it was instruction for what was going to happen next. So I got out of the car and I left my bag on the seat; I hesitated for a second to pick it up, but I knew I wasn't going to need it anymore. It had been a present from Shane on my twenty-third birthday. That felt like a thousand years ago. I wondered what the shadow walking behind me would do with it, the grubby little white bag in which I kept everything I possessed. I wondered what he would do with me. I wondered what he would do with what was left of me.

Here at the edge of the thousand-year-old lake there was no longer a world; there was nothing, nothing to indicate that humans had ever existed on earth, only the smell of still water and the mist drawing in like smoke over the landscape. "Here I am, Mamma," I whispered. Perhaps I was already dead, I thought. Maybe he had already chased me along the road, caught me and dragged me into the ditch, pinned me down and strangled me and cut me up and buried me. Maybe I had already bolted into the shadow that was death, like a roe deer darting between car headlights, incapable of leaving the flickering light, doomed to run into it and be crushed by the coachwork. Maybe I was already travelling outside time, outside the world, even though I was still here, by this ancient lake; I didn't know if I was alive or if I was something else, I didn't know if I was earth or blood or nothing. I hoped that Raksha wouldn't have to see what was left of me. *It won't be me, Raksha.* I wished I could miss out the end. But the end came, and I was there.

And across time and the forest and all the forest's sounds, I can hear Shane's voice. It is close and soft and runs through me like gently flowing water.

"The difficult thing is giving someone something she's never had before."

"Why is that difficult?"

"Because, no matter how beautiful it is, if she's never seen beauty before, she won't recognise it."

"But I was never ever afraid with you, Shane."

He is silent for a moment, before his voice returns.

"But I was always afraid when I was with you. Don't you understand?"

"I'll always be afraid of myself when I'm around you," Shane said, burying his face in my dirty sweater. Darkness had fallen while we were making love, something we were not going to do anymore, and bats with outstretched wings flitted between the night-time trees above. As I lay there watching the tiny shadows skimming like flakes of ash in the air, I knew that if I could do it all one more time, I would choose Shane, again and again and again. For those moments of total closeness, when he was searching for veins along my arm while I was trembling; when I saw the fleeting shift of Valle's face in his; when I was standing by the window about to jump and he shook me, to make me understand that I was hurting him. The giddiness and tenderness when he pulled me in and we collapsed under the window and Shane wept so much I feared he would break. We were horrified by what we aroused in each other, but it was greater than anything else we knew, and only love can scare off evil. But since love is invisible, we have to believe in it, and that was what was hard for me, because I have never believed in anything. Not in love. Not in anything. But, I do believe in death, that death is the end. That is what I hope, that everything really does end here.

When Shane and I got married we stole the flowers from a grave on the way to the church. A bunch of white lilies that he held to his heart as we stood before the altar. Behind it hovered Mary with her baby Jesus. There had been occasions when we had slept in this church, on the floor between the pews, but now we were here to get married, even though neither of us believed in eternity. It was not that sort of age and we were not that sort of people. I looked at him standing next to me in an old suit we had picked up from a charity shop that morning; it was slightly too big and it smelled of mothballs and eau-de-Cologne. He looked happy and fearful, his hair still a little wet – we had bathed on Norr Mälarstrand on the way there – and it looked as though he had just been born. And Shane and I promised to love one another for better or worse. It wasn't difficult to make the promise; I still woke every morning and thought he was the most beautiful person in the world. The difficulty was keeping promises. But that is the very thing about marriage, that the ceremony erases the past and you get the chance to start again. We had never stopped loving one another, hadn't even achieved that; we had tried, but not succeeded. The tears that had filled Shane's eyes when we stood before the higher powers no longer spilled. It was an eternity since either of us had wept. When despair grows so deep, weeping is no longer an option. The church bells rang and when we went out into the sunshine the brightness blinded us and we walked in different directions down the steps, I to the right and he to the left, and we had gone several metres before we realised the other wasn't there. I was contained within myself, unreachable, dazed by the strong sunlight, faint with a hollow, uneasy joy. I don't think we told anyone we were married, not even Nanna. We had no witnesses, no Valle, no confetti falling like rain when we came of church; I don't even know if the marriage was registered anywhere. Nothing was ever real for us; we tried to imitate the rituals of real people, without succeeding. The worst thing is, I believe Shane truly loved me.

"Can't we do something crazy, something totally wrong?" I had said.

"What would that be then?"

"Get married . . ."

He laughed.

"How would that help?"

"I don't know, but we've been lonely for so long."

"Will we be less lonely?"

"We can be lonely together while we wait for a miracle."

"What kind of miracle?"

"I don't know. We'll just wait."

We never said to each other that getting Valle back would help us, but that was the truth.

People always think it was Shane who dragged me down, but that is wrong, I was the depraved one, I was the one who wanted it all to be quick. It was undoubtedly the drugs that rescued me from love; I don't think we ever took as many as we did then, when we were newly-weds. At the end of the summer I discovered I was pregnant with Solveig. A small dark shadow growing in the landscape of doom inside me.

—

It was the first summer and my photograph was now in all the newspapers. I have always thought there is something unnerving about faces, they are so naked, it seems indecent. I would gladly show my fanny to all and sundry, but I don't want anyone to see my face, and especially not my eyes. Raksha and Ivan were sitting at the kitchen table, eating toast, looking out; it was the evening of their second day together. The stream of cars and people outside looked different to Raksha now she wasn't on her own, it had drawn nearer and she could see that all the coming and going out there was nothing to be afraid of. Women walking with heavy shopping bags, deep in thought. An occasional child tearing along the pavement; old people, alone, moving forward so slowly they seemed to be standing still. Like ships on the horizon in the Kattegat, seemingly motionless, but when after a while you looked again they had always shifted a little. There was nothing bad about the people out there.

Ivan said he had to go out into the city to search.

"For what?" she said, afraid he would disappear if he left the apartment, that his memory of her would be wiped in the fresh clear air outside. Instead of answering her question, he looked at her as if she were an idiot. As indeed she was, she couldn't but agree. She felt imprisoned by her fear. She had managed without him for years and now she had allowed herself to be taken captive again. If he left today she would jump out of the window. Certain things never wane and when she laid her head on Ivan's chest at night and listened to his breathing, there was nowhere else on earth she wanted to be. Not even the place where the sleeping tablets took her.

"But will you come home afterwards?"

"Home?"

His gaze always made her feel stupid. The coldness in it, as if he wished her dead. But if she were an idiot, then what was he doing here with her? Perhaps they each loved their own idiot, maybe that was what they had in common.

"I can come with you wherever you're going," she said, preparing herself for an even harsher gaze. But instead the hint of a shine crept into it, not much, but just enough for her to dare to fetch her handbag and put on her coat and stand in front of him, waiting.

"I might be able to help you," she said.

They were down by the waterside in the Haga district. The sun reflected on the water, and the air was soft, with only the faint scent of fire that typically drifted over the landscape at the end of summer. The sound of a plane flying overhead drowned out the noise of the traffic from the motorway. Ivan looked like a little general, scanning the water, back straight, on his guard. For long periods he ignored the fact that she was there, but sometimes they smoked a cigarette together or ate the polony sandwiches she had brought. They were still not speaking. There was nothing to say here either. Nor could they find anything. The landscape was closed, revealing nothing. The trees gave nothing away, they rustled their crowns, indifferent to everything apart from their eternal reaching for the sky. Or perhaps, like me, they had no voice.

"Mamma," I whispered, but no-one heard me.

Ivan had told Raksha he would be able to sense where the murderer was, that he would use his instinct, but actually he sensed nothing at all. And that place was like any other place, grass and sky and trees and the late-summer smell of still water lapping to and fro in the canal. They wandered about as though they were on a large abandoned map, narrow paths over there, clumps of trees over here, the palace there, but it didn't help, the landscape told them nothing. There was no trace of me or the hunter, apart from the flattened grass where the suitcase had lain. The smells were new, it had rained all summer, and nature, growing, striving, kept her secrets.

He came to her every night, defenceless, or bearing only the winged touch still there in his hands. It was as if they entered a room that didn't exist during the day, where they were as one, where there had never been any hostility between them, and every new day they went back down to Haga. She knew he didn't want to go there alone, but each day she was still afraid that he would leave her in the apartment. So she made sandwiches and put on her coat and then she sat down and waited. She would give anything not to be lonely again. It was an awful feeling. She missed the time when he hadn't been there, when she had been sufficient for herself.

At night as I was going to sleep – a long time ago, when I was still alive, when I was still breathing, in a toilet in Central Station or on somebody's floor – I used to picture our planet after we had all gone. The roads without cars, the cities emptied of people, and the stillness that would descend over the world when our species was no longer here, when the factories had fallen silent, when the columns of smoke that had risen out of them for two hundred years had disappeared, when there were no more planes in the sky. In my dreams I would fly over this gentle, hushed landscape and imagine that it wouldn't be long before plants would force their way through the asphalt and the motorways would disappear and in just a few hundred years all sign of human life would be erased. As I lay there I saw the vegetation growing, tendrils winding, trees slowly emerging from the windows of ancient buildings.

The shining gash of Herkulesgatan would be gone, the whole of the Brunkeberg ridge would have collapsed into the old shafts, as if it had never been. Department stores and government buildings and airports would be occupied by birds and the old bank headquarters would have caved in and huge trees would grow out of the ruins, stretching to the heavens. And the branches would be full of insects again, butterflies and dragonflies would return. The thought of everything that was our world vanishing one day calmed me. It wasn't only I who would perish, it was all of humankind.

Ivan told Raksha that something would come to them if they just waited, and time was an asset they both had. So they kept on, spending their days walking around the place where I had been found. The depression in the grass grew less obvious with every passing day. The pale brown patch disappeared, the colour came back and as the earth was touched by sunshine and rain, the grass imperceptibly pushed up. Sometimes it was so beautiful it made Raksha ache; when the sun set over the silhouettes of buildings on the far side of the bay and bathed Haga Palace and the rest of the world in a soft apricot light. She hadn't seen the world's beauty before now: the cobwebs glistening between the sodden tree-trunks, the clean smell of earth emanating from the ground at this time of year. She reflected on the wonder of them finally having a child again together. After all these years. The only thing was, the child herself had gone. In her mind's eye I would be a newborn baby lying in the earth, like a flower, cocooned in a chrysalis from which I would hatch, pure and pink and shiny. And the change was so gradual it was almost indiscernible: at first it had been the murderer they were searching for along the palace shore, but very slowly they changed their tack and it was me they began to seek, without saying it aloud. Neither of them had seen my dead body. They had seen me being born, but they hadn't seen me die.

It so happened that the hunter was a regular visitor to that spot too, but always in the evening, and when evening came Ivan and Raksha would go home. The hunter walked around for a while, taking in the scene and its attendant smells, the earth and water, the strike of sulphur. There would soon be no trace of me left, the flattened, brown grass would be upright, the slight hollow made by the suitcase unnoticeable. He had wanted to leave some kind of sign, but it hadn't lasted. Just before the snow fell that first year he hung my bra from a nearby tree, but no-one saw it before it fell off and was buried in the snow, apart from a child who stood for a long time looking at it, until her father pulled her away.

"Look in the tree, Pappa, there's something in the tree."

It seemed to me there was a special luminosity about this place, but it might simply have been the glint on the water. Sometimes, in my mind, a hole opened up in the heavens above and an ethereal light trickled down through the layers of grey cloud and when it filtered between the trees it was like no other light. It was golden, a golden glow from another world.

Raksha and Ivan started going into the city in the mornings, they followed my footsteps, or what they thought were my footsteps, and they looked so lonely, standing on Herkules-gatan in the autumn rain, waiting. A man and a woman who appeared older than they actually were, paying avid attention to everything that was happening outside the bank headquar-ters. They didn't look like cops or social workers, they didn't look as though they were on drugs, they just stood there, in all their ordinariness and greyness, and scared off girls as well as punters. It might not have been a crime to stand as they did, hand in hand, staring in front of them, but a high-speed train coming down Herkulesgatan would have caused less of a stir. They looked as though they came from a different century: too still, too grey, as if preserved in ice. When I watched them it seemed as though a great divine hand were holding them down to the ground, but I haven't seen any gods here, so it must have been something else.

Sometimes they sat on the steps at Sergels Torg looking out across the giant chessboard and sometimes under the bare trees in Kungsträdgården. They didn't attract as much attention there as they did on Herkulesgatan.

"I love you, Ivan," Raksha said, as they waited in Kungsträdgården, sitting next to each other on a bench covered in bird droppings, each holding an ice-cream cornet. He didn't reply, but that didn't matter, he rarely did. She knew he would love her to his dying day, but as far as he was concerned, that was nobody's business but his own.

We had come from the river into the city, to the hospital. It was as if we had always been by that dark little riverbank with the black grains of sand, coarse sand with flecks of gold, as if until this moment our whole life had unfolded by the river and we had come out of that water with Eskil. When we emerged from an underwater land, reality was revealed to us for what it was, stark and merciless. We stood in the harsh light inside the hospital, under a naked, buzzing fluorescent lamp, illuminated and humiliated, and now when I look at us, I see our clothes are soiled with mud and seaweed and old river water. In this instant we became part of the world, ripped out of the great shadow we had dwelled in together, where we had been invisible to the rest of the world, free. Eskil was no longer one of us, he had been torn from our universe. He lay on a trolley and at last we stood beside him, the three of us; and Raksha leaned over him, wailing, her eyes burning with fear, and we could see that deep inside she was an animal, that behind her human form she was an animal. Everyone conceals something within them that others cannot see; the thought had always frightened me. This was what Raksha had hidden from me. And if I had been granted a single wish, it would have been for her to have Eskil back, and for him to have his Raksha back. I needed nothing for myself, I could forgo it all, if Raksha could only hold her child one last time. But that was not to be; this was the end, I knew.

*

I had known all along that this was going to happen, or so I thought. So why hadn't I said anything to Raksha? Why had I let him walk out into the river? Perhaps because, if it was to happen at all, it might as well happen straight away. Perhaps it was simply that my attention wandered for a moment; we had discovered a beaver's lodge by the huge underwater roots forcing their way down into the river from the trees growing up above, trees that were living off the river water, bowing their crowns over the river's brown membrane. I kept diving down to look at the little den, where I could everything as clearly as if I held a magnifying glass in my hand. Beneath the surface time took on a different dimension; the water's inertia and gentle resistance slowed down earthly time and transformed it into underwater time, time that moved more slowly without the sounds from up above that could measure it out and give it definition. Nothing happened down there, nothing much at least; the shadow of a gleaming perch swimming past a little further on, particles descending in the serried rays of sunlight quivering through the water. What happened down there was slower than anything happening up on land. There was hardly any need to rise to the surface for air; when I was down there I didn't need oxygen, or food, or love. He was collecting driftwood and pebbles at the edge, as I had told him to, and I saw his shins and his flippered feet a few metres away where he was standing. But time moved erratically, for long periods it stood absolutely still and then in a trice it lurched forward. For then I couldn't see his shins; no time at all had passed, and yet they were gone. And here's the thing. Afterwards you see everything as it was, that is the essence of time, you see it precisely as it was, and it is so simple, clear as the sweet river water, and later as the pebbles on his grave, as the deep blue of the heavens arching over us as we lower him down into the earth.

Raksha and Ivan were lying on a blanket in the sun, limp and drowsy with the heat, their legs entwined. It was a world of radiant light, and for a moment everything shuddered and swayed as it always did when you came up out of the river, before the world settled and regained its perspective and its rhythm.

"Has Eskil come back?" I shouted, as I hung on at the edge of the world, even though I could see they were alone. They rose slowly to their feet, I saw Raksha run, then fall and get up again. I dived back down to look for him. I guessed he might have swum out a little; he could almost swim, still doggy paddle, but nevertheless, he moved along with the back of his head under the water and just a little circle of his face above the surface. He was too scared to do proper strokes because they were so slow he thought he would sink; he didn't trust the slowness to keep him afloat, so he swam with his hands whirring like a propeller in front of him. And now he had swum off, despite me telling him not to, without asking, without taking me with him to keep an eye on those inept strokes that made him look like a puppy.

Raksha stands with her cold, mud-spattered child in her arms. In the hospital the clamour returns; there had been no sound at all by the river. None under the water, where the silence was total – that was why we were drawn there, Eskil and I, where the world was mute and iridescent green – and on this day no sound above the water's surface either. It wasn't far to the hospital and they put him on the back seat, but on the way there all noise was absent, we drove through a world that was utterly silent. And then we were standing outside the hospital room where he was lying dead. Or still alive, I thought, because I believed he was alive, even when I knew he was dead. Maybe everyone knew he was dead, apart from Raksha and me. Even after many years had passed, I still don't think she really understood. Perhaps you never do.

"He's in here," a nurse said, her hand on a door immediately next to us. It was as if the door had materialised in the wall the instant she touched it. Without a word Raksha backed away, unable to go into the room.

"I don't want to know," she whispered. And Ivan was somewhere else. As soon as we entered the building, he had gone. So that left me.

"You can come in if you'd like to," the nurse said.

Afterwards someone told us I shouldn't have gone in, but if I could do it again, I would keep going in. Because on the other side there was life, such as it really was. Eskil's half-naked body on the trolley, a heap of wet towels on the floor, spots of bright red blood, a group of adults pressing on his chest. It looked as though they were crushing him, as if they were trying to kill my little brother. Then I heard myself say: "It's not going to work, is it?" I don't know if anyone answered, I just said it straight into the room, to no-one in particular. Or to him, lying there in his bathing trunks, which were still wet. I think saying I knew it had all been in vain was a kind of self-protection. I still believed it might turn out OK, nothing was certain, Jesus had risen from the dead; but I didn't want to expose my trust, my hope against hope. The room spun, twisted full circle, but I was still sitting on the stool, I didn't fall off. It was like watching a film, so I just sat and watched. Since it was a film, it was all right. It was the only film I had of Eskil, and it had a bad ending. After a while somebody shouted that there was a child in the room. I didn't know if it was me or Eskil they meant. I just stayed on my stool. Everything was quiet for a few seconds when one of them standing next to him stopped pressing on his chest. Then another one took over. It was like sitting in front of a television set, and yet this was what reality was; it had been underlying everything, all the time. A crack had opened up that would never be closed; and through that crack there came no light, only total darkness. His hair was wet. What had happened to his flippers? That was foremost in my mind: who had taken Eskil's red flippers? It didn't matter now, because the time for play was finished, childhood was over. In any case, I had always hated being a child.

Enormous clouds are blowing in over the river and the children we once were are running faster and faster under the sky, and the sky is hurrying too, scudding past at speed. But the thought of running away from him never occurred to me; I ran a short distance, then I turned and waited for him to catch up. Every time I had a slight head start he was scared and shouted after me.

"Inni, wait!"

"Inni . . ."

He always thought I was going to run away from him or leave him somewhere. He didn't know I would have guarded him with my life, if only I had known what to guard him against. One night I woke to find him staring at me in the half-light of the room we shared by the river.

"Why aren't you asleep?" I asked, although actually I was too tired to speak and I wanted to return to my dream, where everything was soft and warm. But it wasn't like that for him. Sleep was a restless place and he didn't want to be there; in his dreams there was always something chasing him.

"I can't sleep 'cos I'm frightened, Inni."

"But I told you there's nothing to be afraid of. We're the only ones here."

"How do you know?"

"I just know."

*

We ran beside Raksha along the river, Eskil and I, one on each side of her. Raksha was the best thing we had. When she saw a falling star she shouted out, telling us we had to wish for something.

"Can't you see it? There . . . Now it's falling . . . Look!"

It was the huge comet everyone had been waiting for, the tail of light streaking across the sky, and anyone who didn't make a wish now would miss the moment for ever.

"But our wishes never come true," Eskil said. He didn't understand the importance of the comet, the fact that at this moment the whole world was watching it pass our planet, that it was close to being the end of our world. He looked at me doubtfully.

"Is that true?"

"If it's God's will."

"Is it God's will?"

"We'll have to see," I said.

We believe there is a connection between certain things, but maybe there isn't. Maybe it is all quite arbitrary. In any case, for Eskil it was too late; they told us later at the hospital, however long I tried, I would never have managed to blow enough air back into his tiny soul. *One breath, two breaths, three breaths* and then the wait with one hand on his scrawny chest, completely still, water and sand pouring out of his mouth, and if I just kept going he would soon come back. Since that time I have always had his little mouth against my ear, I still listen for those breaths that never come. The world beyond us both is a faraway murmur, never drawing nearer.

We had reached the end of the gravel road, travelled along it for so long, and around us time had slipped away, it no longer applied to us. We stopped at a farm; it didn't look as though anyone was living there, a grey film over everything, slurry tanks standing open like gaping mouths. It might have been a site he had discovered long before, or maybe he had studied plans of the area. It was as if this particular place had been expecting us. Located slightly off the map, where the rain poured in the wrong direction, up into the sky, a black, inverted rain, ascending against the force of gravity. Adjacent to the large house a barn like a naked skeleton, a few disused storage sheds, right beside the car a mound of dung I was about to step in. These parts were waterlogged, maybe that was why it had been abandoned. It has since occurred to me that this place, so very far in any direction from other houses and other people, had manifested itself there just for us. Wells with concrete covers and further away a pond with dry, blackened reeds round the edges. A tractor, a stone-pit, a solitary cat disappearing behind the house. He would soon be driving on and I still could have run, darted into the forest like an animal, but I didn't. For there was nowhere to run; and even if I did, I would come back here and he would be waiting for me. And why would I run? Why put off the inevitable? All stories end with death, and this one is no exception.

"Don't be afraid, sweetheart," he said, and started the engine. I said nothing, because I had nothing to say and this wasn't the right place, this wasn't where I was going to die. So we drove on. We continued until we reached a lake. I knew he was going to kill me, but I didn't run. Why? Because I had nowhere to go.

If he had told me then that I would never return to the city, that he would strangle me by that little stretch of muddy shore, would I have got out of the car and left? I hope so. But there was no-one waiting for me, I had nothing to hold dear and therefore nothing to fear; indifference was all I had. Dead or alive, it no longer mattered. I was already dead and had been for a long time; we wandered through Stockholm like a funeral cortège, my friends and I.

He said: "I pick girls up on the street as an experiment, a scientific approach to charting what goes on here. From work I head across Herkulesgatan, it's no big detour. You girls are always there, in different variations and constellations. As reliable as Jesus, simple and straightforward."

It is true. We come from nowhere, on our way to nowhere in particular. And money is something everyone understands. There is honour in it; it is untainted. And if one of us suddenly disappears, someone else will come. It is a space in perpetual motion, its door always open to all, where anything goes and where we always are. We expect nothing, we have nothing, we are simply there; and people can do with us what they will. We appeared like shadows in the street-light rain. A kind of forgiveness or comfort flowed from the holes in our bodies and I sometimes thought they came to us to weep. And afterwards we vanished back into the night from which we came. As if we surfaced the moment they noticed us. When they have discharged their effluent into us they want us to vanish, to remove our murky crevices, our averted eyes, and so we do, we absent ourselves, are gone. It is like going to confession, but without God.

"Look, I'm in heaven now," shouts Eskil, his mouth filled with river water. It is a heaven that has come loose from its mooring and rolled in underneath the black earth. When I look up there is no heaven and no Raksha, just an empty chasm where her eyes used to be, a yawning gorge that must be the entrance to the gates of hell.

It is always night-time in childhood. Eskil is standing by my bed again, his hair like a little halo of light round his head.

"Don't be cross, Inni, but I think I've wet the bed."

"It doesn't matter. As long as you're back."

But when I reach out for him he disappears and all that is left is the music and the crystalline light from the room next door. Where Raksha and Ivan are dancing their eternal waltz.

They tell me Eskil is in heaven now. But when I try to go to sleep at night, in the little interlude between wakefulness and dream, I hear his faint voice calling for me once again.

"I don't want to be on my own, Inni."

"You don't have to be on your own. You can stay here with me."

"But that's not possible."

"Of course it's possible. I can hold on to you like a balloon."

"There aren't any balloons here."

He is silent for a moment before saying any more. In the silence I can hear something coming that I won't like.

"I have to go back now, Inni."

"But I don't understand why."

"I don't either, but I have to follow the rules," he says and starts to cry.

"What rules? I don't want to follow any rules."

"I don't either, but we have to all the same."

After Eskil's death I was alone all the time. Alone with my kind, alone in my universe. But one day I discovered I did belong somewhere; I established contact with higher powers. I had fallen asleep by the river and when I woke and stood up, my shadow suddenly had wings. I stood absolutely still, staring at the pearl-grey angel wings quivering on the faded grass. Surrounding me was a strong smell of ether and marble and old feathers and the sound of furious fluttering overhead. When I turned, slowly as in a dream, a huge white bird of prey hung motionless in the air above me. The bird's wings in my shadow had made me look like an angel, that was all. It beat them hard to hover in the air before it flew off. But I never forgot it. I imagined I was in touch with something greater than myself and I too was an angel who could take my leave at any moment; I believed I was immortal. Now, I believe all the bird did was single me out for this hunter.

Massive cold clouds have formed over the frozen river and that year the first snow falls as early as September. It doesn't matter that Eskil is dead, as long as he comes home again in the end. He can be dead for a little while, I think, until we have changed, until we have mended our ways, become different people, less careless. After the funeral, I think, that is when he is going to come back. I look forward to the funeral, as if it were a party. But the funeral comes and goes without Eskil, and I realise that death wants something of us that we are not aware of, and I have to understand what it is. I am death's collateral.

"What's he wearing where he is now?" I ask Raksha.

"Nothing. We put his blanket in the coffin. That's enough. He has everything he needs now." Even though they are open, Raksha's eyes are closed, they no longer see anything. I would have liked that blanket back, as it does actually belong to me, but everyone has forgotten and I wouldn't want to be seen as a grave robber. It is bad enough that I want to dig him up and bring him home. I am worried he is frightened where he is now, in that unreachable heaven beneath us, that he is scared of the angels and the dark and the other dead people; I can picture old men and drunks and suicides roaming around down there. I imagine digging up his little coffin, taking him home and washing the earth out of his eyes.

The small black-clad troupe struggles against the wind with a coffin shining white in all the grey. Around us the world is cold, a dreadful '70s winter that kills everything. Eskil is under the ground by the church, and that is his place now, Ivan says. We are large ants carrying away our dead without understanding why we do it, just bearing them to a hole in the ground the gravedigger has opened. Everyone weeps apart from me, but something inside me has frozen. It isn't just the tears, it is something else. A disillusionment so deep, so penetrating, the freezing point of blood, the ultimate Antarctica of love.

Eskil doesn't exist now anywhere in this world. But he still comes to me in my dreams. I want to go and lie down so that I can meet him and I start sleeping for several hours every day after school, but months pass before he shows himself again. At first I hear his voice but can't see him.

"I'm here Inni . . ."

"Look, Inni . . ."

"Don't be sad . . ."

"Here I am . . ."

I stand on the riverbank with the sun in my eyes. His little shadow appears further down on the shore. He has a bucket in his hand filled to the brim with water and when he runs it bounces and the water splashes out. He races towards me as usual, his arms outstretched, like a miniature aeroplane.

"Shall I show you how much I love you, Inni?"

I try to answer but my voice has died, gone, and just as I move to catch him in my arms and lift him up, he dissolves, like a soap bubble in my hand; and river water and ashes run through my fingers.

*

I would really like to speak to Eskil about what is happening now. About Raksha's silence, about the fact that she has stopped talking to me. As though I don't exist. Maybe she never did talk to me, but at least I had him then. I didn't know how much I needed that little kid. I am always waiting for him to get in touch. Can you make calls from the kingdom of the dead? Can you phone from heaven? If that is where he is. Not that he was in the habit of ringing me before; Eskil obviously didn't make a single phone call in his life, he was too young and he had no-one to ring, we were his whole world. That is the awful thing about families, they are your entire world, there is nothing beyond it. But I can imagine that the means for talking to the dead would be by telephone, and I think we should have made an arrangement, Eskil and I, for finding one another if anything happened. Like the game he loved where he hid and I found him. The one where I walked around searching and pretending I didn't see him, though he was very bad at hiding, always visible in his red dungarees, as conspicuous as a streak of blood in the snow. Sometimes I think the game is still going on, he has just got better at concealing himself. I keep expecting him to pop out from behind a tree by the river.

With time I forget how young he was when he was here, how difficult it would have been to make him understand instructions about life after death and that he would have had to commit everything we said to memory. Did we talk about death before he went? We spoke about the deaths of birds and rabbits and badgers and squirrels, but never about one of us dying.

*

The slope below the grave is bare, just the wind blowing through some trees and further down a man by himself waiting to place the headstone. A seabird flying overhead looks as though it is chasing sunbeams. When the gravedigger is ready he makes the sign of the cross and lowers the little coffin. And the earth swallows up its prey, because the soil is meagre and dry, in constant hunger. Eskil belongs to the church and the gravedigger now.

There is a moment when I understand that he is ashes and dust, but I still keep asking, "Where is he now?" and Raksha withdraws from me even more. Soon she is a creature on another planet. And when she answers her voice sounds as though it is coming from a different world.

"He's in the ground."

"In the churchyard, among the graves? What about heaven?"

"Yes, heaven . . . Heaven . . ."

The road to heaven goes through the earth, she has already told me that many times before. That is why I am drawn there, as though by immense magnetic force.

We stepped out of the car in a single movement. All thoughts of running had faded from my mind; all the thoughts still present travelled in slow motion, as though they were wading through water or lumbering through mud, as though they were waste matter passing through bowels. The trees bent in dark shadows over the lake and the reflection of the reeds made it look like they were growing in both directions, up into the sky and down into the water.

Surrounding the lake was a narrow, dismal shore of coarse-grained sand and black stones, there were streaks of gold in the motionless water and birds in the distance, birds that suddenly rose into the sky and were gone. Churned-up foam rippled at the water's edge; no other person had ever set foot here, on the last shore, or those who had could all be dead now and I would soon be one of them. He took out the knife. "It's time," he said in the same gentle voice they used in the office when they were forcing me to give up my child, when they finally demanded the keys to our apartment on Sockenplan. His jaw was so tight I could see the skull under his face, the skeletal shape, the crude outline of a human being, and I recall how Shane and I had laughed when we saw Valle for the first time, the little frame with its grey edges doing somersaults inside the screen on the maternity ward. "There, now," he murmured as he fumbled with his trousers, before he pushed his way into the empty hole between my legs. There was no pain, nothing mattered any more, this was the end; and I thought, the end comes as a release, the only mercy possible.

I looked up into the sky, so close, lowered like a face above me, like a stream of water suddenly flowing round me, and all I wished for was that I wouldn't wish for anything else. I had wished for the end and now it was here. And yet within me came the pleading, like a bullet from a gun. *Help me, God, whoever you are.* But it was no good. Darkness descended on the world as if someone had thrown a blanket over it.

"Help me, somebody . . ."

Earth spilled out when I opened my mouth, black mud poured out of me, silt and sludge and slime, but no-one could hear me; when I finally called out it was far too late.

"Go on, shout," he said, pulling my head back, and I could hear my screams, echoing across the lake water. Was it really me shouting? Yes, it was, for we were the only ones there, and although he hadn't yet chopped up my body, everything inside me – my voice and my thoughts – was already in pieces. This was what he had been waiting for, for me to beg for my life. A sign. My shouts died away, my head fell to the side and he shook my body as though he had changed his mind and wanted to jolt me back to life; but I was no longer there. He bit me, scratched me with his nails, licked me like an old dog, as if he wanted me back.

Where is the sound of the twigs breaking when they strike my face? I can no longer hear it, the sounds are missing, only the taste of blood and metal and polluted rain in my mouth, and I feel nothing now, nothing hurts. *Do you hear, Raksha?*

I feel nothing now. Everything that was once important has ebbed away, like the tide, like the silvery magnetism of the old moon as it pulls everything towards it. Nothing can touch me now. Heroin takes it all; but when all the darkness is taken, so is all the light.

Just when you think the end has arrived, there is a pause, something in him or in time, a sudden inertia in all his movements. He looks up at the crown of the tree to which he has tied me, he looks over the forest, to the light flowing down from heaven onto the world, as if he is searching for something.

"What are you waiting for?" I want to ask, but there are no words left, all my words are pleas and I don't want to beg, not him, not anyone, I would rather perish than beg for anything. There are no clouds, only the smoky vault descending gently to earth. The last thing I want now is a chink to escape; I want it to be too late, for it to be over at last, for there finally to be something greater than my will. There is: he is holding his hands around my throat again now, and I see the sky above slide across as if on a platter, the vast expanse of the silver sky where all the colours run together like the ink in a water-stained drawing. Why is the sky never blue, why are there never blue skies, why are they only grey-tinged green and violet and yellow?

I see myself lying beneath the trees, collapsed in the mud. He is crouching, staring at me. He touches the bruise on my throat; it looks like a butterfly perching there. My jumper is ripped, my eyes still alive for a few seconds more before they become fixed. In an instant my body transforms into a photograph that has been tossed out onto the landscape, a stone or a leaf. He turns me over and uncovers my shoulders to reveal the marks of wings that have been torn off. It wasn't him; it was someone else who did it, a long time ago. And now, again, he takes out his knife and it shines like a mirror in his hand.

He drops my head into the old slurry pit – but I already told you that, didn't I? That there were such things in those days – because my neck bears the marks of his hands and nails. Then he positions the suitcases containing what used to be me along the motorway, so he can drive past every day and think of me and of what happened in the forest.

Ivan lay watching fleeting beads of light drip through the lowered blinds in Raksha's bedroom and Raksha lay beside him, watching him. When she closed her eyes she saw the birds of prey above the woods in Hägersten settle on the suitcase and try to retrieve the blood-soaked clods that lay inside.

"Why didn't he take her heart, Raksha?"

Ivan's head was in shadow. She took his cold hand and placed it against her cheek.

"I don't know. He didn't want it."

"But if her heart is still there, couldn't they wake her up again?" he whispered, and she thought he didn't mean what he was saying, but he said it all the same. And now he wept for the first time.

If I had still had my voice I could have told them that I hadn't had a heart for some time; I had a knotted, blood-soaked muscle under my ribs, but I no longer experienced feeling. That was what I had striven for, for heartlessness.

"She's no Snow White," Raksha said softly, "and really we lost her a long time ago."

Raksha used to read *Snow White* to me. She read other things as well, but that was the story we liked best. When Snow White's mother tells the huntsman to take Snow White out into the forest and kill her and bring back her heart as proof, a shiver of ice ran through me and I stared up at Raksha to see how she looked, to see if she was transmuting into someone else, but it was the same large, intent face suspended above me like my personal moon. And when Snow White promised the huntsman she would go into the forest and never return if he would only spare her life, her eyes glistened.

"I don't think it's her," Ivan said.

"Then you'll just have to trust me."

"How can I do that?"

Raksha sat up and placed her arms around his back.

"Do you remember that mark on her shin? The one that looked like a little heart?"

It was something they had said to one another a long time ago: one of the gods hadn't been able to resist drawing a tiny heart on me before sending me down to Raksha and Ivan. A little stamp of soft pink. Raksha continued.

"I've seen the mark on a photograph. And they had her fingerprints. I didn't want to say before. Or I didn't understand that we really were searching for her, you and I. And she had a small rose tattooed on her back. She had it done last year when she was pregnant. I've seen that as well. We have to stop searching, Ivan. Do you understand?"

Ivan turned away from her.

When he came out into the kitchen it was so late, darkness had already started to fall. Usually he would get up first, he always woke early and padded around the apartment, waiting for her to rise. It had only been a few weeks, but they already had their ways, and on this day she was the one waiting for him. He sat hunched by the window and drank his coffee without looking at her.

"I'm going out by myself today," he said, standing up.

"But I want to come with you."

"You can't. I have to go by myself."

"I can't be alone. I think I'll die if you leave me now."

She took his hand in hers and I knew she had always loved his big hands. They contained all the sensitivity he refused to acknowledge. He left his hand in hers, like a stone, he didn't move it, didn't answer. She went down on her knees and begged him to stay with her, but he walked away. Still without looking at her. And he didn't come back that evening. But he left his things in the bedroom. A suitcase and some plastic bags and a china dog he had bought in a flea market.

Ivan roamed around Haga Palace in the moonlight. In the background he could hear the gentle hum of the motorway. A narrow strip of shore below the palace, which was in darkness now, and further along grass and trees and occasional street lamps and the light streaming from the little temple. He thought he was walking around searching for his child, his child that society had lost. Those people up there took better care of their dogs than they had of his child. In a way it made me happy that Ivan was sad because I was dead, but I wished he would stop all this now, I wanted him to take care of Raksha. But all I could do was follow at a distance as he ran and stumbled on the muddy wet grass. I saw him stand up again and run on, from one end of the palace to the other, towards the motorway.

One night he walked up to Herkulesgatan. Light shone from the banks' windows, and the open mouths of the multi-storey carparks ejected the balmy air that used to keep us warm when it was cold. And that is how it is: at first we are invisible and then we are everywhere, huddled in our padded jackets and furs, frozen, waiting. Blank, eyeless buildings, the scent of eau-de-Cologne and patchouli, and after a while the men who step out like shadows from the architecture. Nanna stood alone on the pavement with a tape recorder beside her and a globe under her arm, wearing a hat I had never seen before.

The globe was bright blue and the flex trailed behind her when they walked away. They walked away together.

In the soft glow from a night lamp in a hotel room by Tegnér-lunden she takes something, as soon as they have come through the door, with her pants pulled down over both of her hips and one of her buttocks. Ivan looks away when she pushes the needle through her skin, and she waits for it to arrive in her heart. When she has finished, she collapses onto the floor, lying like a bundle of rags under the window, not unconscious but unreachable, and he lifts her onto the bed. For several moments he gazes at her lying on the bedspread; she must be asleep or perhaps just keeping her eyes shut, but they move like small living creatures under her eyelids. She has a large scratch on her neck, a blood-red weal, as if made by a claw. Gently he rolls down her tight jeans. I know that lying there she is floating in another world, a better world.

When there is nothing left on her lower body apart from a pair of faded knickers, he turns on the bedside lamp, removes the shade and passes the naked bulb back and forth over her legs. I realise he is trying to find that little heart that once was on my leg. He turns on the ceiling light, but still finds nothing; he runs his hands up and down her legs. When he turns her over she smiles and mumbles something. I think she is like an angel lying there, an angel just fallen from heaven.

Her breathing was so light, so imperceptible, and night crept into the room and filled it. Nanna looked so very young when I saw her with him, intensely vulnerable and innocent. When it was fully dark and only shafts of yellow light filtered in from the street and the buildings opposite, he stood up and took off all his clothes and left them lying by the bed. In the half-dark it looked as though someone must have squatted there and left a little pile of turds. He lay down behind Nanna and fell asleep.

He never came back to Raksha. Having waited for weeks, she went to the station and took a seat on a high-speed train south and then walked all the way to the apartment block by the river where, in another century, she had once lived. From inside the apartment she could hear the sound of the television, but he didn't open the door. In a broken voice she shouted through the letterbox, but there was no reply. She sank to the cold floor and sat motionless, but for the slight movement of her eyelids in the darkness. Sometimes the light went on in the entrance hall and she blinked at the fluorescent lamp for a few moments before it went dark again. She sat in the corridor, freezing in her thin coat, her teeth chattering, like a little animal. I believed it was my fault she was sitting there, but I couldn't help her. If only I could have told her Ivan was sitting on the other side of the door, listening to her breaths.

After two days she took the train back. The journey was quiet, she was alone in the carriage for most of the way, sitting by the window in the bright sunlight and seeing the trees thin out until they disappeared completely and were replaced by bare, drab landscape. She imagined she was bound for the under-world, that the conductor who periodically swayed through the carriage was her escort. He smiled at her every time he passed, as though he had personal charge of her journey. Perhaps she had never properly left that first time many years before. She had walked away from Ivan then, with me at her side, in the belief that she was saving us from something, at least that is the way I see it, that she left so that I would escape their war, but Raksha's life thereafter had just become a period of waiting for him to come after her, of waiting to experience again the shining light she had once experienced with him. Now she was really leaving, without the hope that he would come running. She believed she was on her way home at last, that nothing was waiting for her, that what had begun one night at a fairground in Ängelholm twenty-five years earlier was finally over.

Only children believe we can have everything we wish for, but I sometimes think there is no such thing as children, the idea of the child is simply an illusion. So-called children are merely smaller in size and more easily deceived, they live with adults under duress, like any cuddly toy or pet. You hold out a dog-eared photograph of a gleaming baby, so people will think you are virtuous. As I did, thinking I was the Virgin Mary in the beginning when I was out pushing Valle in his pram, when he was newborn. But a human is neither good nor evil; she is like a wasp, part of the ecosystem.

There was a curse on our family. With the huge waterfalls and the polluted water came the darkness, and it kept on flowing through the generations. When I was a child I believed I would be able to lift that curse, but I went along with it instead. It was so easy, there was a golden line to follow, as plain as the river lying heavy on the landscape.

It is very easy to kill someone, so much easier than you might imagine. I think that was what he said. It was the only thing that surprised me, his sentimentality, his difficulty in letting me go, his unwillingness to leave me there by the lake. Why did I go with him? I went with him because I knew he wanted to kill me. I recognised him the minute he appeared in the street; there was something about his eyes, he looked like anybody else, even attractive, but his eyes were like a reptile's or a dragon's, glinting cold. Everyone on the street knew who he was, and everyone was afraid of him, avoided him and his car; but not I.

I always liked the idea of dying by my own hand, of taking control of my own life, the only way of rebelling against the world. But the truth is I was too weak to put the knife to my throat myself. And I always knew I would die young. This is eternity without me.

LONGING

Lake Vättern lies like a gash in the landscape, a gigantic water-filled groin that opens up when you come down the E4 motorway from the north. It is one of Europe's largest lakes and little Solveig walks along the shore every morning with her satchel. I have seen her going back and forth between the house in the forest and the school beside the deep lake. She is constantly sidetracked and is always late, because she keeps finding things. She has coins and stones and other treasures hidden in every drainpipe. She knows nothing other than life here, in this little town with a church on every corner, where the houses rise steeply up the mountain sides; round her neck she wears a silver cross that she touches when she is anxious. She prays to God every night, not because she believes in God, but because that is what you do here. She prays for puppies and kittens and white parrots. Her world is filled with small animals, just like Valle's, cats and deer and foals and little birds, an entire Disney World.

The shimmering blue mountains all around mean that it is always cold; the town lies trapped in shadow and the lake is never warm, even in summer, for it is so deep, over a hundred metres at its deepest. Solveig knows that she was born of wolves and that a human family has taken mercy upon her. She knows I am dead, but not how, and she knows that Shane has gone, but not why. And this is what hell is, watching your children live on without you. You think you will escape sentence by dying, by being murdered and dismembered and dumped in white suitcases and eaten by flies, but it isn't enough. The punishment is having to watch, without the ability to get involved. But the truth is, life is better for them now that I am no longer part of it.

Valle has already moved numerous times and I think he struggles, though he never says anything; he would never complain or make a fuss, but several times I have seen him crying when he is on his own. He mostly keeps to himself and no-one seems particularly attached to him, neither children nor adults. Perhaps it is because he forgets to wipe his nose and round his mouth, and he always has a streak of milk and snot on his upper lip. Maybe it is because he eats faster than the others and with his mouth open, maybe it is because he has grown rather fat. Only a mother could love him. He sleeps on a rug outside his foster parents' bedroom, because he is still too frightened to sleep alone. Like a little dog. We are the ones who made him scared of the night.

It was a dog that discovered me, but sooner or later I would have been found by a person, given that the suitcases were so close to a human thoroughfare. It was as if he wanted everyone to see me, to see what he had done. In the late autumn of the first year he hung my bra on a sapling close to the place where one of the suitcases lay, but the snow came early and when it melted my bra was gone. He kept some of my things and buried them in a wood close to the house where he lived at the time. A small mirror, my earring and a stocking, which swiftly decomposed, like a flower. I think he wanted to sink back into the mire where his soul belonged, he wanted to come forward, to be punished, but his courage failed him.

He preserved his memories as I preserve mine. For him I was the writing on the landscape, a secret message for an undisclosed recipient. I still don't know what the message was. We know nothing of what is in a person's heart, we can only guess. It would have been better if I had disappeared without trace, if no-one had needed to see my dead body; it wasn't even a body anymore, it was offal, carrion, shapeless lumps as far from their origins as the body parts glistening in the refrigerated cabinet at the cash-and-carry.

The crowns of the trees above are moving; it looks as though they have come unmoored and are drifting on the white surface of the sky, as if the sky itself were an immense lake in which the treetops are being drawn irresistibly to its murky depths, leaving the roots floating on the top like massive black hands reaching for heaven. I think it must be the birch trees tinkling like a thousand tiny bells and making a speckled dance of light that stipples his freckled hands. And now the numbness comes, spreading through my body in swirls of gurgling silver, it comes when there is no more chance of escape and I feel as though snowflakes are falling inside me. A feeling so raw, so pure, so cold, transcending anything I have ever known.

A tremor passes across the lake, an invisible wind ruffing and scuffing the mirrorlike surface. When I try to say something, blood spills from my mouth. It doesn't matter, in any case it is too late to say anything now. This is death's vantage point, the hunter's angle. My body is lying on the grass, a leather glove turned inside out. The eyes of the person lying on the grass are half-closed but there is still a glimmer of light beneath the eyelids. Why does that not go out, if it is all over anyway? And where is the blood coming from? Bright red foam at my mouth and he hasn't used the knife yet. And now the world is finally slipping away, like a ship, or a sandcastle swallowed up by the tide. Just as Eskil slipped from my hands so long ago. Brown water flooding the world, running into my eyes, death filling my veins and everything else, the layers of tissue in the orbs of my eyes, the ragged membranes in my lifeless womb, a mounting black slime slowly smothering my vision. Retina and sky merge into one, black ink overflows from the glass that is the world. His face is still suspended above me like a mirage, an image that jumps and shudders and shakes, as if someone has cut into your gaze with a knife, or sliced into the very perspective. I will pray to anyone at all now, I want an angel to come and devour me, I want darkness to surround me, for light and time to vanish from my eyes. I see everything slip away, the grass and the trees and the little slope down to the lake and the firmament above me with a scattering of clouds sliding slowly past in the opposite direction. Now his face is my entire universe, the only thing filling my eyes. The intense grey of the gaze, the prominent bridge of the aquiline nose, lips that are flat and half-open and saliva dripping onto my naked face, water coursing from the openings for his eyes and the dark hole of his mouth. I wish my last picture could be something other than this, a tree or a flower or Raksha's face from long ago, but it is too late for wishes now. And I hear Raksha's prayers running through me like old rosary beads. But I didn't believe in God and God never believed in me and I never wanted to be saved; nothing scared me like salvation. *So see me now, Raksha, as I walk into death, as I walk into the murderer's world, see how I walk in with open eyes. See me now, Raksha, as I soar into the heavens never to return.*

The ripples on the water have settled into a mirror surface of leaden gold, the setting sun behind the pine trees, the birds caught in a wing-beat. Every image is frozen, like my body, rigid, fixed, a photograph. Like the pictures of me that will appear later in the newspapers. The black-and-white one where I have permed hair and eyes as deep as graves; I look bloody awful, but Shane said it made me look like Bambi. We took that picture in a photo booth on Kungsholmen.

He must have picked up the knife, for then small droplets of blood flew through the air, some as tiny as pinheads, sombre spatter on sombre sand. Soon I was lying on the shore in seven pieces. Soon he had scooped out my womb and pulled out my intestines. The world was broken now, seven fragments of mirror lying on the grass, seven bits of heaven reflected, seven sections of the hunter's unknown face. That is why it is so hard to remember; because all experience comes piecemeal. It has always been this way. There is never a complete picture of the world, never a single picture. Something in my vision began to tremble and spin before the picture could appear and then there was no picture at all. Just slivers of reflected light and voices and wisps of heaven. But now I was rendered harmless, no more images would come to me, and nor would I try to say anything else. Tongue cut out, head tossed into the sludge, face streaked with mud and grit.

*

I think of Valle when he was newly born, how quiet he was. I was waiting for the cry but it didn't come. Why isn't he screaming, I asked the midwife. She shook her head and smiled, wrapped him in a blanket and laid him down with me. As if she didn't know the answer either. But he was alive, he was lying there with his round eyes looking up at me, he was breathing, he was moving his little hands, they were opening and closing. He didn't ever cry much afterwards either, just lay quietly in his crib under the window, looking up at the sky, as if he already knew he was alone in the world.

And now? Now he places what is left of me in two suitcases and puts them into the boot of the car. My blood is still on the earth like a shadow, but the earth here is mostly sand and ancient shells and it will soon sink in. He stares out across the water, calm and focussed, so much in the moment that the colours of the landscape assume uncommon depth, and everything strikes him with intensity, sharpness, like the reflection of something not of this world, the smell of water and earth and blood, the sound of the torpid lake water, the lapping of tiny waves. If anyone had asked him he would simply say he was performing a deed everyone else would have liked to do; make me dissolve, turn into earth and flesh and matter for the stars, put out the light in my eyes definitively. Someone has to do it, and he is the one with the courage. That is how he would explain it, if anyone asked. But no-one ever does.

After we die, the place we occupied in the world is filled by the living sooner than you would think. It doesn't take long, something to do with time and gravity and how your space immediately contracts, seeming to shrink, in the end eliminating the room we took up on earth. Even if the laws of physics had been on my side, it would have been impossible for me to return. If I suddenly showed up at Valle's and Solveig's, they wouldn't recognise me, although they think they miss me. What they miss is an old fairy tale that finished long ago. Valle remembers us, but his memories are mere snatches now. They nestle inside him like glassy wicked stones and he brings them out as seldom as he can. Perhaps so that they won't wear thin.

I try to find a bright memory inside him, but there are none. None in me, and none in him. I don't know if it is because shadows always gather in memories. Or maybe the occasional bright moments don't count in the great darkness of what is left of our lives. I couldn't look at photographs of him even when he was living with Shane and me. Not even on the good days, and there were such days as well. Many days were full of brightness, untainted, many days I would stay away from all the bad; and we had a good time, Valle and Shane and I. Even if it was sometimes boring in the way it is with a child when you stand pushing a swing in some godforsaken playground, though in your heart of hearts you are filled with tremulous, whirling joy at the beauty, light and miracle of

141

your child's being. But in all the baby pictures in our photograph album, Valle looked so alone and helpless, as if trapped and defeated by the camera's empty flash and the very idea of being a baby. I can still see the little quiver of the dummy when he had sucked so hard and created a vacuum that finally relaxed.

Even in those days I would start weeping the moment I opened our album because I felt sorry for him sitting locked in the picture, sucking on his plastic dummy, and I couldn't reach him, couldn't comfort him. The photographs were time that had passed and had made the undone done. And so it still is. Where have those albums gone now? I have no idea what happened to all our things after my death. It doesn't matter, here you have no need of things, and maybe it is just as well they have gone. Valle and Solveig have created new pictures, they have new family trees.

The earth's surface is covered with the dead; we are a dark mixture of ash and gases and organic material that you tread on every day. Certainly not on purpose, but it is a fact, every day you tread on us and force us deeper and deeper into the earth. The living have always been afraid of the dead, but there is nothing to fear, our space on earth is soon filled by those who are left. Just look at Solveig on the sofa, lying on Ellen's knee with her eyes closed with the news on in the background. There are reports on the television of blood and earth and mortality and tonight there has also been an item about me. It isn't a problem, because Solveig isn't listening and anyway she doesn't know it concerns the person who was once her mother. I hope she never finds out. There is no place for me in the house by Lake Vättern; Solveig is consumed with the people around her, Ellen and Johan, whose love will come to be a shining light inside her. I often wonder who has taken my place on the street, who is looking after Nanna, and I wonder if anyone rings Raksha now that I never do.

I come to them in their dreams. I blow gently on Solveig's face as she sleeps, but perhaps I just drive more and more shadows into her when I try to fill her with light. I wish I could give her a heart that can endure both love and tragedy.

Sometimes when I am there she wakes up and calls for her mother, and, because I can't reply, soon the other mother is sitting by her bed.

"Were you calling?"

"I dreamed you'd gone."

"But I'm here. I'm always here."

As a mother you have to last at least twenty years, and that is a long time, but I think Ellen is the type who will manage it. She has an inner calm and as she says now in the dark of the night, she is always there for Solveig and the other children. Perhaps she does slightly prefer her own children, her birth children, but I hope Solveig also arouses a special tenderness, as she lies in bed, warm and soft, stretching out her arms to be picked up even though she is really too big. Her eyes are pale blue, her mouth as small as a woodland strawberry.

"What happened to . . . to my . . . mother?" she might suddenly ask on such a night, and each time the question makes her more uneasy, since after all her mother is sitting right beside her on the bed, Ellen's cloudless face suspended above her like a lantern in the half-dark room.

"Was she very lonely?"

"Yes."

Every time Solveig wakes at night and asks for me, I think I will have to stay away in future. All I have to give her is anxiety and broken sleep. They have told her I was ill, but she seems dissatisfied with the answer, as if she knows instinctively it isn't true.

"Why couldn't they make her well again?"

"She was very poorly and in the end her heart gave out," Ellen says, stroking Solveig's soft cheek and glancing aside, the way you do when you tell a lie. And it is obvious she can't tell the truth. But I'm still sad. Your mother is a mound of flesh in the forest, Solveig, I whisper.

*

And I am grateful, I really am. I could never have given Solveig everything she has now. It is difficult to explain. It is not that it is clean, because it isn't, we made everything cleaner than this, Shane and I; we were constantly cleaning, like maniacs. But there is a tranquillity about these people. Trivial things, like Ellen taking the time to fill a spray bottle with half washing-up liquid and half water, to save on washing-up liquid. That sort of thing shows attention to detail. She takes her time, she isn't on edge. She and Johan are in a place they want to be and they are not going anywhere else. She can't imagine another life. This is enough for them: to be woken early by the blare of an alarm clock and go to work in the care service and the library and come home again to cook a meal and clean the house and play with Solveig and the other children. Ellen and Johan find beauty and order in the world and have a natural place in it. In my head I had hundreds of plans for different lives and didn't know which of them to seize upon. And so I seized on none.

"And then I came to you," Solveig whispers in the small vestige of night still resting upon her room like a gossamer of blue. She is soon sleeping again. Peaceful and safe in the house by Lake Vättern. A light pours from the black water at night, as if a higher being lives deep in the lake. I don't hear what Ellen says in reply, for when she says it I have already left.

I am the one bringing troubled dreams to her, the silent wing-beats of the night. No, I have no wings. It is just a metaphor. But sometimes in the past it did feel that way, that there was something monstrous moving on my back, as if there were an

145

alien presence within me that would force its way out between my shoulder blades at any moment.

Sometimes I used to think that Valle would be fine regardless, that someone touched by a love like Shane's and mine would never forget it; it was like an elixir or a shining aura that would always have an effect on him. Now I think the elixir we passed on to him was harmful. Our desperation and disquiet flows through him. Our longing for death.

I can still hear Shane's voice, though he left me a long time ago, but his voice remains inside me, like the soft purl of water. Or was it I who left him? You leave each other so many times before you finally go, in the end you don't remember who left whom. Perhaps it was love that left us both, it tired of us and moved along. I don't think we deserved it. Whatever love is. I think it is a place in the light where nothing can catch you.

Solveig often says it. "And then I came to you . . . And then I came to you . . . And then I came to you . . ." As if, by repeating it, she will understand where she comes from. Maybe she is only trying to erase what was there before, to create her own lineage, starting from when Ellen and Johan appear. Certainly, she was in my womb for months, but it could have been anyone's. She must have heard my voice and Shane's, but she would doubtless have heard many other voices. The women at the local authority office; a variety of people in the street talking bullshit right next to my enormous stomach. And those two hours at the hospital after the birth when she lay and looked up at me, only I remember those. For her that time is gone.

Valle is alone in the forest in Havsmon with his knives and in the half-light of dusk he appears lit up from within, like a little cherub. No-one has taken my place in his life; he is still waiting for someone to love him.

He is so like me, it frightens me sometimes. I can see the deep pit inside him, opening and closing. I daren't look in on him, I imagine I would destroy something. His existence is so fragile, the eczema makes him sore and he finds it difficult to sleep at night because he has such dark dreams. The nightmares come from Shane and me. I have seen inside those terrible dreams, seen him hunted by a pack of wolves that want to kill him. The wolves are us and we come out every night. If I had a gun I would shoot them.

At school he is on his own, no-one ever speaks to him. When he asks if he can join in, the others just shrug their shoulders and carry on as they were, and Valle doesn't know what to do. Other kids take a shrug like that as permission to participate, but not Valle. He tries to walk quietly away so that no-one will notice him. He hides his loneliness from his new parents; he knows that no-one likes a boy without friends. Sometimes he stays out in the afternoons and says he has been at a friend's house. Then he will go into the forest, sit on the big stone by the lake and whittle sticks into weapons. I don't want him to carry a knife, but it makes him feel safe to have it in his rucksack, shining, wrapped in newspaper. At dusk he returns to the house in Havsmon and has the same feeling he has at school, of not being truly present for the others there. They are never unkind to him, never a bad word, but they see him come and go as though he doesn't really exist in their world. Every day newly pressed clothes are hanging by the side of his bed. They often ask him if he needs anything, but he doesn't understand the question and would never think of anything he needed of his own volition. If it weren't for the dogs he would run away. It is the only time he is happy, when he is with the dogs in the forest, when they run towards him through the trees so fast that all four paws leave the ground. Does he remember the dogs we used to play with on Floragatan? Does he remember that he once lived with wolves?

He has already moved many times. He has only lived with these new people for a year. The house in Havsmon isn't very far from Solveig's, just a few miles north. Neither knows of the other's existence; I don't think anyone told them they have a brother or sister. Perhaps it is just as well, as they wouldn't be able to find each other anyway.

I would say to Valle and Solveig that if you don't see any point to all of this, to all the hurt that always hurts, to the impossibility of the three of us ever being together, it is because there isn't any point. I believe that in the end what matters is accepting your place in creation. You have to learn to love your fate, or at least accede to it, regardless of its price, regardless of its hell.

There was only the two of us now. I imagined my grave would be the lake, that he would drag my body into the water and let it sink. I pictured Eskil sitting on the lake bed waiting for me, so I felt no fear. The effort to live as the creature someone had once made me, God or Raksha or Ivan or whoever it was, the creature I had never managed to be, was over now.

Drowning is said to be a gentle death, almost erotic. But the body doesn't want to die, it can't give up, its every fibre is focussed on survival. It is a human pretence, to say that death is like falling asleep. It isn't like that even for those who die in hospital; they suffocate slowly, as if smothered by giant hands.

But drowning was not to be my fate, for now he was strangling me by the water's edge. That was what he had been waiting for. Finally he was equal to the gods. I too had been waiting, waiting for someone with the courage to kill me.

I assume it was something he wished to prove to the world. His strength, and the inner resemblance to a god that only he knew of. When we drove through the forest I had been frightened, but when we reached the shore the fear had vanished. I stepped out of the car as if I had already arrived in the kingdom of the dead. Weightless, speechless, cold. I lay down on the shore on a blanket that he fetched from the car and he wasn't instantly transformed before my eyes. His gaze didn't darken with hatred the way it sometimes could with some of the men on the street, when my naked body and my naked face suddenly filled them with rage. This one was still as a lizard before he throttled me, his touch on my body cautious, bloodless, slightly awkward. Then he lay on top of me and tightened his hands around my neck. I didn't scream, because I couldn't, my vocal chords were ragged and I was bleeding all over my lungs.

Valle ran away and when he was found in Stockholm the people in Havsmon didn't want him back.

"We don't think it's a good idea," they said, wringing their hands.

"Children in this situation often run away," said the woman in the social services office who was responsible for him now. "It's a way of testing you. To see if you really want him."

Valle was sitting in the next room, waiting, but they didn't know that. He didn't hear what they said, but through the wall he felt the frostiness grow, felt the chill radiating from the room. The couple looked down at the table, their hands entwined.

"No, we don't believe he wants to be in Havsmon. And the truth is we can't cope with him anymore."

From the room next door Valle saw the pair from Havsmon being led along the corridor, their eyes cast down to the floor. He thought about the dogs and wished he could have taken them with him to wherever he was going next. He thought more of the dogs than they did. They showed the same cool friendliness to the animals as they did to him. If only he could have gone back and stolen those dogs.

Someone came into the room and told him he was going to be driven to a temporary family in Vallentuna where he would stay until a new home was found. Valle walked out to the taxi and immediately fell asleep on the back seat. When he woke two strangers were staring in through the window. All he hoped for was dogs, that these people would have dogs too. But the new people had no dogs and the silence spread like a vapour through the rooms. He didn't know what to do with himself in the house and he felt as though he was being watched as he sat on the edge of the chair, waiting. They asked what he intended to do with his life. He had no idea, he was eleven, he didn't even know what he was going to do with the next hour. Did he ever think about us, about Shane and me? We were no more than a flickering candle inside him that he could never really grasp, a warmth seeping up. There was so much time that only I could remember, existing in him as mere slivers of light. I hope he has my love in his soul, the love from the first years of his life; I hope it can stay inside him like a protective serum. But I often think it must be the reverse, that we have poured poison into him and this is what prevents him accepting the loving care of these people. That must be it, but the thought is so painful it flies away before it can take hold.

I used to hate the people who had assumed responsibility for Valle and Solveig, I despised their smugly virtuous lives, the fact they could already have so much, they had surplus to give to an unknown child. Now I hate only myself. I see Valle sitting in his clean, sunshine-yellow room in Vallentuna, not touching the things they have given him, not daring to move anything from its original place. He makes his own bed every morning without anyone asking him to and the only things in the room he picks up are the dog posters that belong to him and he can look at them for hours. The people have suggested he could put them up on the wall, said it might be nice to have them framed, but he doesn't want to. He wants to be able to get hold of them quickly if anything were to happen, if he suddenly had to leave again. There are children in the house, but they are old, teenagers, always on their way out somewhere. They call him their little kid brother, knock on his door and come in to look at the dog pictures, but after a while it goes quiet, they walk off and Valle is left alone in the room he dare not touch. Sometimes the older ones have presents, small things, cheap, but nonetheless: a packet of chewing gum, a bouncy ball, a Disney comic. In the mornings Valle is so quiet that in the room around him a circle forms and becomes impossible to penetrate. Every time he attempts to say something his face fills with blood and every time it gets harder. They let him be and in the end they forget he is there. All the time he has that comic-book sense of there being five mistakes in the room to spot: his head, both his arms and his legs hanging point-lessly over the chair with feet that don't even reach the floor. No-one says it out loud, but it is as clear to him as if they had shouted in his ear.

When he ran away from Havsmon he regretted it instantly, but he couldn't go back because he was ashamed. He didn't ever want to leave the dogs. He travelled by train to Stockholm and walked around for days before they found him. Something draws him back to the city and I suspect it might be Shane and me. If only I could make him understand there is nothing here, that under its elegant surface the city is raw and danger-ous. I hope he doesn't run away this time, but I recognise the instinct to flee, the desire to escape from the world the moment it comes close. Inside, he is already on the run. When he lies in bed in the afternoons he is in another world, a world I hope doesn't claim him completely. It is like a drug and it makes me frightened. So I look away.

One day, when I had just begun to show, we went to the social services office, Shane and I. It was quite a while before it was outwardly noticeable though, because I was so thin. I think Solveig was trying to hide away from us in there, and I can understand why, we had nothing to offer her on the other side. We told them the truth, that everything was falling apart and they would have to take her as well. In fact, Shane and I didn't see eye to eye; he thought I was awful, I was giving up too easily. Maybe I was, but he didn't know what it felt like with the needle against my vein, aware of the baby fluttering inside and not knowing if it was withdrawal or my anxiety that was waking her out of her dormancy. He didn't know what the danger felt like sweeping through my blood into hers, surging straight from paradise into me and making her quiet. Into us, for it was the same sick blood that flowed between us; we were still as one.

I had taken drugs when I was pregnant with Valle too. But that time I didn't know what was in store, I didn't know that I was carrying inside me a real child with bright eyes and a ticking heart and breath of untouchable delicacy. Valle had been the child who was going to change everything; and he had changed nothing.

After we had signed the papers Shane stayed away more and more, and when he was there he didn't look at me, he looked

at something further away in the room. I wasn't taking anything now. I drank from time to time, vodka or red wine, and
I took a few pills, but none of the things I craved. I lay in bed
for days on end, watching the sky skim along outside and
feeling the baby move inside me, first like a spider and later
like a little fish or seal. An elbow, a knee, the weight of the head
between my legs, and we spoke to each other wordlessly as I lay
on my side with my hand pressed to my stomach, as if goading
her until she kicked back. Solveig was born that same year on
New Year's Eve.

It was one of the first warm summer nights, when the heat lingered long after the sun had gone down, hanging like a haze on the asphalt far into the night. When I had seen him circling us for a while, I walked over, bent down and met his eye on the other side of the car window, and when he had lowered it, in an infinitely slow electric motion, I asked him to take me somewhere.

"Where do you want to go?" he asked.

"Away from here," I said.

And when he leaned across and opened the door I entered his kingdom. It was like stepping into a different world. Inside the car it was still and oppressive, sun-hot seats, stifling air, classical music coming softly out of the radio. He said nothing, he didn't look at me, and I don't think I even said my name, perhaps he already knew what I was called. He put his foot gently on the accelerator and we moved smoothly away past the bank headquarters and the multi-storey car parks. And I saw it all for one last time: the girls standing around in their short fur jackets and their tights, smoking their way through the night. Above every girl hung a little cloud of smoke like an umbrella. I imagined it was Nanna leaning against the entrance door to the bank, an open book in her hand, but when we drove past I could see it wasn't her. And I thought how much I loved those girls, loved them for their simplicity and sensitivity, for being quite unafraid, and only here with them had I felt loved. It was the last thought I had, before we joined the motorway and drove on into the wide night.

I tried to say something when he entered me, but when I opened my mouth earth spilled out.

My soul had been loosened from its moorings many times and I had been in that floating place, looking down on myself, but this time I wasn't coming back. I knew that he would kill me, knew that I was going to die. A storm passed through his body, something shaking him, perhaps just the rush of orgasm. Saliva dribbled from his mouth onto my face. And the pictures came faster now, flickering shreds, black cracked mirrors, huge arrows fired into me from a giant bow far away. Who aims pictures at us from far-flung worlds? Pictures that will become our lives. Like the picture of me as an insect, ravaged by unseen wounds and injuries, a subhuman filled to the brim with filthy lake water threatening to spill out at any moment and drown everything around me. Is it Ivan's picture? Or Raksha's? Or is it the blessings and curses of the gods? You run into the arms of death, you seek a huntsman and a slaughterman. There is no way to withstand what lies ahead. And then he picked up the knife again, and I thought that was a good thing, for no-one would recognise me now, no-one would be able to identify me as anything other than earth, blood, waste. I had come into the wrong world, where I was never meant to be. I wanted it to be as if I were never there.

The sound of my heart beating across the landscape is deafening, and then it stops. I see the world around me disappear. It doesn't hurt. It doesn't matter anymore.

The only thing he kept at his own house was an earring. Doubtless he still has it, though probably stored away in a safe place. Perhaps he buried it in a plant pot so it would be close at all times; it was right by him on the occasions he was questioned by a police officer over my death. Yes, there was just the one earring, I only ever had one, in my right ear, a butterfly earring Shane gave to me. There was nothing symbolic about it. I don't even like butterflies. They are insects in disguise. He wanted to keep something, as a denial of total separation. I have realised, now that I have had the time to study them, that this is why murderers often slip up. They get caught because they find it difficult to say goodbye, they linger at the scene, leave clues on the body and take all kinds of trivial things. A lock of hair, a skull, or, in my case, an earring and the key to a locker at T-Centralen station, where I kept all my worldly goods. They were few in number, but they were mine. He never used the key; he threw it into Strömmen Bay and before long they opened the locker and disposed of my things. My suede jacket and bicycle key, my big tape recorder and the little plastic wristband they give you in hospital so that you don't lose track of your baby.

I remember the smell of that night. The stench of blood. The smell of genesis, the primeval odour of birth. Lake water. The same as the smell in the delivery room, around newborn infants. Seaweed and algae. Blood and excrement. Solveig exuded an intoxicating fragrance, as though someone had just lifted her out of a lake; but two hours later she was gone. That final night in the world, I remember the reek of lake and old vomit assailing me, the evening light hurtling down between the trees and the faint whir of the electricity cables above us. And the luscious scent of June, when the air is sated with moisture and sweetness and newly formed blossom.

June is the month of madness, when the sky is never dark; when sexuality, the beast within, awakens; when the flowers and caterpillars burst out of their cocoons and swaddling-clothes, brimming with chlorophyll and lust for life; and when the hunger stirs in creatures such as him to rape and strangle someone. But never will you find the person you are all searching for, never will you discover who he was. Someone picked me up in the twilight on Herkulesgatan one night in June; someone was with me in those last hours by the edge of the lake in the forest. I am sure that on that night by the lake, man and beast became one.

People say the dead know everything, and only the dead know the truth, or at least we think we do, and that makes us quite irritating. It gives us a superior attitude, unconstrained by fear of losing something, for we have lost everything already, even ourselves. Living a lie is over, the words speak for themselves. And maybe we do know a little more, since we have so much time to take a look around, when every moment stretches to a thousand years in the special time prevailing here. We see everything we didn't see before; whenever we return we hear new things, we see the fall of light a little more clearly and it has always shifted slightly since the last time we looked. Later when we are given passage, we revert to what came before, to the great anonymity, to the chain of life and rebirth that the body is part of, and we become flowers, trees, worms, butterflies. At best. Very likely most of us become ash and stardust. But you have to be patient, you must wait for permission to pass. The last time someone speaks our name on earth, we get our leave to travel. We need hang around here no longer, authorised to sink back into what came before. The silence of eternity. That is what we hope for. Yet no-one who loves me mentions me anymore. It is others who prattle on, people who write in the newspapers, folk who know all about everything. But I can't help hoping that someone will utter my name, that Valle will suddenly say "Mamma" and mean me.

*

It is the same with the murder series constantly on television, people in them spouting off all the time. Sometimes they catch my eye when I go past. Everything on television is about murder now. I don't know why, but people seem to love it. It is no different on there: the police officers and criminologists each acting as some kind of hero, sitting in immaculate rooms, with sleek hairdos, discussing the killer. And meanwhile my world is conjured up, and ever so subtly beside their glossy world a dangerous underworld emerges. Full of junkies, whores, crooks and other desperados. It tends to be the extras who play those parts. But really the only person of interest to them is the murderer, and of course the dead woman doesn't feature. Yes, it is usually a woman and she is just a brief glimpse, a blur of green body, and then she is gone, out of the picture, disappearing into the depths of nothingness whence she came. I think the principal characters in the television series, deep down, are impressed by the killer, by his will power, by the Napoleon flair with which he vanishes into the night with no trace left behind. What can the dead woman offer? Nothing. And anyway she has nothing to say.

Valle came up to Stockholm and there he stayed. After Havs-mon he had gone to Hjo and after Hjo to Jämtland, where he lived for a while when he was young, and after that he lived in Mora and eventually in Södertälje. When he ran away from Södertälje, it was only a few months before his eighteenth birthday. So they let him go his own way and he rented a subleased apartment that they paid for. Then he must have lost that place, because the next time I see him he is sleeping in a doorway. The stone floor is so cold against his face, against his soft, warm cheek, but lying there, drifting within himself, he doesn't feel it; he senses nothing of the world around him, has only the embrace of absence inside rocking him gently to sleep in the wind. He sleeps in stairwells just like his mother, but I have the impression it is harsher now, more dangerous, or maybe it only seems that way because my child is the one sleeping there now. I don't remember being afraid myself, I felt free and invincible when I slept outdoors; I thought I had found a way to cheat the system, to charge along outside time and society, like an animal, not imprisoned inside a cage but unconfined, whilst the rest of the world was kept captive behind its bars. Well, you know where that freedom took me. And now I am afraid when I look at my child.

It is obvious Valle was drawn into my world. At first I was secretly glad, flattering myself that he went there to search for me, but it hurts when I see him waiting for a dealer to come and give him the promised land that evaporates so rapidly. He looks so small, so slender, in his hoodie and bomber jacket, like a child waiting for his parents to take him to the cinema. But I assume he must see what is in my world, as if a hidden trail lies within him that he has to follow, an instinct. Skinny legs in black denim disappearing into a pair of trainers. His hands deep in his pockets, his shoulders hunched, as they are all the time, as if he is always slightly cold; and his wary watchfulness. He has that chemical, unnatural air about him now, as though he isn't human but belongs to an army of the dead. It wreaks its effect on Valle as rapidly as it did on me; the heroin seizes you with a force greater than any other and it refuses to let go. Though that last bit isn't true; it is you who won't let go of the heroin. I still love the word, but no longer feel the physical manifestation the word produced, the inner rush.

I watch him as he sits on the sofa with a needle in his hand and a flex wound round his arm. Lying beside him are a girl and a boy, knocked out, already half-asleep, smiling. And when I see him sink backwards and throw back his head, suffused as he is now with the great namelessness, I see that this is paradise, this is the paradise on offer to people. I reach out to touch him, his head resting on the other boy's shoulder, almost affectionately, but they have already forgotten one another, and I am the one always forgetting I don't have any hands. And now I see how close it comes each time, death sweeping across the room, its big fist ready to snatch one of them at any moment. Should I hope for it to be over quickly? Should I hope for a grave for my child? What should I hope for?

*

I look away again and when I do I see Solveig and she seems to be forever suffused in a glow. That is why I named her Solveig, so that she should have her own inner sun that would always shine on her when we were there no more. Shane and I decided on the name together, before the thought of giving her away entered my mind. Then I found out her name doesn't even mean sun; it was Raksha who discovered it in a crossword clue, that it means the one who fights. That may be true, and the whole fighting thing might be a good idea, but Raksha could equally have made a mistake, and as far as I am concerned, it still means sunlight. Whatever the reason, Solveig goes through life as though she was never left a changeling in the forest, as if nothing could ever damage her. Do you know where she has got that security from? From me. I gave her away so that she should walk free. If she had stayed with me she would never have started at university; I have always been afraid of those people, in their towers. But Solveig walks through the ancient university buildings with her head held high, a special kind of pride surrounding her, and even from afar you can see that she likes herself. That is another thing I couldn't have given her; from me would have come shame and silence. She sits for days on end in the reading room of the huge library in Uppsala. It looks like an old museum, from the outside like a palace, and some of the books are the size of coffins. The mere name of the library makes me nervous. Carolina Rediviva in gold letters over the entrance. But Solveig moves around so easily in that world. As she seems to do in all worlds, as if ignorant of rules and boundaries, or just pretending she can't see them. Except that she has a girlfriend now. Called Clara. I have heard Solveig call her name.

*

Clara always wears a black leather jacket, even inside the library, and she has febrile eyes, eyes that I see are to fall in love with, their intensity and lustre like pure honey. It is cold in their world now, late November, the trees are bare and the leaves lie stiff and frosty on the ground and I watch Solveig and Clara standing under a tree in Slottsparken, kissing, heedless of the cold around them. Breath steams from their mouths, and all the time Solveig's hands are feeling under Clara's jumper. Vaguely I remember that touch of soft skin beneath my hands.

I wanted to bathe in Shane's gaze for ever. But our love was like a stagnant pool of stale, sick water. We were bound together by invisible cords and in the end all we were capable of was wounding each other.

"But at least we did our best," he whispers across time and all the noises of the forest, past death.

"Do you really think so?"

"Yes . . ."

"In that case, Shane, our best was lousy."

He laughs gently. "At any rate, the best thing we did was have Valle and Solveig."

"Wrong again, Shane. Having the children was the most appalling thing of all."

"I'm not afraid of what's ahead. I'm not afraid of anything anymore," Shane said the last time I saw him. It was in the cemetery, I still had the identity wristband on from the maternity ward. We sat between two graves and talked. He was thin, translucent, and he couldn't forgive me for what I had done to us by giving up Solveig. He didn't say as much, but he didn't need to. He didn't look at me, he looked at everything else apart from me, at the crowns of the trees and the clods of earth and clumps of grass he was scratching out of the ground. I wanted to tell him that he had to look at me and that the only thing that could be forgiven was the unforgivable. But perhaps it was a long time since he had looked at me, perhaps I was simply a reminder of all our failures. I asked him if he was going to Istanbul. "Maybe," he said, "maybe not." I dared not ask anything more. He spoke to me as if I were a stranger who had taken a seat beside him. When the silence had lasted a while I walked away. Now I see the scarlet patches on his neck.

I was always going somewhere, always in a hurry; I went with strangers because they were strangers, because they had no notion of who I was. Just as I didn't; there was no-one more of a stranger to me than I was myself. To wake up naked with blood on my thighs in a bike shed on Kocksgatan didn't make me afraid. Only when there was something to fear was I afraid.

"It's because you're a flyer that it's always so fast for you," Shane said tenderly, taking my face between in his hands. If there was a good interpretation and a bad, he always chose the good.

"I'm not a flyer," I said. "I'm a drug addict."

Shane saw things no-one else could see; that was why I wanted to be with him and it was why I wanted to be away from him.

"You pretend to belong to this world," he says some time at the beginning, when he still laughs about me forgetting that we were supposed to meet, when I have been gone for days and can't remember where. But I am not good enough at pretending, and something else constantly draws me in, away from him, away from reason. Sometimes I think it is because I see more clearly than everyone else, and I understand more, that I take the drugs. It was the aforesaid angel that unlocked the world for me. Every time it beats its wing inside me, by some topsy-turvy law of nature I fall upwards, against gravity, with the birds and the light. But how can I explain this to Valle? And to Solveig? How can I explain that there is something greater than all the rest, something greater than our life, something greater than Valle's eyes looking at me and believing I will choose him over drugs? I must have been born with a monster in my soul.

I accept they took Valle from me, but I can't accept the way they did it, coming so early in the morning, without notice, snatching him out of our bed. I could have taken him to the social services office myself and sat him down in the playroom and when he was engrossed in one of those toy cars I would have walked away and never gone back. But perhaps they knew I planned to escape with him to Istanbul. Sometimes I think that if they hadn't taken him, we might be there now, Valle and I alone by the Black Sea, winter on its way and the tourists departing, and I would be clean, and there would just be the two of us and nothing of what has happened since would have happened at all. We might have been able to live with Shane's mother. But then I recognise that it is probably as well it ended up the way it did, their stealing him so brutally from my arms, that a single trauma is a good thing, a single rupture rending everything apart. So that for the rest of his life he knows I would never have willingly given him up. Not how it was with Solveig; I handed her over, like a parcel.

One day I could stand normality no longer and that was when I crossed over to the other side. It was like walking through a glass wall that smashed soundlessly into a thousand pieces. I stood in a rain of broken glass with my first syringe in my hand and if I could, I would tell you how beautiful it was, as if all things were illuminated from within. Once it has been within reach, there is no way back. You can never return to the earlier world, the one that was there before, even if there were a previous world to which you could return. For me it was never about that. And it wasn't about the physical experience, nor the abstinence, but there is a total stillness and clarity that you can't live without once it is revealed. The world outside has been emptied of meaning, and you begin to understand that it has always been that way, it is raw, ugly, unjust. No-one tells the truth about it, but that is unsurprising, because no-one tells the truth about anything else either.

But now I was lying in the mud by the little lake with a human shadow over me. The trees bent their huge, dark crowns to the lake. I had always thought they bowed their delicate necks over the water in prayer and finally, helplessly, were drawn down, driven by thirst towards death. A hundred years might pass before they drowned, but slowly, imperceptibly, they were on their way. Never in my entire life had I begged anyone for anything; I had never bowed down, like the trees by that lake, to anyone. Instead I had been smashed like a withered branch.

I thought of the angel's wings I once believed were mine. But there were no angels, and a darkness enshrouded my vision, and I died.

He leaned over my dead body, which was lying like a pall on the earth, a puddle of human scraps in blood-soaked shreds of clothing. His face was unmoving, frozen like the world around us, and my head looked so large lying there, as if it belonged to an animal.

"I only wanted to be with you," he whispered to what moments ago had been me.

Time must have flown in Valle's world for he looks so different now. He is bigger, as if he has grown several sizes since the last time I saw him. I couldn't believe it at first, but he has actually given up drugs and as a result that unnatural look he had has disappeared. It is something of a mystery, as he hasn't become religious, he hasn't been in rehab, hasn't fallen in love and I don't think he has suffered a lightning strike to the head; he has simply stopped, and his life is calm. Perhaps the physical exercise has saved him; he works out for several hours a day. At first I thought all those muscles looked odd, as though he were wearing a suit of armour under his clothes, but I suppose it makes him feel invincible. In that case, it is a good thing, if he considers himself more whole, and if he knows he can defend himself. Now that I have grown used to it, I like watching him; he is changed, but still the same, and his skin is glowing and alive, his eyes are as clear now as they were when he was a child. But sometimes I think his life seems so bare and lonely and I am more anxious for him now that he is clean and no longer has something to protect him; and I can't help wishing him the gentle veils of heroin and a single mission that fills the world.

He looks like Shane did at that age and I am almost embarrassed when I see him, as if I am gazing at Shane again. I was so deeply in love with Shane, but falling in love is quite difficult to understand from eternity's perspective and here it is incomprehensible that the tiny reverberation sounding through your body when reason leaves it can have such massive consequences.

Valle looks very much alone walking between job and gym and the little apartment and then sitting the whole evening in the ice-blue glare of the computer screen. And that is life, getting up in the morning, getting dressed, working to earn some money, and then coming home and having something to eat and letting your soul be sucked in by a television or a computer. What else would you do? There is still a silence around him, and it seems that with each year it increases. Sometimes a girl will arrive on the scene and stay for a while, but then she disappears and Valle flies off on a new trip. Always travelling alone. He has a tough job in telesales, but he can handle it; he works incessantly and he gives his all in every telephone call, a place where he isn't afraid to speak. When he has free time, off he goes again; he is good at saving money and he has already been around the world several times and he never looks happier than in that moment when the engines roar and the plane is hauled into the sky as though by some mighty force. I often think about all he has seen on his journeys, the things imprinted on his eye. The Inca Empire. Beirut. The seas off Alaska. The cities in South Africa. The skyline in Shanghai.

Thousands of planes are suspended around the globe, looking from a distance as though they are crawling, when in fact they are streaking along. From above they look like lanterns floating on water. Valle is sitting on one of those aeroplanes right now; I don't know where he is going, but the plane is moving eastward and in the cool of the cabin with the sun shining in through the window and a grey Moscow lying below, he is half asleep. He loves nothing more than flying, as much now as he did that very first time at the age of two when we went to Istanbul, and he spent the entire flight standing stock-still in the seat by the window, staring out.

"What can you see?" Shane asked from the next seat, a protective arm around him so that he wouldn't fall off if the plane were to make a sudden lurch. I thought: Why do we have to return to earth? Why can't we stay up here forever?

"The first time I saw you I knew I wanted to have a child with you," Shane says. It was so weird, we met and ten minutes later we were sitting in a bed under an open window; we had said nothing to each other, just left together. A party at which neither of us knew anyone. Rather like our entire life, a giant party where neither of us actually knew anyone. We walked away to that room with the roof lights, the one he used to borrow from a lady in Mosebacke with a view over the whole city where you could always see the sky. We didn't sleep together that first time, we just sat all night looking at one another. It was a long time before we did. It felt as though we had just arrived in the world, we were newborn, like nascent stars at their most vulnerable, material from stellar explosions re-forming. But I would never say that to Shane. There are things you cannot say. I don't think I ever said I loved him.

"But you don't know anything about me," he says a little later, when night has returned. We haven't turned on any of the lights; it is easier to talk when we can't see each other. His voice is as naked as a fluorescent tube in the dark.

"Maybe not, but I know I like the person I become when I'm with you."

"And who do you become?"

"I become no-one."

*

The sun was on its way back after night-time, a soft, downy light rising from below, from the ground and the trees, the way it does on certain nights in early summer, when in a burst it starts to flood the world. When I saw my reflection in a toilet mirror in McDonald's, streaks of mascara had run down my face, like black tears; though I wasn't sad, I was happy. I had made myself up to look dangerous.

"You're sweet," Shane said.

"Come on," I said, and we took the metro to the end of the line.

"What if things are happening too fast for us?" Shane asks. I don't think things are moving fast enough. I have always wanted to do everything fast. Love, do my first syringe, have a baby, die.

At night for the first few weeks after we found out I was pregnant with Valle, we lay in a bath in the Hotel Admiral until the water grew cold. On the surface around us floated strands of hair, soap residue, particles of food, semen. Shan had said he wanted us to give up drugs now. "Yes," I said. It was obvious we ought to quit, we ought to quit no matter what, but it was something people said, not something we really meant. But this time he did mean it; he said he would bind me by my hands and feet if I tried to leave. So those first few weeks we were clean, for the first time since we had been together, and wide awake with the harrowing thirst in our blood. Through a window in the bathroom we saw the little band of darkness that was night at this time of year, the dark striation drawing in across our part of the planet only to withdraw at once. All I could think about was the fierce desire as the dark liquid was forced out of the syringe into my blood and spiralled through my body until it met the very source of life. When we slept together it used to feel as though Shane was making love to my naked heart. And now – no feeling at all.

From here I see everything so clearly, from here I see all the twists and turns. One night some time later, when we felt slightly better, I left the Admiral, going out without knowing why. We had celebrated Shane's birthday that night in the window.

"What do you wish for?" I had asked him as we sat in the light of the candle on the Black Forest gateau we had pinched.

"You," Shane said. "I'll never wish for anything else if I can be with you."

"You have me already," I said. "You have to wish for something else. Something nigh on impossible."

His eyes glistened. He didn't look at me when he spoke.

"Every time I go to sleep I'm scared you'll be gone when I wake up."

"Me too," I said, because I was as scared as he was that I would leave. At first he had tied me to the bed, but now he didn't. We weren't sick anymore. The rope lay coiled up by the window.

"But do you need me at all?" he asked.

"If you only knew how much I need you. I would be an angel without you."

After he had fallen asleep I went out and came back with a silver packet. On the metro it gleamed so brightly in my bag I thought everyone could see it. I lay down on the bed and floated away. I had got into the first car that stopped, without checking to see who was sitting inside. When I lay on my stomach on the backseat with a man on top of me who wasn't Shane, I thought I would die, actually die, but I didn't. I stood up and walked back along the narrow wooden bridge over the water past the National Museum and the Grand Hotel, and on through Kungsträdgården to Sergels Torg.

Valle was born and I recognised that we were on the lowest rung over the abyss and that below us was only a gaping black gorge of nothingness. When we left Danderyd Hospital I was afraid they would stop us, but they didn't. We ran across the car park with Valle in the carry-cot, like thieves. He was so sweet with the creases round his eyes. He didn't need to be sweet; it was enough that he existed, was our child. Shane had said he wanted to protect me from all that filled me with fear, from the demons and vampires flocking around us as we lay on the grass in Berzelii Park the first summer after Valle had arrived. We were contained in the boundless radiance of baby-hood, in a dome of sunshine and sky under the trees with the little boy between us as proof that we would never forget one another now; and I think he really tried, he did his utmost to shield me, but he could never save me from myself.

I wish I could say I did all I could to protect Valle, but it isn't true. When he was newborn I thought I would kill myself if I failed to keep him safe, and it was easy not to take anything for the first few weeks; Shane and I were basking in the endless glow there is around a baby. But after a while it started to hurt when I looked at him because he was so defenceless, his little mouth and wide-open eyes seeking me out with such trust; I was terrified that he was dependent on me to survive. It was as if, suddenly, I saw us from the outside, a panoramic picture of us walking under that vast sky with him in the buggy; and

I could see how fragile it all was, how the black birds of doom were circling above our small apartment on Sockenplan, how ridiculous it was of me to believe I could do this. So one day when Shane came home I was sitting with a syringe in my arm, and the moment he opened the door, I pressed it in. Shane's face went white, he stopped in his tracks and just looked at me as I let the wave take me and its force fling me into another world as it always did. He carefully took Valle from my arms and retreated to the bedroom with him. I think in my mind it was up to him to take care of Valle now, so that I could let go for a while, but after a few weeks we were both shooting up. At first – it was later that same evening – I promised I wouldn't take any more, but my one relapse had scratched the fragile surface on which our lives played out and without voicing our intention, we started again. At first only a little, and then as much as before. And later even more than before, because we couldn't face what we were doing to Valle. People say that you can't choose to die if you have a child. But you want to die precisely because you have an innocent little child. Children are the mirrors of death; you see yourself in their eyes, grotesquely magnified. You see yourself succumb, that it is inevitable, that you do them harm. You see it is all your own fault.

Shane made me stop breast-feeding that day, announcing that was the way it would be from now on, and I didn't dare argue. Perhaps everything would have been different if I had been able to carry on. Breast-feeding a baby was the best thing I ever experienced. When I took him away from my breast the last time, something inside me shattered, not that I blame anyone other than myself, but nevertheless I want to explain that something broke, I even heard it, a strange crunching sound deep inside my body. And yet for the next three years we would fight to keep him. Why? When we could have let go there and then and allowed him to be free of us.

Why should you tell the truth when it is so easy to leave things as they are? It is something I constantly ask myself. But I realise I haven't been alone in all the lies. Lying is part of human nature, an ability refined by evolution. You have to presume that people lie, not the contrary. But I would like to tell the truth. For Valle's sake. The notion of doing the right thing for once, even though it is too late.

Nanna dropped by from time to time. She lay beside me on the bed with her big books. Stoned and beautiful in her sunglasses despite it being winter. Outside, the snow fell soundlessly and she read aloud to me from a book about snow. Her books were always on the theme of snow.

"This is the end," I said after she had closed the book.

"No," she said, "this is the beginning. We have a little baby. We have to be stronger than we are now."

She used to have conversations with Valle when he was inside me; it felt pretty silly, but good, and Nanna always knew what to say. She talked about herself, and sometimes she talked about me as if I wasn't there.

"Hi, little person," she said to my stomach, patting it. When she spoke I saw thousands of shadows behind her head, shadows of all of those she had driven away with into the night, the ones we made a living from. She said she would take care of the baby should anything happen to me, she would be there come what may. Then she disappeared again. There was no-one who could make herself as invisible as she could when she wanted to.

"I'm here," she said every time she appeared, only to vanish once more. When she hid behind her hair she looked like a tiny animal.

"Can't you see the sky?"

"No," I said; his large head was in the way and all I could see was him. Thunderstorm eyes staring at me. Wide with lust, icy with loathing. The passage of an instant and a thousand years there in the forest. I could feel my heart, filling with blood and emptying of blood and then filling with blood again, I saw my arms drop to the ground, and what had been my body was still. If I could do it all again, would I go with him? I fear that I would. This moment was the culmination of a thousand and one other moments. And the silver packet twinkled in his hand.

His pale grey eyes are flecked under the vaulted lids; he has a graceful, almost subtle way of moving, like a dancer, with an elegance to all his movements, and he doesn't look dangerous. And as for his face, it is transfigured before me, the leaden eyes suddenly filled with blackness, an eclipse of the eye, the chill of death pouring from his soul. Desire, pure and raw. When he looks at me his stare is so intense it burns my skin. He touches my breast, he touches my face, my lips and eyes, and in that stare, lust and hate are forever intertwined. Here am I, naked and cold before him, and he severs my head from my body as if it were an insect's, and for one reeling moment, though my head is disconnected from my body, my eyes are still alive and for a few split seconds I do indeed see heaven, before it burns out and the light disappears and cold water bubbles in, between my skull and brain.

Did I really think he would kill me? Yes, maybe I did, but I didn't think it would be the end; I believed all along I would return, as someone else, that I would be forgiven. Forgiven for what? I don't know, simply forgiven. For being born, for existing in the world. A murder victim. And then a revenant. Lost. Liberated.

It is eight thousand metres as the crow flies from Haga Park to Hägersten where my body was found, twelve thousand by car via the motorway. Maggots, some of them still chrysalids, are crawling around me. The odd fly, green. Lethargic, barely moving. That first autumn people everywhere are saying it was someone with a head for maths who murdered me. A hunter or a dancer. A scientist or an architect. To which I could add the judge I slept with towards the end; he used to hunt in the forests outside Uppsala, but maybe he never told the police that? As far as I am concerned, it makes no difference who did it, who is guilty of my death, I mean. If the gods were put on trial, they would all be acquitted, and I have always known I would die young. And I am like Snow White, afraid of nothing, not of huntsmen or forests or murderers. My problem is that I didn't want to be saved.

All I know is this: if I had managed to escape, I would have had nowhere to go, and if I had been able to say who he was, if my tongue hadn't been cut out and my mouth filled with earth, no-one would have believed me. So what does it matter who did it? I got into his car and we drove past the high-rise buildings and the fields and on into the green landscape and that was the last time I saw the city.

Thus it is: suddenly you are holding a dead girl in your arms, cold and white as marble, despite the fact you thought you would simply drive her back to the city afterwards and drop her off in Kungsträdgården and see her disappear between the overblown cherry trees. For something else took over, from nowhere, without warning, like a wave rising inside you, and once there it obliterated all else, flooding the world in a gruesome black ooze of water; you couldn't find a way to withstand it, and nor perhaps did you want to. You were filled with a godlike strength, controlling life and death, heaven and earth. Immortal. Invincible. This demon, for it is a demon and a god of sorts that takes up residence in humans, has lived in him for many years and only shown itself from time to time, the shadow brother or furious genie someone has accidentally let out of a bottle. Afterwards it seems to him it was all a dream. But he can't take anything from that dream, he can't keep the dead girl, he has to part with her in the forest. He will always remember me with tenderness. Yes, tenderness.

In any event, now we are in the forest by the thousand-year-old lake and an organ that must be my womb lies in his hand, grey and glistening and bloody. It looks as though it weighs so little, no more than a hen's egg.

I could have asked:

"Will we come back again? Can you promise me that I'll come back to my children?"

But I had no children to come back to; there was just me and that city and its architecture of cruelty.

You can see the resemblance to Eurydice. She has already been raped by the gods and for her it is all too late. It isn't that Orpheus wasn't permitted to turn his head and look at her, she couldn't care less about that, it is simply that she must have a pretext for remaining in the underworld. You need an excuse for choosing darkness.

Shortly after I had met Shane we went into the city one evening to buy shoes, and I went off for two weeks. I was going back to him the entire time, to everyone I met during that period I would say I was going home, and it was the first time in my life I had felt like that, that I actually was going home. "I'm going home," I said to anyone who asked, and I was so tremendously happy when I said it. But for all that, I didn't go home.

Solveig must have persuaded Clara to go with her from Uppsala to Stockholm, where she is living now, because every time I see Solveig, Clara is around. She is still constantly in that leather jacket, indoors as well, and her eyes are just as intense when she looks at Solveig, filled with light and loving kindness. Solveig has started wearing a suit, and shiny shoes and a coat from the NK department store. Every day she enters one of those sky-blue buildings next to the Museum of Natural History and stays inside for hours. Time is movement. Maybe so. Nothing here moves; it is all in a state of perpetual doldrums.

When Solveig and Clara talk about their lives, it sounds as though their words are coming from a book. They never speak about me, and nor does Valle, when he speaks at all, perhaps because they don't know much about me. Solveig knows only what she has been told. She knows that I am dead, she knows that I was an addict and that she was taken into care at a very young age.

But one day she goes into a record office and looks everything up. She spends an entire day in the Stockholm City Archives on Kungsholmen and reads everything there is to be read about us. I see her sitting alone under the little green lamp in the dark reading room. Next to her are the nine cardboard boxes in which all the details of our lives can be found, the police investigations as well as the reports from social services.

She stares for a long time at the small passport photograph of me affixed to the first page, the photo that was in all the newspapers. The one with the frizzy hair I had at the end, and where my eyes look harder and deeper than before. I look straight into the camera's flash, but you can see that I am already far away, distant and unhappy. Maybe she recognises my eyes and her own narrow face, covered with freckles. The photo was taken a few months after her birth, in the spring. It was for a new passport so that I could follow Shane to Istanbul, which was where I thought he was, but by the time the passport arrived I was already inside those suitcases, stinking to high heaven.

She stares at length at the photograph, large, round tears rolling from her eyes, each one making a tiny sound as it plops onto the table. It is here in the underground corridors of Kungsklippan that I become her mother for the first time, when she sees the little black and white passport photograph taped onto a stencilled sheet. It is when she reaches the end of the story, where it says that, even before she was born, we asked them to take her. By then she has already seen the sketches and photographs of my dead body in pieces. In the documents it states that we presented ourselves five months into the pregnancy, it states that we wouldn't accept any of the assistance they offered us and that we wanted to sign the papers as quickly as possible. It doesn't say that this was the only thing we had to give her, it was the only thing of value we had to offer, a life without us; it doesn't say that we were in such a hurry because we were afraid we would change our minds. It does say she has a brother, named Valentino, born three years before she was.

*

An odour of lake and forest emanates in waves from the old documents and I can see she feels nauseous now; she has her hand over her mouth and her brow is glistening with perspiration, her face grey. I wonder why Clara isn't with her. But she is not in the city, I realise, for when Solveig calls her and weeps into her phone, she can't come, but her voice is tender and close. And I don't think this is me, I would never hurt Solveig, but suddenly there is a trickle of dark, slimy water between her feet and a roar from deep inside the building. And now the black water surges along the corridors, it rises in the reading room with the green lamps, dark and full of earth and ash, and Solveig drops all the papers and runs, up, towards the light. The documents once written about us are carried away in the river of black. Outside in the light she sits down. She opens her hand and in it is the photograph of me.

Are you still listening? It doesn't matter if you aren't, I long since gave up caring whether anyone heard what I said. In my experience most people are so self-absorbed they find it hard to hear anything other than their own thoughts. You see impatience squirming through them like a snake when it isn't their turn to speak, and then you want to come to their rescue and let them carry on. But there are exceptions, those who quieten when they hear another voice, like Shane, and Nanna.

Many of those I met on Herkulesgatan were there to talk. That was the most trying aspect, it was easier with the ones who just wanted to get it done and didn't drag things out; I felt sullied by their words. Some of them thought they were finally *sub rosa* and began their confession as soon as the car door slammed shut. My job might just as well have been that of a psychologist or a priest. You get slightly better at listening when you are dead, because you hear everything then. When you have time to replay all your conversations, you hear the nuances in what was once said and you miss nothing, which is awful too, as it is too late by far. But if this is the penalty, all this listening and rewinding, then what is the crime? I will never know.

I don't recognise the world I grew up in; it all looks so different, people moving in a different way, more diffidently, more self-consciously, as if great mirrors were held in front of them.

They all say everything is worse, but maybe it is also marginally better. It must be the disappointment of soaring expectations that clouds their view; it is always best to assume nothing. Or perhaps it is the same old raw human spirit masquerading as the future that blinds me. The exhibitionists are still there anyway, standing in the tunnels with their trousers open, but as they only expose themselves to children, adults of every new generation believe they are a thing of the past. Most of the shops have moved away from Herkulesgatan down into a shadow world, an old-fashioned high street shop being almost impossible to imagine now, like mediaeval cripples earning money from their misfortune. No, it hasn't completely disappeared, but it is smaller and mostly frequented by undocumented women, the ones with less than nothing. But really everything is the same, just new places and new variations on the old theme.

At the spot where our house once stood I watch the river, its emerald-green water flowing along, the black water lilies reaching for the surface as I once reached for Raksha. There have been so many times I have thought I should stay away, not disturb anyone, leave Valle and Solveig to become the people they will become without me. Hanging in the little chantry in the church by the river is the same Jesus as when I was a child. I used to look into his kind eyes, the only gaze I wasn't afraid to meet. He too had made a mess of things and his father must have been angry with him as well, because he left him hanging there, bleeding and forlorn.

One day Valle was standing on a chair with a rope around his neck. His eyes were as steady as glass, a film of fever on his face, and he looked utterly calm, still, as though suspended in a kind of serenity. I know how that serenity feels. The sun shone outside his window, which was slightly open, and a pale winter light was streaming into the room. Things lay all over the floor, clothes, dirty plates, pizza boxes. The rope was strong, I could see, and I stayed close beside him without knowing what I ought to do. It didn't matter, there was nothing I could do anyway. He was somewhere else, in another world. Soon he would be far from here.

"Mamma," he said plainly, into the room. Then he lifted up his feet, but he didn't kick the chair away. I heard his rattling breaths, as if they were my own, but I couldn't do anything. The rope tightened and he stopped breathing. I shouted, but my voice made no sound. I tried to pull him down, but I had no hands. I tried to hold on to him and force the rope out of his hands, but I had no earthly power, nor power of any other kind. I saw my child dying in front of me and the world grew still, the remains of the world that I was in, the remains of light.

Why shouldn't he kick the stool away and be free? I knew how lonely he was, knew how long he had struggled, and so much in his life had turned out fine now, without being *good*. Should he live for me to be able to drop in on him from time to time and gaze at his handsome face? I thought: If he can just get through the next few seconds, nothing will ever hurt him again. I imagined him coming to me, although I know it doesn't work like that. The word "peace" passed through my thoughts. And I remembered he loved flying. So I whispered to him, told him he should fly away, fly out of time. I don't know if that was why he suddenly managed to wrench off the rope and he fell to the floor. His body trembled with weeping, he retched and coughed, and from above it looked as though someone had taken hold of him and was shaking him. And then he grew still. Sunlight filled the room, a rainbow arced in the sky between the high-rise buildings, and I let him be alone. You might think I made that up about the rainbow, but I didn't. I may have invented some tiny detail in the story, but the rainbow outside Valle's window that morning, that bit is true.

I didn't think I would dare look in on him again after the episode with the rope; I was sure I would find him in the morgue, as cold as snow. But one day I couldn't stop myself taking a little peep, and when I did, there he was, sitting at a café in the sun with Solveig. Solveig!

The first spring sunshine had arrived and Solveig was wearing a big yellow quilted jacket. Valle appeared to be so happy, almost carefree, his eyes bright and full of light, and he looked straight at Solveig without lowering his gaze. It can't have been the first time they had seen one another, they must have met before, because I noticed they already knew each other and were talking about things they had clearly spoken about earlier. Solveig must have gone back to the social services and asked them to give her his name, and because Solveig is Solveig and possesses the charm of words, she must have left the office with his name in her pocket and then one day stood at his door and told him she was his sister. And now they were sitting there, she with her Elvis haircut and he with the enigmatic little topknot on his head that made him look like Little My. They laughed a lot and I laughed too, though I made no sound. I had never heard him say so much, words spilling out of him like pearls. And now that I saw Valle and Solveig together, I could see their likeness to Raksha and Ivan, and in their happy faces I saw glimmers of the people who had once been my parents, like faint eddies in a pool. I was struck by a new and violent sense of loss at the unexpected realisation I was missing myself, and I had to look away for a moment.

She had been so scared, Solveig said, that they would be alike, and scared that they wouldn't be in the least alike. But most of all she was scared that he would shut the door in her face when he saw her.

"But I've never been happier in my entire life," Valle said.

"Did you realise who I was?"

"At once."

"Even though you didn't know I existed?"

"That's my little sister, I thought."

Valle worked at Arlanda now, selling perfume and cosmetics in a glossy mirrored tax-free shop where he could see the aeroplanes take off. He must already have told Solveig he used to take drugs, for now she asked:

"Why did you stop?"

"I don't know. I just did."

And he said he had always known he would take his own life, ever since he was a child, alone in the forest with his knives and the dogs; it was the thing of which he was most certain, that he would die young.

"Why are you telling me this?" Solveig said.

"So you're not afraid."

"But I am afraid."

They sat in silence for a while.

"What keeps you here?" Solveig finally asked.

"I don't know. I just don't seem to be able to get away. And I'm frightened I would be reborn as something even worse."

"OK," Solveig said.

"OK?"

She looked at him and then said:

"I'm not going to try to stop you if you really don't want to stay, but obviously, I'd be really happy if you did stick around."

Part of me can't wait for humankind to perish as a species. It is a childlike notion, that the world should have shuddered to a stop the moment I breathed my last, when he strangled me in the forest. But I know that only my world stopped, your world sped on without me. Life was what it was, and so was death.

Another part of me wants everything to carry on, for humanity to have another chance, just as I sometimes wish for another chance myself; but those thoughts lead nowhere, only down into the darkness. Still, I sometimes send a prayer into the nothingness, even though I know there is only the void of the spinning solar system and the cold chalky light of the Milky Way. I pray for Raksha and Ivan and I pray for Solveig and Valle. *Keep these people in the light. Guard them from evil forces.* Sometimes I fear I might accidentally be worshipping those evil forces.

One day I will let go and reel back into the nothingness whence I came. I watch Raksha for hours and wish she would utter my name; I need to know that I still exist within her, but she has no-one to whom she could say it. She has a coffee with Sylvia every Sunday and sometimes she cuts her hair. That is the only time she speaks to anyone, but she never mentions us. Not me, not Eskil.

She still has two children, just as I do, for you always have your children, and death can't change that, neither for me nor her. You can't stop being a mother, no matter how much you might try to break free. For a while she had Ivan, when he reappeared after my death, but then he moved out again and now she has only Sylvia. Sylvia, with her dandelion hair, who chatters on into the air about nothing as Raksha sits listening, hands on her knee. My longing to return is fading, the sense of loss subsiding; here there is only the wind and the faint scent of eternity and oblivion. When I look at the people I have left behind, they too are strangers.

Sometimes I think I would like to ask Raksha what she meant when she said she couldn't be my mother any longer.

"But how could I say anything so foolish? Of course you were my child," she might mumble as she lies half asleep in the bath and lets a sleeping pill disperse inside her.

"So it was just that you couldn't cope any longer, with being my mother?"

"But obviously I wanted to be your mother. That's all I've ever wanted."

"But that's what you said."

"Yes, but we say a lot of things we don't really mean. Stupid to go through life believing something like that. I was in the depths. Literally in the darkest depths of the damned river. You shouldn't believe everything you hear."

"But you weren't happy before that either."

"Wasn't I? No, maybe I wasn't. Some people will never really be happy. But you can't be as precise and pernickety about words as you are. That way disaster lies."

"My disaster has already happened, Mamma."

You are eternally joined to the person who killed you and getting used to that is the hardest part. To see into the people you love is one thing, but to see into the one who murdered you is something else entirely. You have to face your own death, over and over. For a while I wondered how he could carry on living with me on his conscience, but not anymore. The human capacity for suppression is infinite; memory is only one part of the psyche and the task of the organism is to rearrange memory to prevent the person going under. A long time ago I considered revenge, it smouldered inside me; but the feeling is no longer there, and even if it were, it isn't feasible.

Inside him is a barren, desolate wasteland, and yet he has that particular body language of so many madmen; something about him seems entirely open and candid and he readily connects with people. Maybe he doesn't radiate warmth, but he has a presence, an intensity, something that intimates he is rather different. But no-one would think he was dangerous. And if the images of death ever surface inside him, just before he falls asleep or just after he has opened his eyes in the morning, they are torn, fragmented, out of context. It is like a film he might have seen in the cinema long ago. I believe he expends a great deal of energy keeping me at a distance and in the end there is only a narrow shred remaining on which to live; his life diminishes until there is almost nothing left. In recent years he has withdrawn, he no longer stands at the fence chatting to the neighbours and not long ago his wife moved out. I heard her say it felt as though she loved an empty shell.

From here I see myself from the outside, like a photograph, and time and time again I see myself with Valle, sitting at a plastic table in Burger King waiting for a pimp or a dealer. When I look now I see he has fallen asleep in my arms. It is just after midnight and he has dark shadows under his eyes. Why don't I go home? Why do I just sit and let time go by? I know that in the end they will come and take him if I don't change. Is that what I want? Is that what I wanted all along? I can't make sense of it any other way, because I let it happen.

BREATH

Shane was in Istanbul again, Valle would soon be three and I didn't know how long we were going to be on our own, so Valle and I wandered around the city together. We sat in Kungsträdgården and looked at the pink trees that had just burst into bloom. Valle was no longer a baby, he was a miniature person, sitting there, looking at me. Sometimes he reached out his hand to catch the tiny petals swirling in the air like snow. I longed for Shane to ring, but when he did, I didn't know what to say. When I think of our life now, it seems as though it was all about standing in separate telephone boxes trying to get hold of one another. The feeling of suffocation when we couldn't. And then when we did hear the other's voice, when it was suddenly so close and meant everything in the world, then we had nothing to say.

"Where have you been?" he shouted from an infinite distance.

"Only here."

"Can I speak to Valle?"

"Not at the moment."

"He's there, isn't he?"

"Yes, where else would he be?"

One day we were offered the chance to live at Harry's on Floragatan. I had lived there before and Shane and I had been there often while we were expecting Valle. Harry had two massive grey dogs, Great Danes, and he always wanted people around him. He had nothing else to spend all his money on and someone off the street was always living there. Many was the day I lay on his huge bed watching the flicker of the television. There was the constant sound of voices elsewhere on the same floor where I was languishing in a haze on the bed, under which was a pharmacy fit for a king, everything you could possibly want. I think all that medication had something to do with his job.

This city is full of men in need of company and not all of them are after sex; many daren't, they are too old, too scared, or it is something else, they want a thrashing or to be rocked like a baby. Sometimes Harry asked me to watch over him when he wrapped himself inside his plastic bags and masturbated. When he came I had to pull off the bag, quickly, so he didn't suffocate, but I never had to touch him, he did that himself. I tried it too a few times. When the air supply is choked, it creates a rush in the body like heroin, but it is faster and harder, and more dangerous, I think. I didn't ever feel anything sexual, it was more existential for me, hanging for a second on the edge. From time to time he would get girls to do things with the dogs, but not me. I would never have done it. That is a lie. I would have done anything for access to his chemist's shop. He just never asked.

We stay there for weeks. Valle runs in and out of all the doors, delighted with the vast halls after being used to our little two-roomer. We play with the dogs and sometimes he is allowed to take them out with Harry to Humlegården. Most of the time I lie half asleep under a radiator. I keep thinking we should go home, but we just don't make it, and Valle loves being with the dogs. Do you remember, Valle, how much you loved those huge dogs?

All the lights are on at Harry's around the clock. It is never night-time. From my position lying on the floor underneath the hot radiator I see the towering canine shadows. I am so cold, despite it being warm outside. The treetops rustle in the gentle breeze, the soft tinkle of a thousand tiny bells. In a distant part of the apartment I hear Valle's high-pitched voice and it sounds as though he and Harry are racing from room to room. Valle's squeal, the sound he makes when someone tickles him, and a lower, deeper voice, also exuberant, open. I think of the games we played when I was a child, of being in constant fear of the other children. They always knew what they wanted, they always had a plan, and they had willpower, a desire for something that fuelled them like electricity. Valle was never afraid of anyone, he liked them all.

Nanna with her bleached hair is a silhouette in the bedroom doorway against the fiery radiance of the sunset.

"You've got to get out of here, now."

That evening we leave Harry's.

Nanna pushes Valle in his buggy and takes us down under the ground where no ill can befall us.

"I've been looking everywhere for you."

"We were only here."

"I thought you were dead."

"Here I am," I say, holding out my hands as if I were a gift.

Nanna doesn't laugh. It is a long time since she laughed.

"Where are we going?" I ask instead.

"We're going home."

"But I don't want to go back to Sockenplan."

The metro plunges into the rock above us and I can't hear her reply.

Dirty blankets everywhere and the bundled shapes of people sleeping in the dim ash-yellow light. This is where I have friends, I have Nanna, and she is afraid of no-one, ever. Folk here move slowly, as if under water, and there is no light, only the occasional flash of a torch and the glow of the fires. Someone might get angry, grab someone else by the throat or give them a sudden thump, but it amounts to nothing and is soon over; and no-one hides anything down here, so there is nothing to be afraid of, there are no secrets, no-one is worth more than anyone else, we are all equally worthless, we belong to no-one, we have nothing.

The first time it was Shane and I who lived here, and that was a long time ago, when we had only just met. We slept close to each other by a warm concrete wall and the sound of the metro trains rushing past never stopped. Water ran down the wall, waste water probably, but it was always warm there, like lying next to the sleeping body of a giant, and the sound of the water calmed me. That time I thought we were free, autonomous, because we had nowhere to live. Now I have Valle with me it is so different. If Nanna wasn't here I would leap in front of a train with Valle in my arms.

I watch Valle and Solveig all the time, and all the time they are together again, one always where the other is. Valle stays over at Solveig and Clara's and there he can sleep without nightmares. The summer is warm and they keep all the windows open, and the sky retains a faint blue tinge throughout the night. Valle sleeps on his stomach in the moonlight next to Solveig and Clara, entangled in one another like baby animals in a den, and I think that nothing could hurt them now they are no longer alone in the world. Clara takes photographs with her huge camera and hangs them up all around the apartment, and Valle's eyes are happy as he sits with them in the boundless summer light. Early in the morning, before the city is awake, they go down to Lake Råstasjön. They dive into the dark water and disappear and each time they come up again it makes me dizzy, seeing their wet heads break the smooth black surface as they draw air and summer into their lungs. The dark motionless of the lake water and the relief of drawing breath again. The light piercing your eyes and the world returning. From above, my children's heads look like water lilies, alone in the black sheen of the still water, and from higher up like tiny pinheads, until finally they are invisible and there is just the lake's shiny surface reflecting the clouds. You might suppose it is a dream, a fantasy the dead indulge in to pass the time. In that case, perhaps life was also just a dream.

In the end it is easier to look at the murderer than those you love. It hurts less. I wonder if he is afraid of what is to come, afraid of the fires? I believe he is, even though he has been a confirmed atheist since childhood. He is older now, weaker, and he finds it hard to see. I have watched him fumbling for pieces of furniture in his house to avoid tripping over. Is he imagining a classic hell, with fires and pitchforked demons, women's muffled screams, children's unrelenting cries, a rubbish dump of human remains in searing flames that do not cleanse? Or is it merely a sneaking unease that he will be engulfed in greyness, lose his human form? I could quell his anxiety with the following simple information: the human being is alone in eternity, there is no heaven, no gods, no Father Christmas, we are entirely outside the scrutiny of higher powers. There is no punishment, but neither is there forgiveness. When the end comes, you are alone. You fall headlong into nothing.

I am looking forward to seeing him die. I hope it hurts. I hope he is afraid, as I was. Fear is the worst thing, the hope of escape, before the realisation that you won't. I will be there, wishing him a lonely suffering, on a level with the torment of Jesus.

It was June, early summer, my last.

We sat for a while, gazing out over the misty green landscape and listening to the purr of the engine until he switched off the headlights and turned to me.

"Get out of the car and wait for me," he said, and I got out of the car and waited for him. Then I heard his voice beside me.

"Shall we get going?"

I stepped out into the gentle rain, summer a chamber of damp around me, the trees standing high, their crowns heavy with rain. All the noise had gone. The birds, raindrops, the hum of the engine, the perpetual buzz of electricity cables; the world was silent, soundless. How can anyone be stupid enough to try to hide in a telephone box? That is the kind of question you ask yourself in retrospect. Telephone boxes have disappeared now, but you remember them, don't you? They were everywhere, you stood inside one, drenched, like being in an old jar of formaldehyde at the edge of the forest. He was waiting for me in the car, the headlights illuminating the world of rain around us, and the rest of the world seemed to have been swallowed up by the creeping mist that evening and we really were the only people left on earth. In places the sky was so low, the treetops vanished into the cloud. And didn't I tell you that I tried to run? I hurled myself out of the telephone box when he came back, I ran into the forest and he came after me and threw me down on the ground and took me like an animal in the mud before he dragged me back to the car.

The mist infiltrates all the hollows and seeps into the ground with the blood from my nose and mouth and all the sounds truly have stopped, the whistle of the storm, the breaking branches, the beat of the rain against my face and the awful screech of the birds, as if the sky has absorbed the world's noise, and one of my eyes must have filled with blood for suddenly half the world is in darkness. Red water rising across the landscape, mounting, though it seems to be trickling down over the trees behind glass. Like human waste, effluent, sliding slowly down the world's protective glass film that has never allowed me through; I have always stood outside, watching life unfold inside. Crawling like an insect on the outside. And now the forest opens out, the trees become sparser and there is the road again, winding through the countryside like a grey streamer. And I must have run in a loop, for now the car is standing in front of me, a cold, alien object in the landscape, belonging in the world of people, shining dimly in the greyish green and yellow of the rain-drenched light. The car door is open like a mouth and he looks at me, standing still as a beast that has already vanquished its prey, still as someone who knows that people like me will always run in circles, and in a few strides he is beside me and drags me down onto the ground and sits on my chest. His clothes are covered in mud and sand, everything is wet, dew and rain and water from the underworld gradually rising below us, the dark water of death, and beneath my shoulders I feel a gentle pull, as if it is the earth that is taking me back and not he who is despatching me. Now he is the giant bird of my childhood, sitting on my chest, pecking out my eyes.

The smell of the lake spreads like an open wound, the same smell that once filled the delivery room, of sludge and seaweed and untainted putrefaction, the inside of the body exposed, the soul laid bare as the flesh it is. He quietens and stares at me with a primordial gaze, lacking all humanity; such a look, fixed and cold, a frozen fury, pure instinct.

"You came back to me."

My voice is no more, water and earth are clogging my throat and my lungs are filling with blood. What would I say if I had a voice? What would I say if there was still time? I don't know.

By the time we were back in the car after I had tried to run and the road was growing narrower and the forest encroaching more intensely, I had decided to offer no resistance; I wanted to meet death without begging for mercy, but my body would not be defeated so easily. In the end something else took over and I hit out and screamed for Raksha. But, when his hands squeezed my neck and he raped me, then came the numbness, purling through my veins, bringing stillness, and I was no longer afraid.

I lay on the shore in pieces and there was nothing left to fear. It all happened quickly now, the light disappeared from the sky and it was dark by the lake. He washed his face in the sweet lake water and sat for a moment, staring out across the water and the silhouettes of the fir trees on the other side. Then he dragged the suitcases down the small bank and in them he carefully laid what was left of me. I was a pile of flesh on the grass. I was raw nature, a shapeless bright-red pulp of meat bearing no resemblance to a person, I was the precursor to earth and stardust, a corpse among corpses. Was this desire in its purest form? To conquer the other person's body?

It is as if the lake sucks in everything that lives; the smooth water absorbs the last of the twilight glow, the flowers and trees are magnetically drawn to its silvery surface, shrubs and saplings lean in its direction, as if bent by a wind. The same applies to the sky, which sees its reflection in the black lake, and to any careless child in summer when the water is smooth and warm. They reach for life, and they meet death.

"My child . . ." Raksha calls from somewhere far, far away. The treetops spin around above and I think they are birch trees; they sound like birches, the faint rustle or swish in the wind, the flickering, fractured light descending through the small green leaves. It is so long since I was in touch with Raksha. I had thought I wanted nothing more from her. No questions, no presents, no telephone calls. But now I wish she could come to this forest outside the world and hold me while I die.

"Is there anyone there? Raksha, are you there? . . . Raksha, I think I've messed myself . . . Are you there, Mamma?"

There is not an awful lot of blood when you cut up dead bodies and he was painstaking and careful, almost tender, when he moved my body around on the shore. He looked like someone who had done it before and he took his time, wasn't rushed by darkness falling and the moon emerging from behind the trees as if someone was shining the icy beam of a giant spotlight on him. And he wouldn't leave a single trace, not a strand of hair or a fragment under my nails.

My head drops onto the wet grass. A gentle rain settles over the little forest and a cold streak of light spreads above the trees when he drives back to the city with me in the boot. The church service is still on the radio but he changes stations, to the news. *The Falkland Islands have just surrendered to Great Britain. The last battle was waged with bayonets and machine guns. A bloody moon rises over Europe.* He arrives at his home, spends a long time washing his hands, face, neck, genitals, he has a shower, washes his hair, vacuums, scrubs, cleans all the windows, falls asleep early between soft clean sheets. It is like an inner renewal.

Many times I had imagined that death didn't want me; it took a taste and spat me out. But in the end it had obviously changed its mind. What can be said about that? It was a shame I couldn't stay alive, but no-one survives life.

We sat beside the angels at the altar in Klara Church and shared a hamburger. Above us was the painting of Jesus when they took him down from the cross. It was night-time and there was only the faint sound of someone asleep between the rows of pews. Valle was sleeping in his buggy next to us. Nanna had a cat with her that she was looking after for someone. It climbed around on the altar for a while before curling up on her knee and falling asleep too.

"You need to go home now," she said.

"I know."

"When it's light, take the metro."

We were silent. I thought I could hear the sound of the candle flames burning around us.

"What about you? Don't you want to come?"

"I'll stay here."

"Sometimes I think he'll never come back," I said.

Nanna pulled the little smile that meant she had already seen it all and she wasn't impressed.

"Yes he will. People always think that when they've left someone."

The cat woke up and stretched. I recalled all the times I had believed Nanna had gone forever and then suddenly she was back on Herkulesgatan, like a wonderful old ghost.

"Sometimes it feels as though you only exist inside me," I said now, "as if you're someone I've invented."

"Sure, but you could have invented something better while you were at it."

"But I think you're the most beautiful thing I could ever have come up with," I said, and her eyes glistened. She lifted the little cat up to her face and kissed its pink nose. The cat shut its eyes.

"Come on. No time to be sentimental now, babe. That won't help either of us."

Shane was back. One day he was simply standing in front of us while we were walking along. He was pale and sunken.

"Hey, mate," he said as he stepped out of our doorway, and he crouched down in front of the buggy. Valle's eyes widened, he cautiously put out his hand and touched Shane's face. He said nothing, just looked intently at his dad, without blinking. Shane lifted him up and held him to his chest and I could see him crying silently into Valle's hair. I didn't ask what he had been doing, I was too proud for that, and nor did he tell me, but I think I understood by then that he was sick.

When Valle had fallen asleep I took my first needle for weeks and it left me unconscious. Now I think it would have been better if I had taken death's hand for once. Instead I dragged myself through light and dark to resurface in the subdued lamplight where Valle lay sleeping in his old cot that was actually too small for him.

"Why doesn't he say anything?" Shane asked after Valle had fallen asleep in my arms. It was the only way to get him to sleep, even though he was too big. Shane had tried to make him say something. Valle looked pleased, but he said nothing, just gazed at Shane with quick bright eyes.

Before, words had come and he talked all the time, a gentle babble pouring out of him, though the words were hard to distinguish. Some individual words were quite clear – doll, lion, doggie, Mamma – but now they had gone.

"We don't talk much," I said.

I believed that words were just a way of hiding things you couldn't bear to know. Without words the world lies before you, naked and true.

Shane had bruises on his chest that hadn't been there before. At night I lay and looked at him while he slept. He was so handsome, the thin, pale skin on his eyelids that always gave him an expression of vulnerability, the hair on his neck curling under the smooth black hair on top. Sometimes he slept so deeply I thought he was dead. "You're alive, aren't you?" I whispered, and felt his ribs. He was breathing, but I could sense he was far away.

That last period we had with Valle was the calmest for us. We took stuff, but not much. It was almost as if we couldn't be bothered. We bathed in Barnhusviken and walked in the warm weather that had arrived in the city despite it only being April. Valle got a dolphin balloon at Gröna Lund that he wouldn't let go, even when he was asleep. We sunbathed in Kungsträdgården and I read aloud from *The Wizard of Oz* in the twilight while Valle fell asleep on Shane's chest. Valle laughed again, but still he said no words. It didn't matter, there wasn't much to say. Other than the three of us belonged together. I remember thinking we were like a family, people who belonged together.

It was early one morning and the three of us were asleep in the large bed. Valle must have sensed that his present life was about to end, for that night he had come in with us. Quick footsteps across the plastic mat and then he crept under the quilt beside me, his little body made cold by the night. I lay awake while he gradually warmed up beside me, thinking about him still wanting to be in with us, and that night I swore that we would finally go to that home by the sea for mothers and children that had been offered to us, though Shane wouldn't have been able to come with us. But how many times had I had that thought? Valle and I would never go to the sea.

In my mind I can still see the picture of us that last night all tangled up together, from just above, as if I were a bird on the ceiling looking down at us. Shane lying behind me, his leg round my waist, his black hair covering his face, Valle curled up under my arm like a little hedgehog.

We were woken by the harsh sound of the doorbell. The room was light. And suddenly it was full of people putting his things into large boxes. The sound of wings was deafening, I couldn't hear what they were saying, and small white feathers filled the air like snow. A pillow had been torn open. By me? By Shane? Not Shane. He just sat and stared at me, a hat pressed to his heart as his only shield, while one of the women picked up his child and carried him out of the room. And now Valle could speak again, calling for me in a tiny, broken voice. "Mamma . . . Mamma . . . Help me, Mamma . . ." Then the door closed and there was silence. As if he had never been there, as if we had never had a child.

It was that night Solveig came to be. We summoned her from the darkness, though we both knew she should have stayed where she was. Unborn, safe, ensnared deep within nothingness. When we made love we did it robotically, like two dolls. The image of Valle quivered between us and the orgasm hurt, as if a baby was bulging out between my legs again and dropping to the floor.

I stood for days on end outside the building that had swallowed up by child. Sometimes I went up to someone and asked:

"When will I get my baby back?"

I was so afraid they would ask which baby I was talking about, but they almost never replied, just hurried through the doors with their handbags pressed to their hips, as if it was their bloody handbags I wanted. Standing there alone, looking at my shadow on the wall, it was as though I had never had a baby boy, never pulled Valle's buggy up and down all the hills in this city. But most of the time I simply stood and watched them. Sometimes I ran up and grabbed at the coat of one of them I knew. Well, I say knew. They knew everything about me, but I knew nothing about them. All they wanted to find out was whether I was high. "Are you high, Kristina?" You're damn right I am, I screamed, kicking out at them. Was that their only question? I had lots of questions. I wanted to say he was better off on the street with me than with strangers, I wanted to say that I was his mother. Sometimes I saw children's shadows at the windows and I heard the trill of their laughter from behind the closed face of the building. One night I threw a stone at a window and scrambled inside, but there were no children; I ran down the empty corridors calling his name. Empty corridors filled with icy silver moonbeams, and room after room filled with the same compassionless silver. I tried to find everything they had written about us, in case there was some evidence against me, but I found none.

*

On Herkulesgatan Nanna was huddled against the wall of the bank reading a book, her white hair like a curtain shielding her from the world. She had always looked at me as if she were seeking the good in me. No-one else did that, they were all trying to find the bad.

"Come on, love, let me warm you up," she said, stretching out her hand.

"You won't go, will you?" I said.

"Leave you? Never."

It was the last time I saw her.

For nine months I took almost nothing. I slept most of the time, lying under the window, half dreaming. Shane came and went and at night he lay behind my back with his hand on my stomach, as if sheltering the little creature inside from us. He kept falling asleep everywhere and was just getting thinner, even though we ate at McDonald's every day. It happened fast, he went away for a few hours and when he returned he was thinner still, as if something were consuming him from within. At night I dreamed about an animal that was eating him alive. It was huge and black and lay like a shadow behind him in the bed where I used to lie and hold him. He slept more and more and when his own clothes no longer fitted, he started wearing my jeans and jumpers.

Shane lay and listened to my stomach, a small, hard womb protruding like an egg from my soft belly. I thought about Valle all the time, that he would be reborn. The idea intensified the longer time went on, that he was the one growing inside me. Somehow he had turned up inside me again; I had been given a new chance and no-one knew. At the social services office I scarcely listened to what they were saying about him. They could say whatever they liked about the little community by Storsjön, about the people who had taken pity on him. Because only I knew that he was with me. I tried to tell Shane once, but it made him angry and he shook me by the shoulders. It hurt, not so much a physical pain, but that he didn't believe me. He had always believed me, he had always defended me and what I thought. So I was alone in my belief it was Valle. Perhaps I knew it wasn't true, but I entered that fantasy like walking into a room.

Later we were allowed to go to Jämtland to visit him. On the train I wasn't thinking about where we were going. Inside I was vacant. I had showered, made myself look nice, put on makeup, worn a coat with a fur collar. I couldn't fasten the coat over my stomach, but it was thick and looked good. I felt grown-up in it. The landscape was unreal; outside the city the sky was so wide, it was everywhere. It was a long time since I had seen a sky, for there were none in the city, you could catch an occasional glimpse of a pale blue square and then it was gone.

235

Now it stretched without end beyond the train window, as if we were riding through it. Maybe at that point I was happy, the baby's unhurried movements under my ribs were a world of its own, untouched by any danger.

Shane muttered to himself the whole time and walked back and forth down the train. As soon as he sat down he sprang up again, as if he had burned himself on the seat. I was calm, for me there was nothing at stake anymore, everything was inside me. The people were waiting at the station. They drove us into the country in an immaculate, newly washed car. They chatted to us, were unbearably gentle and kind, as if they were being paid. Well, they were. My fur coat looked a wreck on their pristine seat.

"How was the journey? It's a long way."

"How lovely to meet you."

"We've baked some buns."

"I think he might be a little bit shy at first."

"But we've plenty of time."

"Maybe you're hungry."

On the way I started to feel afraid; I couldn't cope with all the friendliness, I had no way of dealing with it, my entire repertoire was built on self-defence. We sat in the back of the car in silence. I was scared my voice would sound too loud and harsh if I said anything, like a chainsaw obliterating every-thing in its path. Shane answered their questions anyway, but his voice was thin and adrift and the words kept ebbing away before he could finish his sentence. They obviously knew we were expecting another child, but they didn't mention it. They must have thought we were idiots. If they did, I could only agree. We drove past something that looked like an ocean; they said it was Storsjön. They said Valle had been bathing in there all summer. It was as if they were talking about someone who had nothing to do with me. My Valle was floating in amniotic waters again.

We stepped out of the car at a yellow wooden house by the lake and a moment later I would come crashing out of my dream. We walked slowly through a garden and into the house. There were children's things in the garden, a little bicycle and a blue tent, and there was a small sandpit filled with buckets and spades. Valle was sitting on the floor playing when we entered and he didn't look up. An elderly woman was sitting at the kitchen table. He had grown taller, even though only a few months had passed, and he was wearing clothes I had never seen. Someone had cut his hair short and it was shining in the bright sunlight. I stood at the door and looked at him. Shane did too. The baby must have been woken by the sound of my heart and it made such an energetic movement, it had to have been visible through my jumper.

"See who's here, Valle."

Valle looked up. What was in his eyes? I don't know. The baby moved inside me and it was suddenly quite clear that it wasn't Valle who was hiding inside, waiting for us to become other people. He was sitting before us on the floor, utterly real, in jersey dungarees, in that yellow house where the light streamed into all the rooms like water.

After a while he walked up to us. A little while later he sat on my knee and ate some biscuits. It ought to have made me

237

happy, but it only made me sad. His hair smelled so sweet, as it always did, like kitten's fur. I wept so much I made it wet. He patted me on the cheek and then he wanted us to walk around the house. Everything was perfect, like a doll's house. He had his own room with yellow walls and brightly coloured cushions on the bed. Later, when he wanted us to go outside, the sun was so strong I could hardly see. When we left he was sitting on his little bike, waving. Beside him stood his new parents, their big wings folded around him.

Autumn came and the one inside was growing and in time she started kicking Shane's hand with her tiny feet. Shane sang a little tune to her and I could feel her quietening down. One day without any forethought I said:

"When the baby's born we're going to take her to social services."

Shane's eyes glazed over.

"You're just frightened. We'll manage it this time. We're different people now."

"Aren't you frightened?"

Shane's hand cradled the baby in there more firmly.

"It's good to be scared. You said that yourself. That way you shape up."

"But we're not shaping up, are we? That's the thing with us – we don't shape up."

"Someone has given us another chance, I know it. Wait 'til you see her. It will all be different when she's here. She's going to bring *us* up."

It is a human weakness, overestimating your own capacity for change, it doesn't just apply to addicts.

Some distance away from Herkulesgatan the murderer was already setting the wheels in motion in his daydreams. Like a prisoner of himself he was driving back and forth along the roads looking for something, animal or human, girl, child or woman. He had no idea yet who I was, but he knew what he was looking for and I fitted the description. Someone going through life like the living dead, someone who no longer believed in salvation. A cold wave rose up in him at the thought, until finally it was all that was left in his soul. I imagine it is the same with the heroin that fills every artery and every nook inside you. Soon our paths would cross. It would be an accident, and yet not; it would be the last event in a long chain of chance events that are called a life. One night I would be standing in front of him on Herkulesgatan in my fox-fur boa.

I bought that boa after I had given birth to Solveig. And I finally acquired a short black skirt and a pair of high silver boots. Every time I caught a glimpse of my reflection in a shop window I wanted to laugh. But at last I knew who I was: I was just the picture of that figure in the reflection, the woman in the fox-fur boa. It was clean as a cut, and it was true.

The labour pains were much worse with Solveig. But I wanted to suffer the worst of all pains. I didn't want her to come out, so when it was time I refused to push. Shane had said he would only accompany me as far as the hospital doors and then he would go. Unless I changed my mind, as he put it. But he only said it to make it harder for me, it had been arranged long before. We had both already signed the documents and it couldn't be changed now, and besides, even if we kept her, in the end they would take her, in a year or two. This way she would be spared that. And so would we. So when it started – it was in the morning just after we had woken up – we took a taxi to the hospital. And it happened quickly this time, in half an hour I was on the floor groaning, blood running between my legs. In the taxi Shane held my hand tightly the whole time and every time I was gripped by a contraction he held on to me. He helped me out of the car, gave me my little case and my handbag and I walked towards the entrance on my own as the taxi door closed behind me. But I had only walked a few metres before I was seized by the brute force again and sank to the ground. Shane was back at my side, he picked me up, the only thing in that disgusting hospital environment that smelled good. He carried me up to the ward and I was hanging around his neck, and for a moment, between the pains, we laughed at ourselves in the stark, grainy light of the lift, at me the weight of a whale and him thinner than ever, and then, when I was lying in a bed in a hospital gown, he left. I would have left as well if I could, to escape the last bit. They might as well have put a little bowl under my fanny for Solveig to drop into and drown straight from the womb.

Deep down I had been hoping she would never come out, that time would be frozen and she would stay inside me forever. The only time I felt whole was when I had a child in my belly. That was why they had to use a ventouse to get her out. In the end a doctor stood between my legs, pulling on the traction chain until he was red in the face. The pains had long since subsided, it hardly hurt at all now, and I thought it was better for her to die in there, so that she could skip being born and I could be her grave. But in the end something deep inside came loose and burst out of me. Solveig's head had a scratch and a bump, but it was still small and round and beautiful. I breathed in the scent of newborn baby; I said her name was Solveig, they had told me I could decide; they stitched me up between my legs and left us on our own. Gradually the room around us filled with a cold, pale winter light that settled on her face. Soon the sound of footsteps and voices would be everywhere, but first it was just the two of us. The final moments are mine and Solveig's alone.

There are certain images you have to keep to yourself, or they will disappear; you have to keep them within, unalloyed, untouched. You have to try to ensure that the words don't destroy the pictures so the clarity and pain are lost. It doesn't matter that they hurt, as long as they are pure as glass.

"Doesn't she want to say goodbye?" I heard someone whisper in the delivery room. No, I didn't want to say goodbye to Solveig; no matter what I did, they would still have taken her from me. The only thing I had left to give her was to surrender her, instead of tearing her tiny pink body apart. As we had done to Valle. As we had done to one another. To God and the Devil and everyone else, I say: The one who loves a child most can also give it up. So I lay with my face to the wall and heard their whispering voices retreat down the corridor. And when they had taken the thing that until moments before had been as much a part of me as my gut, I picked up my belongings and walked out. The fur jacket, the bag, my book and my bicycle key. The milk seeping from my breasts was grey, grey as dishwater, as if my body knew no child would ever drink it. Soon I was sitting on a toilet floor in Central Station with a needle in my thigh. I never saw Solveig again.

It is the final days. We are still roaming around the city where the water lies dark and motionless between the islands: he, the man who is soon to strangle me, and I, the person I was when there still was a me, when I had a living body, when I still had time, when I still had children. I don't really believe I ever stopped bleeding until I died that summer. I still do have children, but they're not with me. They weren't with me at the end either, but I will always be Valle and Solveig's mother. Death can change much, but not the fact that Valle and Solveig came from my body. Maybe there are other people, like Ellen and Johan in Jönköping, upgrading them both to new and better versions now, but they originate from me.

We will meet soon. He has already seen me, but I haven't yet seen him. And now I watch myself walking along the streets that are shiny with spring rain, and I am searching for Shane, because he has disappeared again. We saw each other in April in Klara churchyard and he said it was a crime against nature to give Solveig away and then he never came back. I didn't know then it was the last time I would see him.

"I miss you," I said, but I didn't dare touch him as he sat leaning against a gravestone.

"Do you?"

He seemed surprised and kept looking around as if he was expecting someone.

"Are you waiting for someone, Shane?"

"I always am."

"I mean someone in particular?"

He shook his head but didn't answer. I was the only one speaking.

"Every time I wake up I think you're there and I reach out for you. Then I remember that you've gone."

"Where is she?"

"I don't know. Somewhere."

He fell silent and picked at the grass. I looked at his hands while I spoke. His wrists were so thin and pale. The tattoos had faded.

"But she's alright where she is. You and I can't have any children. I know that now."

Summer is almost here now and I still believe I am going to find him, even though I think he is wrong about us and Solveig. It is the only thing I have to hold on to, that the reason we didn't keep her was because we wanted her above all else. But Shane will never forgive me and actually it doesn't matter, he will never come back, because now time is up. As I walk along looking for him, I finally realise how awful it is to wander around asking for someone, when you should know where that person is. Shane told me so many times.

"Do you understand how humiliating it is when you have to ask around for your girlfriend?"

"Wife!"

"Yes, but what bloody difference does it make if we're married when I don't know where you are?"

"It matters to me. I know I'll always come back to you, even when I walk out."

"Oh, right, am I supposed to be happy about that?"

"I think so."

"The worst of it is that I am."

"What?"

"Happy when you come back."

And the person who is about to take me out of the world is going to and from work, where he has a lot to do, because he is at the age when you do have a lot to do, when you have a career, and for a while now he has been preoccupied with me. It makes him distracted and absent-minded, but also wide awake, and he moves through the days as lightly as air. For some time he hasn't known what to do with the energy that fills him. He already dreams about me at night, a recurring dream, of lifting my head off my neck, as easily as with a doll.

The first time he saw me must have been on Herkulesgatan when he drove past in his car. What is it about my appearance that makes him want to kill? That I am already dead, that I won't defend myself? In his imagination he marks out the lines on my body where he plans to make his cuts. The idea of my neck pleases him most, the mere thought of tightening his hands around my throat makes him gasp for breath. His fantasies about me guard him against the abyss, how he will let the light fill my eyes and the oxygen rush through my blood one last time, before he squeezes again. In this he is like the gods who play with us for a spell before they let us go. And the choking is nothing new. Practically every man nowadays wants to have his hands around your neck when he comes; I don't know where they got that horrendous image from. But it makes them come straightaway. And when they come they shout for God. Sometimes being on the street really is like being in a bloody church.

He watches me on Herkulesgatan from a distance. Perhaps he has been standing there looking at me many times already. I ought to drop this question and let it go, but it keeps coming back: Why did he choose me? I will never know. Does it matter? At any rate this is the first occasion we speak to one another, because suddenly he is standing beside me with his pale eyes and I think he is shorter than I am, but it might just be my high heels.

"Good evening," he says.

Summer fog used to be treacherous and we were driving into it now, fluffy and soft from a distance, as if it wanted to protect the world from something awful. As we drove into it the light disappeared and the air surrounding us became cold and raw and dark. The mist swallowed every sound, it sucked in the birds' cries and the hum of the overhead cables, and you were filled with a vast emptiness without knowing where it came from. We drove into the mist and there was no way back.

I looked at him sitting next to me, motionless as a sculpture in the last dim light. I knew I had reached the end, there was no point in running this time. Did we say anything, or did we sit in silence? Does it matter? We drove into the mist as if it were an alien world and a few hours later he would return alone.

"Are you really not scared?" he asked.

"No, I'm not scared."

"Not of anything?"

"Only people who hope for something are scared, and I don't."

He was quiet for a moment and then he said:

"You can tell a mile away that you're not afraid of anything. That you don't need anyone at all in this world."

"I did once. But that was a long time ago."

He gazed out of the window, his voice quite soft.

"The hardest part of killing someone is having to put out

the light in their eyes. But once you make your mind up, it's as easy as flicking a switch."

I said: "Throw my things into the river. I don't want there to be anything left of me in the world."

I went on: "And one more thing. Don't drag it out. Don't hurt me more than you must."

When he finally pulled up by the little slope leading down to the lake, it wasn't the car that stopped, but the world outside, for it seemed as though we continued our journey while the rest of the world stood still, waiting, holding its breath, like a tide that would suddenly turn. I fell backwards through time with him by my side, down to its very beginning. The church service was still coming out of the radio, but it was fainter now, I think they were playing Stabat Mater and the windscreen wipers swept slowly across the glass and it really did seem that we were falling together, downwards in time, and suddenly I was a mother again and I sat in the delivery room with Solveig in my arms. She still smelled of blood and vernix and then she was gone and a little boy like Valle lay next to me in the narrow bed on Sockenplan, his hair soft and downy, sweaty with sleep and sun, and then I wasn't someone's mother anymore but I had found Shane, he was standing in front of me on Rådmansgatan and I stopped and threw a coin in his cap, and I was drawn to his world, like a magnet. But then he was gone too and I was a girl again in Alvik and I lay on a car bonnet beneath a slender silver moon with the sense that I bore the universe within me. And I carried on falling and there I was again, further back in time with Nanna and I had the first syringe in my hand, and quivering on its tip a crystalline droplet, translucent as a little mirror before it burst, and I can see now, as clearly as through a magnifying glass, that it never was a choice, it was something else, something inexplicable, a breeze or the breath of an alien being passing through me, a moment of greater clarity than any other. And then I was back by the river under a yellow sky, kneeling in the cold water with Eskil in my arms, his little chest still, his eyes pale and motionless, and then, like a miracle in time's reversal, I was a big sister again and I lay in a large bed with my nose pressed to the milky fragrance of his soft neck while Raksha and Ivan bellowed at each other with the force of wild animals for whom love was forgotten. Then I see them again, Raksha and Ivan, and now just the two of them, as they looked when they met for the first time at a funfair in Ängelholm. She who would one day be my mother wears an A-line coat and Ivan has a beer glass in each hand and in the background a bluish landscape rolls out under the sky like a glittering map. Inside those two simmers something unknown, and it might be happiness or the first hint of sadness, but whatever it is, this is the way it feels when life eventually begins, and you have waited for it for so long, for something to happen to you, and I think Raksha has been waiting for something that will uproot her from her old world. And now it starts, with a kiss, in front of the giant yellow Ferris wheel that has been shunted around Sweden all that summer in the late '50s.

I will never know where she comes from, Raksha, what darkness she travelled through to reach us. All I know is that she moves in with Ivan after the first night, that the past is a firewall of black inside her. Beyond the wall lies all that was once burned away by a mighty conflagration.

This is my last picture of the world and it is of Raksha and Ivan, the world's starting point and its beginnings, and all the time he sits in the seat beside me, the hunter, and he watches me. And not only time stops in the end, but we stop too, and everything around us is still, a world of rain and dark water falling gently through the trees, and we have reached the place that is to be my grave.

His hands tightened around my neck like a rope, his face and hairless chest pressed against me. I couldn't breathe, my lungs gurgled as the air sacs burst, I tried to cough, I saw things. Maybe they were apparitions; I think it was the Virgin Mary again, when the angel visited her, and now I could see how frightened she was, how she imperceptibly backed away towards the wall, and I saw the angel rape her, saw it hold her hands to the ground and ejaculate into her, I sensed the smell of death on them, sweet and cold and stale. And now the seed plunged into her soul with its fearful tidings. She would bear a son and lose him. She would be given a child who would be killed before her eyes. For what? I will never believe that Mary understood. I will never believe she accepted her fate.

Then I saw myself, I saw the grey foam bubbling out of my mouth, a mixture of earth and blood and ragged mucous membranes. I saw myself lying on the black mud, naked, twisted into a strange position that made me look like a plucked chicken or a doll someone had thrown away at childhood's end. A streak of blood on my cheek, my eyes wide open but extinguished. My thought was that I didn't want Raksha to see me like this, I didn't want anyone to see me, I never had.

But I can still see those children Eskil and I were, as we ran together beneath a pale sun, a piece of silver in the sky burning through the haze, a sun shining on two children who were all alone by the river under the great heavens, running. They are alone in the world, those two children, and when I watch them now the rest of the world has receded like a tide, waiting, quivering and quaking, in the grip of the moon before it starts to trickle back in microscopic rivulets that soon will fill the world. Such is grief, threatening at any moment to fill the entire world with its stinking black water. The children's bodies are white and naked against the inky silt on the shore and she, the girl who once was me, is always slightly in front, and the boy running after her is so very small in the wideness of the landscape. And if you zoom in on him you can see he has freckles, a shower of pale dots on his chest and arms. And he has little bags under his eyes, small folds that are always there because he struggles to sleep at night. If you zoom in even closer, you can see that his eyes are bright green, a special green colour that exists nowhere else in the world apart from in his eyes and in the Kattegat seen from heaven. I go there often to see that shade of green again.

"Is that you, Raksha? . . . Is there anybody there? . . . My head aches so much . . . I have so much pain all over . . . Where is my head? . . . Please help me get my head back . . . Was someone shouting for me? . . . Raksha, were you calling for us? . . . We're here! On the black shore under the heavens . . . Now the tide is coming in . . . It's washing over us . . . Raksha! . . . Mamma!"

"Don't shout," he whispers, and his face is closed like a marble statue's and there is nothing that scares me more than the stillness. It is the ones who are calm and never get angry who are dangerous, that I have learned on the street; they are the ones who do terrible things in private. I see the predator in him, the silhouette moving slowly like a shadow that I could reach out now and touch. And the words pour out of me and I can't stop myself.

"Please, please, please don't kill me. Don't hurt me."

This is the moment he has been waiting for, when I finally beg for my life. "Get onto your knees," he says. I kneel in the mire. He presses his thumbs on my throat and squeezes.

He let me return for a second before he gripped my throat with his hands for the last time and held on. The iridescent green light in the forest gloom came back once or twice, and the sound of the birds, before they disappeared forever.

SNOW

At my funeral it was snowing, the whole world was covered in a thin layer of snow, and when Ivan came walking up to Bromma church it looked as though it had been snowing inside him, for now he was quite silver-grey.

"Hello, Ivan," Raksha said, waiting on the church steps with a little bunch of flowers in her hand. When they walked together along the rows of pews, they could have been a young couple about to be wed, but they weren't. They were already married, and they had never been young. There were only the two of them there, apart from the priest and the organist and a sexton who stayed in the background. They sat right at the front and listened to the priest talk about the battle between light and darkness. From above Raksha and Ivan looked like two children in the large nave, sitting, their heads bowed. As soon as the music sounded, Raksha started to weep. She wept noisily, her mouth open like a child, runnels of snot and tears dripping onto her knees. Ivan took her hand and held it in his. Her legs shook and jerked like a panic-stricken deer.

When it was over they followed the gravedigger to the grave. A cold sun on the snow, the air clean and raw. A few snowflakes swirling around.

"Are you going home now?" she asked, while they waited.

"Yes, I'm going home now."

"It must be windy there by now."

"It's always windy there."

She wrung her cold hands.

"I was never very good with all that wind."

"Neither of us was particularly good at anything," he said, looking down into the hole that was to be my grave. That was the way it had been. They hadn't been particularly good at anything.

My body, or what was left of it, was lowered into the ground. Ivan thought Raksha would try to throw herself into the hole after me, so he kept his hand on her arm, but she stood perfectly still, staring ahead. The white coffin was lowered into the frozen ground and the grave was filled with earth. Outside the church they took each other's hand, and then they parted forever.

After all those years Raksha filed a petition for divorce. Ivan signed and returned it to the authorities. She was in the bath when she opened the letter declaring them to be divorced. She slid under the hot water and retreated into herself. Whatever it had been, it was over at last. She took her pills again and the old world opened up inside her, the world no-one else had access to, the one that was gentle and beautiful and light. Ivan sat on his balcony in the sun in his hat and gloves, waiting for spring. He sat so still the birds mistook him for a lifeless thing or a piece of furniture and would settle on him for a while. There he sat, waiting for the end to come.

There is still no stone on my grave. A simple wooden cross has been there all this time. Raksha has always intended to organise a stone, but it hasn't materialised. Every time she is there, she thinks she is going to arrange for a gravestone, but the years have passed and become decades. Before she leaves she usually kisses the grass growing on my grave. I have seen her kiss the snow. Sometimes she talks to me and occasionally might castigate me, but that is alright, I deserve it. Sometimes she sings a song in her rough, gravelly voice.

Little Raksha, an old lady now with silver hair, lying on her flower-patterned kitchen sofa all day long, deep in her half-dreams. She always has done this, I suppose. From death's perspective, life appears to be a strange dream without logic, so for me her daydreaming is starting to seem less peculiar. But the other day she suddenly rose from the sofa and took the turquoise telephone receiver down from the wall and ordered a gravestone, as if all she has ever done is order gravestones. She must have worked it all out long before, because in an instant she has the telephone number on a piece of paper in her hand. The statute of limitation has elapsed and they will never exhume my remains now. She said on the telephone that she hadn't decided yet what should be on the stone, but she knew it had to be rough-hewn and simple and that my name had to be in gold. And also, she added quickly when they had finished and were on the point of hanging up, and so quickly the man at the other end could hardly hear, it had to have this on it too:

HERE LIES THE DAUGHTER OF A HAIRDRESSER

Crazy little Raksha. She has never been a hairdresser, at least not a professional in a proper salon with a trolley full of expensive hairsprays. She cut my hair and Eskil's and Ivan's and did some of their friends and a few neighbours by the river and, later, on Svartviksvägen and she still cuts Sylvia's. Just imagine this is the epitaph she has been working on for the last twenty-five years. But perhaps she was only thinking that my profession wasn't appropriate for a gravestone, even if I had nothing against it myself. It is the truth, and it isn't any less true for being unseemly. Besides, you are allowed to lie on gravestones. People lie all the time, about everything, and especially on gravestones. *Greatly loved and sadly missed* it often says, although it isn't true. Sometimes it does become true after death, as it has for me and Raksha to a certain extent. After my death something between us eased and suddenly she could cope with me, maybe even love me. And I have always loved her, I still do, in the same way I did as a child, even though here those sorts of feelings fade over time. I still like seeing her small brown hands and the floral housecoats she lives in, the same ones she had when I was young, I think. When she lies in her bath with a tiny angel on the rim and blows one smoke ring and then a second into the first, I think she is sending a little message to me and to us, those who were once her family.

Love is like snow coming to swathe the world in its light, and then it vanishes. I look for Nanna but she is hiding, as always. Until one day I see her on Herkulesgatan again. From above, her blonde hair gleams against the grey asphalt, the grey granite buildings. She is older and thinner, almost hollowed-out, but she moves as fast as she did before, as if the streets are hers and hers alone. She must have climbed out of a car because all of a sudden she is standing there next to a pillar, rummaging in a big bag. An old man glides up to her on a bicycle with a tape recorder on the pannier rack and together they walk down to Sergels Torg and on towards Klara churchyard.

Everyone on Herkulesgatan is always on the way to somewhere else, it is the only thing you talk about there, but no-one tends to get further than the morgue. I always thought Nanna would be the one to get away. Long ago she used to say she would take me with her to the great glacier at Kebnekaise, where there is no fear or dread, only light and sky and snow. We were going to take Valle with us and no-one would find us there. It didn't happen. I never saw her again after I had lost him, and the glacier is on its way out too, melting like the Russian tundra and Antarctica. Everything disappears, everything you love dies.

The day I came across Solveig alone by the dark stone in the churchyard was like dying again. Ghostly and thin in her coat, she looked so pale. She wasn't weeping, she was simply standing with her hand in front of her mouth, looking as though she was freezing on the warm summer evening. Clara stood a short distance away, leaning on a tree, smoking, looking at Solveig. After a while Clara walked up to Solveig and put her leather jacket around her shoulders. On the gravestone was his name: *Valentino.*

"Are we just going to leave him here among the dead?" Solveig's voice was small and hoarse.

"Yes."

"It doesn't feel right."

"It's what people do though, we just go."

You might be inclined to consider it a mistake, a temporary relapse, that he couldn't manage the same strength as before after being clean for so long, but I don't think it was. And a morphine death is gentle and kind, the sort everyone dreams of. I believe he had been alone for a long time and he didn't know what to do with all he was suddenly given, and maybe it was difficult for him to emerge into the light so abruptly, to find he had a sister like Solveig out of the blue. I know what hope can do to you.

*

Sometimes I think Ivan and Raksha were reckless people, careless about things that were important, lying for days by the water, drinking in the sun, forgetting all about us. But I believe it is just the same as Shane and me: you hope the children will save you, you forget they are so small, so helpless, so easy to harm when you call them forth from the shade of their unborn state with no comprehension of what you do.

Shane and I truly believed the children would save us, we told each other all the time: "When the baby's here, there'll be no more problems." How wrong we were. When the children arrive, the difficulties really start.

I returned to Herkulesgatan but everyone who had been there before had gone. Someone said Shane was in prison in Istanbul, someone else was convinced he was dead. No-one knew where Nanna had gone. It was as if there had been a nuclear war and only the nastiest people had survived. Many of them had been afflicted by that illness and it had all happened fast, they had instantly disappeared from the streets and been isolated in the major hospitals. That was where Shane was, though I didn't know it then, just a few thousand metres from Herkulesgatan where I was wandering around without him. He died only a few months after me, and just like me he ended up in a bag of sorts, a black plastic cocoon that they put straight into the ground.

I didn't attend any of the scheduled meetings with the authorities and I didn't write any threatening letters, I didn't complicate matters for any person on earth; the awareness that Solveig and Valle would be better off without us had finally sunk in, as a simple truth. And I didn't give it much thought, but I must have assumed it would be an overdose, that somehow it would happen naturally, in accordance with evolution, Darwin and all that. There is no gentler death.

I didn't deliberately run into his knife, I was running away from something else that scared me more than death, and he happened to be standing there with his blood-soaked dreams.

What was I running from? The short answer is that I was running from love. The long answer is far too long, and anyway there is no-one who bothers about long versions anymore. You are given only one chance, and you can never come back to this planet again. All that exists is the flickering little candle flame that is your breath. Look after that flame, Solveig.

When I looked in on you and Clara the other day I decided it would be the last time, from now on I am going to let you be. You are so beautiful and so grown-up, I am always slightly frightened when I see you. Next to you I feel like a child, for you are older now than I ever was. Possibly it makes me rather jealous. Not jealous as such, I would give you the stars if you asked me to, but when I see you I think I would have liked to be part of all that too. Love, time passing without you thinking about it. The seasons. The weather. I would have liked to be grown-up, I would have liked to experience one more summer.

I am sad that as soon as you found your brother, you lost him. But I believe you are strong, tough, like a tree. And the apple often falls far from the tree. Isn't that what they say, those in the know?

I am going to stop disturbing you now. Perhaps you didn't even hear me, but mistook me for a bird of the night or a grim story you once read in the newspaper. Don't believe everything you hear. And don't believe everything you think. Don't worry if people gossip about you and your origins. The brightest flame casts the darkest shadow. And you know, most of what I have gleaned about time and space and eternity is what I learnt listening to your lectures at the university. And it is fortunate I am dead, for how would I dare speak to you, standing there in the stream of light through the high windows with your suit and your Elvis hair, making everyone listen to you? Your explanations about the origin of the universe actually comfort me most, especially the story you tell the students about the birth of stars. About everything once upon a time being gathered into one small particle that exploded one day, about stars being formed from a vast exploding cloud of gas and then the stars themselves exploding and the heat producing carbon and oxygen and nitrogen and everything needed for you and Valle to come into being one day inside me. The same substances, as it happens, that are involved in the decomposition of a body and turn it into stardust. Accounts of how the universe continues to expand make it easier for me to let go, the thought that we are part of the same state of perpetual motion. I think, whatever happens to us, it has been only one second in eternity.

"So let us keep fast hold of hands, that when the birds begin to sing, none of us be missing."   EMILY DICKINSON

SARA STRIDSBERG, born in 1972, is a writer, playwright and former member of the Swedish Academy. Her first novel, *Happy Sally*, was published in 2004, and her break-through came two years later with the publication of *The Faculty of Dreams*, her second novel, which was longlisted for the Booker International Prize in 2019. Her novels have been translated into 25 languages, and she has been shortlisted for the prestigious August Prize three times, including in 2012 for her collection *Medealand and Other Plays*. She lives in Stockholm.

DEBORAH BRAGAN-TURNER is a translator of Swedish literature, and a former bookseller and academic librarian. She studied Scandinavian Languages at University College, London, and her translations include works by Per Olov Enquist and Anne Swärd.

FOR
VERONICA
WEDGWOOD
THESE
Studies in Seventeenth-Century
History

edited by
RICHARD OLLARD
and
PAMELA TUDOR-CRAIG

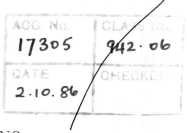

COLLINS
8 Grafton Street, London W1
1986

William Collins Sons and Co. Ltd
London · Glasgow · Sydney · Auckland
Toronto · Johannesburg

British Library Cataloguing in Publication Data

For Veronica Wedgwood These: studies in
seventeenth-century history.
1. Great Britain—History—Stuarts, 1603-1714
I. Tudor-Craig, Pamela   II. Ollard, Richard
III. Wedgwood, C. V.
942.06   DA375
ISBN 0-00-217517-7

First published 1986

Made and printed in Great Britain by
William Collins Sons & Co. Ltd, Glasgow

CONTENTS

ILLUSTRATIONS

PREFACE

Veronica Wedgwood's historical writings have been so widely enjoyed by the general reader and so justly acclaimed by her fellow scholars that the editors of this volume of essays written in her honour would only find themselves repeating what has already been said, and said much better and more authoritatively, if they were to attempt to describe her achievement. The bibliography compiled by Jaqueline Hope-Wallace is perhaps better testimonial than we could give.

Yet perhaps they may speak for the other contributors in singling out the grace of mind and of personality that gives to her work, as it does to the privilege of her acquaintance, its special quality. Veronica Wedgwood brings the same gift of intuitive sympathy to all her friendships, of the past as of the present. She walks beside them instead of going back to meet them. Such insight reaches the simplicity of wisdom.

The editors wish to thank Mr Stuart Proffitt of Collins for the scholarly care with which he has guided the book through the press.

Richard Ollard
Pamela Tudor-Craig

INTRODUCTION
Elizabeth Longford

A characteristic pleasure of Veronica Wedgwood's friendship, which I have enjoyed since we were undergraduates at Lady Margaret Hall, consists in her modesty and sense of fun. In various forms these qualities permeate the whole of her *œuvre* and emerge as the virtues of balance, perspective, tolerance and understanding of human motive, all presented with the spice of wit and irony in a general atmosphere of good humour. One would be as surprised to find angry dogmatism in *The Great Rebellion* as to meet gunmen on duty in the Palace of Westminster.

The Wedgwood voice is above all persuasive. A short passage from *The King's War* (the second volume of *The Great Rebellion*) will recall its characteristic tone:

> He [Charles I] had failed in war as he had failed in peace, because he never fully understood what one of his secretaries had once said: 'There goes more to it than bidding it be done.' For the King, a thing wished for, a thing bidden, was a thing done. But closing the gap between bidding and doing is the whole craft of government. That craft Charles, King by the Grace of God and Divine Right, never mastered, never even saw that he needed to master it.

The voice, though not raised, is compelling.

Not that she is incapable of trumpet calls; another of her excellencies is the power to march and counter-march vigorously over great distances of time and space. In *The King's Peace* and *The King's War*, which together compose *The Great Rebellion*, she achieves a superb panorama of Britain before and during the Civil Wars. Far from having to look for needles in bundles of hay, the beguiled reader finds that the wide canvas and magnitude of the setting serve only to point up each separate event. With such a gift it is absolutely right that she should turn now from biography and narrative in the seventeenth century to the splendid panorama of world history.

Here again she disclaims any dogmatic pretensions to a 'theory of history', though fortunately she cannot avoid numerous scholarly and stimulating generalizations. As a world philosopher *malgré elle*, she brings out impressively the human instinct to 'carry on' whatever the impending disaster. No doubt it was disgraceful of Nero to fiddle while Rome burned, insane of the Romans to practise luxury as usual while the Empire was falling. Nevertheless, London's 'carrying on' during the Blitz was morally rather than practically different from the Romans' performance, and we must all in a sense keep on fiddling if we are to survive. This is only my opinion, formed after studying her *Spoils of Time*, volume one of her history of the world.

Looking at her work as a historian more minutely, one is struck by her effective, because selective, use of detail and especially of original sources. Quotations seem to be dropped into the text almost casually, as a great cook light-handedly adds some essential ingredient to the noble dish. There is no overloading. Yet the temptation to overload is among the major ones that beset the historian. How authentic sounds the voice of the contemporary diarist compared with one's own summarized version of the same event. Moreover with original sources in one's possession, there is a genuine fear that failure to use them fully may deprive readers of evidence that they cannot obtain elsewhere.

Veronica Wedgwood has solved these problems of overloading by exerting the same instinctive judgement that her ancestors showed when they picked up a piece of their pottery and decorated it with classical elegance and grace. *Meden agan.* Nothing in excess.

With classical grace there goes also a certain reserve. We know from her writings that she likes people – her *Spoils of Time* is a narrative of peoples – and particularly likes people who are 'lively', 'curious', 'hard-working', 'energetic', 'confident'; she dislikes about equally the 'languid' and the 'hot-headed'. But she herself prefers not to work within a university in spite of her many opportunities to do so. 'The behaviour of men as individuals', she writes, 'is more interesting to me than their behaviour as groups or classes.' And I once heard her say in an interview that she needed to be independent and detached.

She is a rare spirit, sometimes reticent, always strong. Above all she makes the reading of history an experience not to be missed.

I am grateful to her publishers for giving her friends and fellow historians, through this *Festschrift*, the opportunity to express their admiration for what she has written and is still writing.

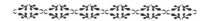

THE APOLOGY *
J. H. Hexter

THE FIRST PARLIAMENT of James I opened late in March 1604.[1] Early in June, a committee of the House of Commons set out to prepare a document to satisfy his Majesty about the actions of the House during a ten-week session which had not gone very well.[2] June was two-thirds past[3] when the committee reported a document called the Apology and Satisfaction of the House of Commons.[4] Here is the story of that apology.

The late days of May and the first in June had been hard ones on Members of the House of Commons who held that body in any esteem. First, the King peremptorily called the whole House of Commons to Whitehall and scorched its collective ear with a tirade.[5] A day or so later had come a conference of a House com-

* Only in reading the galleys of this essay did I notice a most unfortunate omission. Glancing through the footnotes, I did not see a single reference to Geoffrey Elton's 'A High Road to Civil War?' published in the *festschrift* for Garrett Mattingly, *From the Renaissance to the Counter-Reformation*, ed. Charles H. Carter (New York, 1965), pp. 325–47. That study focused with great intensity and perspicuity on the legislative history of the Apology, as it moved from the floor to committee, back from committee to the floor, and finally back to committee once again in June 1604. Of that history, Professor Elton's account is definitive. It is the point from which my assessment of the significance of the Apology starts. In writing that assessment I referred back to it again and again not only for the precision of its detail but for the crispness of its judgments. The accident of my failure to refer to 'A High Road to Civil War?' would be an act of gross ingratitude and a serious impropriety in scholarship.

[1] The Journals of the House of Commons (hereafter CJ), 1, 139.

[2] CJ, 1, 139–306.

[3] CJ, 1, 243b.

[4] The most readily accessible edition of the Apology is in J. R. Tanner (ed.), *Constitutional Documents of the Reign of James I* (hereafter Tanner) (Cambridge, 1930), pp. 215–31. Unfortunately, Tanner edited out several passages of consequence to the story that follows. The version that appears in William Petyt, *Jus. Parliamentarium* (hereafter Petyt) (1739), pp. 227–43, contains the passages that Tanner excised.

[5] CJ, 1, 227a–228a.

mittee with one from the Lords about wardship.[6] The Commons
had given its committee elaborate and careful instructions on
how to proceed in the conference. At the meeting, however, that
committee had been the unhappy recipients of an irritable blast
from the Lords, who had contradicted each point that the committee made,[7] told the House to take care what it did,[8] expostu-
lated with it, and admonished it.[9] The Lords particularized their
denunciation of the iniquities of the House of Commons by
censuring the Members for having 'spent our time in matters of
privileges'.[10] By their close parallel the two denunciations of the
Lower House stretched both the long arm of coincidence and the
patience of the House of Commons to breaking-point. In the
midst of its debate on what to do about these cavillings at the
business the House chose to pursue and at its way of going about
that business, 'in which many particular actions and passages of
the House [had been] objected to', Sir Thomas Ridgeway, 'one
of the knights of Devonshire', declared that it appeared his
Majesty had such a mistaken impression of the proceedings of
the House in general, and especially in the matter of wardships,
that it was

> necessary and safe for this House, and dutiful and convenient in
> respect of his Majesty, instantly to advise of such a form of
> satisfaction . . . as might in all humility inform his Majesty of
> the truth and clearness of the actions and intentions of the House
> from the beginning, thereby to free it from the scandal of levity
> and precipitation.

Ridgeway therefore moved that 'a committee be named to take
a survey of the proceedings of the House' and to prepare a document to present to the King to vindicate its actions.[11] The
language of the debate on Ridgeway's resolution heated up
enough to lead the Clerk to omit some of it when he transformed

[6] CJ, I, 229a.

[7] My interpretation of 'opposition of reason to reason': CJ, I, 230b.

[8] My interpretation of 'precise caution in proceedings': ibid.

[9] ibid.

[10] ibid.

[11] CJ, I, 230b–231a.

his rough notes into an official record.[12] The House adopted
Ridgeway's motion, and put the preparing of the vindication of
the House into the hands of that same large committee it had
selected two weeks earlier for the conference on wardships, the
one in which the House had run foul of the Lords in the first
instance.

On the day James had summoned the House to appear before
him and indicted the whole course of its actions since the opening
of Parliament, the slender record of the meeting in the Commons
Journal does not tell whether he suggested that the House owed
him an explanation of its undutiful behaviour. In any case, what
he had said seemed both censorious enough and far enough off
the mark to suggest to the House that it have a response prepared
for his satisfaction. The King gave belated thought to the sort of
document the creators of the earlier Humble Answer in the
clash over the Buckinghamshire election were likely to produce
after three and a half months of cacophonous and gritty proceedings in the House. He decided under the circumstances that
he would do well to apply a bit of ointment to the lacerations he
had inflicted on the Members by his sharpness of tongue. So four
days after the House had chosen a large committee to prepare a
point-by-point vindication of its actions James sent a long
message to persuade it that no such course was necessary.

First, he addressed himself to 'the motives of his . . . unkind-
ness'. He had been upset because despite 'the long continuance
of the Parliament' so few 'matters of weight' had 'passed, and
that matter of privilege had taken much time'. He had been,
thereby, 'moved with jealousy' that proceedings had not gone
'as . . . he expected'. What he had said to the House when he
summoned it before him just a week back was not, he alleged, a
condemnation, but only an 'admonition as of a father to his
children', a reminder to them of that 'expedition', that speed,
'omitted and desired'. He did not think that the House had
'denied' him 'anything which is fit to be granted'. He was touched

---

[12] He omitted the explicit concurrence of one Member (Sir John Hollis) with Ridgeway's resolution, and buried what looks like an attempt of the Speaker to divert the
House from the general course on which Ridgeway's motion set it into a confined
response on the matter of wardship. He also wholly omitted his own phrase that had
described what the House aimed to do as 'to right his Majesty's conceits' – meaning, I
take it, his conceptions or misconceptions (CJ, 1, 984a).

by the concern of the House at the displeasure he had expressed and at its 'desire to give him satisfaction', and he noted happily that since he had dressed them down the Members were moving faster 'in those things' that he 'desired to be in effect'. And so, putting an end to this somewhat ambivalent capitulation, he 'wisheth we would not trouble ourselves with giving him satisfaction; and he giveth what time we desire for finishing the matters of importance pending'.[13]

James's back-pedalling did not work as he intended. The House did not revoke its charge to the committee to prepare a satisfaction for the King. It did not rejoice because James had said he was satisfied that it had meant well. That was not the kind of satisfaction that his tirade on 30 May had seemed to demand, nor the kind the House wanted to give him. If on 5 June the Members found the King's expression of his *gracious* satisfaction with their previous *good intentions* less than they wanted from him, it can only be because they also wanted an expression of his *rational* satisfaction with their previous *good actions*, all the actions from the beginning of the Parliament of 1604 that he had ill-advisedly criticized them for. What they wanted from James was a due vindication of those actions and of the grounds on which they had taken them. They wanted to tell him that they were right and that they had been so all along.

So, despite James's assurance that its labours were unnecessary, the committee that the House had chosen set about carrying out its instructions. On 20 June the Commons heard the draft of the document its committee had prepared. The Clerk began to transcribe it into the Journal. He ordinarily did this with formal addresses of the House to the King to make them matter of record. Three hundred words into the 5000-word document, the Clerk stopped copying. 'The Form of Apology and Satisfaction', as the Journal called it, had been twice read; it had also been 'debated and argued *pro et contra* whether the matter and the manner fit'.[14] At least seventeen Members spoke to that issue, but our only record is silent as to the substance of the arguments. The tenor of the debate evidently stirred doubts in the Clerk's

---

[13] CJ, 1, 232b–233a.

[14] CJ, 1, 234b, 995b.

mind whether the Apology and Satisfaction would ever reach the King – doubts serious enough to make him stop copying it, but tentative enough to lead him to leave eight pages of the Journal blank after the early sentences he had copied, just in case.

Nine days later, the House recommitted the 'frame of satisfaction touching the proceedings of the House'. It insisted that members of the committee who 'found any cause of exception or were not present at the former several meetings' of the committee 'might be commanded to attend'. It wanted the committee members to resolve their differences so that they could report to the House 'some . . . resolution . . . for further proceeding or surceasing'.[15] Although the committee was 'appointed to meet on Monday next, 2 July', it made no subsequent report to the House. On 7 July, James returned to tirade as an appropriate mode of parliamentary address; he tongue-lashed the House of Commons at length, made a sarcastic but ambiguous reference to apologies and apology-makers, and prorogued Parliament. And that, as far as any parliamentary action went, was the sticky end of the Apology – a report buried in a committee by recommitment, apparently because there was not agreement on it in the House.[16]

That really is about all there is to say for pretty sure about the Apology and Satisfaction as *a political event of 1604*. It was a true non-starter. In a session in which the House of Commons had insisted that it was a court of record and established the position of its Journal as its record, the Apology did not make it into that record; it was thus a political wraith without substance, the event that did not happen.

We really do not know, have no means of knowing, how this came about or, rather, did not come about. There is not enough evidence for confident inference. At best we can set bounds within which whatever happened happened. At one extreme we may suppose that as the session moved towards its close and attendance slackened, especially at committee meetings, a small cluster of Members got control of proceedings in the committee charged with preparing the vindication of the House and seized the

---

[15] CJ, 1, 248b.

[16] *State Papers, James I*, vol. 8, p. 93.

opportunity to write the eloquent and rather high-flown declaration of principles that the never-on-the-record Apology contained. When the whole House heard this somewhat inflammatory document read, the Members were resolved to keep it off the record. So they effectively bottled it up in committee for the rest of the session.

The other extreme alternative is that most of both committee and House were satisfied with the 'matter' of the document. The King's advisers, however – courtiers, placemen, and privy councillors – were anything but happy with it. Particularly unhappy were those advisers on whose counsel the King had followed courses that so seriously alienated a House of Commons which had been ready to give the King his honeymoon session. It was late enough, near enough to prorogation time, for a small group to put a brake on the actions of the House despite the annoyance of the majority at their stalling tactics.[17] Such a group could prey on the anxieties of the Members. Those Members were fully in agreement with the substance of the Apology; after all, it was just what the Commons had insisted on despite the King's request, two weeks before, that the matter be dropped. Still, they might well worry that the 'manner' – we should say the 'tone' – of the Apology would exacerbate the already roiled temper of the King, a King who might be ruling them for decades to come. In good faith and in the interest of harmony such men voted to return the Apology to committee. There was little time left in the session, so the tactical skills at sabotage of a minority kept the document bottled up until Parliament was prorogued.

On the basis of the available evidence neither of these scenarios is improbable; both are indeed about equally probable, as would be several alternative scenarios less extreme. Only of two boundary statements can we be sure. First, there was no intense passion on the part of an overwhelming majority of the Members to get the Apology as they had received it on to the record and so to present it to the King. Had such a passion existed, there was no

---

[17] The extraordinary pains of the House to instruct the committee members on their future behaviour – dissenters who had spoken against the Apology on the floor or stayed away from committee meetings were to be 'commanded to attend' – can be read as pressure for action, as can the House's order to the committee after recommittal that it meet promptly: CJ, 1, 248b.

obstacle to prevent its consummation in action. The House could have done it and did not. On the other hand, the House of Commons did want to vindicate its action during the session. It had regarded such a work of vindication as necessary on 1 June in the face of the savage going-over it had suffered from the King. Four days later, however, the King had done an about-face. He had come as close to open repentance of his earlier outburst of temper as a king well could. The House had been offered an easy way to establish amicable relations with the powers-that-be if that were its first purpose: just drop its aspiration to an apologia. The House did nothing to accept the hand of peace the King had extended. It did not, as far as the evidence takes us, reply to the King's message of 5 June. It did not stop the work of the committee that it had assigned the task of vindicating its actions from the beginning of James's first Parliament. If it had done so, it would not have had an Apology and Satisfaction before it on 20 June.

A message the King sent the House on 26 June, between the reading of the Apology on the twentieth and its recommittal on the twenty-ninth, may account for the submersion of the committee's report, although ostensibly what the King said in his message had nothing to do with the Apology. It did have to do with one of the principal concerns of the House – taxation. James said he had been advised that it was customary for his subjects to grant a new ruler a subsidy in his first Parliament. He had permitted Members of the House to forward such a measure, and he knew that of late some of them had been pressing for a grant to be made to him. In the meantime, however, he had learnt that the custom was not as alleged – misadvised again! – and that the people were still paying instalments on the great tax of 1601. He therefore urged that nothing further be done about a levy at this time.[18] Though not especially graceful, the message was certainly gracious and welcome. The Members could now go home and tell those who sent them that after the four high-priced Parliaments at the end of Elizabeth's reign they were to enjoy a respite. The King's generous gesture may have made language in the Apology, which hitherto rang sharp but true,

---

[18] CJ, 1, 246b–247a.

sound merely petulant. And that is really all we can say for sure or for probable about the course of events.

If the Apology has any significance, then, it cannot be because of what it did politically at the time it came before the House, or because of what immediately happened in the political context into which the Apology was, so to speak, dropped. In context – the Parliament of 1604 and its immediate sequel – the Apology dropped into the void. If the document is not all sound and fury, it will have to be because of what it says and what its authors meant by what it says, and who its authors were. Regardless of what the House did about the Apology we need to know what its authors meant to do in writing it.

At the simplest level it is reasonable to suppose that the authors of the Apology meant to carry out the instructions of the House to the committee of which they were members. The House instructed the committee to 'inform his Majesty in the truth and clearness of the actions and intentions of the House from the beginning'.[19] To do that the committee had to show not only that in general the actions were right but also that the House was the right body to engage in those actions. That is what the name given the document – 'Apology and Satisfaction' – signifies.

And that of course tells us what at a minimum the document represents. It represents its authors' opinion of how the House saw its own actions; or, put another way, saw itself not only in action, but in justified or right action. In the matters they dealt with the authors of the Apology had to be, if not right on target, at least in the target area. If they had not been, if the House had regarded what the Apology said about its actions as merely absurd, the Members would have disregarded the document, not treated it in the ambivalent way they actually did.

The authors had also to think the King would not regard what the Apology claimed about the House to be pure piffle. Unless the King might conceivably be brought to see that the doings of the House since March were justifiable on grounds that he might acknowledge as justifying, the whole exercise would be a waste of time. Thus, we may be sure that the Apology is *not* the sort of document which the Communist Manifesto was: a statement of

[19] CJ, 1, 230b.

principle based on a theory wholly alien to the powers that be, and intended to rally a party aiming to overthrow those powers and be their replacement. Since it aimed at the assent of the House of Commons and at the agreement of the King, its assertions can not lie too far outside the bounds of their shared opinions. Unless the authors were lunatic – and of this there are no signs – the Apology must be close to the centre, the golden mean, of those opinions.

It is these implicit constraints on the authors of the Apology – there is of course no evidence that the authors perceived them as constraints – that make the Apology so significant a document. Let us list the things about the Apology that render it significant.

1. It explains exhaustively the grounds for the positions it takes.

2. It aims to come acceptably close to the common opinion of the House of Commons and to persuade the King.

3. It is a document of *justification*; that is, it seeks to state what the Commons did *rightfully* during two busy months, and therefore what the rights of the House are with respect to the matters they concerned themselves with.

4. Because the Apology is about what the House actually did *and* its right to do what it did, it aims to state the opinion of the elective representative body of England about its own place in the political order, its duties and its privileges, and their source, and to do so in the context of immediate political actualities.

So the Apology is an extraordinary document and, for our understanding of how the House of Commons saw itself at the beginning of the seventeenth century, a most important one. The House did not present the Apology to the King, true, but no one in the House appears to have suggested that its committee had got everything wrong about the House's own view of what it was and what it was for. As far as the evidence goes on those fundamental matters the Apology may have been precisely right and had to be pretty near right. For our purposes it does not matter at all whether the authors of the Apology were 'sincere' or 'meant' what they said. They were certainly intelligent: both the intellectual and the rhetorical quality of the document itself testify to that. They were intelligent men who, by inclination perhaps, by circumstance surely, were trying to formulate the self-appraisal of the House of Commons in a way that the House would recognize as appropriate. Every matter on which the authors of the Apology touched maps for us an area of concern of the House of Commons in 1604, or at least an area which contemporary experts – the authors – perceive as of concern. The length and intensity of their responses in the Apology provide us not merely with points but, as it were, with the areas and contours of the concerns and preoccupations of the House as a cluster of contemporary experts surveyed them. As a 'constitutional' document in the sense of an enactment or judgement having the force of law, the Apology, then, is literally inconsequential. As a set of clues to the way the House of Commons perceived itself at a moment in the history of human freedom when the House was entering on a crucial role in that history, the Apology is of enormous, indeed of unique, value.

In its vindication of the House, the committee was touchy. It was also compendious: it left nothing out. It explained to the King why what it had done about Church reform,[20] and assarts,[21] and purveyance,[22] and wardships[23] was the right thing to have done, though he had mistakenly thought they were the wrong things or had misunderstood what the House was in fact doing. The Apology also explained why the House had not done what it had not done about Scotland, and why it was right not to do it.[24] Because the King had charged the House with being too touchy about its dignity and its privileges, and with spending too much time on such matters, the committee tried to show that the House had been quite right to be touchy, and had spent the proper time on slights from all sources – from the King, from the Bishop of Bristol, who wrote an adverse pamphlet about the position of the House on the union with Scotland,[25] and from the Warden of the Fleet, who refused to surrender to the House a bankrupt

[20] Tanner, pp. 226–7; Petyt, pp. 229–31.
[21] Tanner, p. 227; Petyt, pp. 231–2.
[22] Tanner, p. 222; Petyt, p. 232.
[23] Tanner, pp. 228–9; Petyt, pp. 233–7.
[24] Tanner, p. 226; Petyt, p. 228.
[25] Tanner, pp. 225–6; Petyt, pp. 227–8.

member seeking to escape his debt by invoking parliamentary privilege.[26]

The Members of the House, the Apology said, even had good reason to complain among themselves of the usual incompetence and negligence of the Gentleman-Usher through which was 'frustrated' their 'loving and just desire to hear your Majesty's speech the first day of Parliament'. (As he had done before at the opening of Parliament,[27] and as most of the Committee members knew by experience he had done, the Gentleman-Usher had failed to bestir himself to inform the House of Commons that proceedings were about to begin.) Even worse was the Yeoman of the Guard who stood watch at the door of the Parliament House. When the Members of the House of Commons, finally aware that the opening of Parliament was about to get under way without them, rushed up to catch the King's speech, the Yeoman barred their entry. Since the inadequate space behind the bar reserved for Members of the House of Commons was probably already full of gate-crashers, that was not wholly unreasonable. Gratuitously, however, and in the manner naturally adopted by the equivalent of a traffic cop at the equivalent of rush hour, the guardsman addressed the Members in language 'very opprobrious' which 'might have been not unfitly applied to the peasants of France' but was not appropriate when its object was 'the whole flower and power of your kingdom'.[28]

Now, clearly, for these misdemeanours King James was in no way responsible. The sycophancy of the higher officers of Church and State, the negligence and idleness of some minor officials, the petty tyranny of others, the tenacious timidity of yet others, caught, as the Warden of the Fleet was, in the No Man's Land where the law is at once uncertain and severe – these are sources of inconvenience and indignation and the staples of satire always

---

[26] The warden had refused because he was in reasonable fear that if he obeyed the House the creditors who had got Sherley gaoled in the first place would hold him, the warden, liable, for the debts of the man for whose custody he was responsible: CJ, 1, 149–208 passim, esp. 200, 203.

[27] Petyt, pp. 221–2. This passage is omitted by Tanner in his reprinting of the Apology. For a previous similar episode, see John E. Neale, *The Elizabethan House of Commons*, p. 340.

[28] Petyt, pp. 222–3; omitted by Tanner.

and everywhere from Chaucer to Gogol. Yet the authors of the Apology devoted more space to these trivia than to the union with Scotland and the reform of religion taken together. They spent more than twice as much space on them as they did on the long-standing and recurrent abuses of purveyance.[29] And, although the King's profitable right to revenue from his wardship of all minor orphans who held any of their land directly from the crown was increasingly archaic and grotesque, and directly touched the purses of many Members, it received little more attention in the Apology than the cluster of random minute pecks at the dignity of the House described earlier.

This peculiar disproportion between cause and effect, this excessive boggling over and muttering at trifles, raises questions about the Apology and the state of mind responsible for it. How does one account for the hypersensitivity to which the Apology gave vent at the slightest lapse in reverence for the House and its privileges? In seeking some explanation we do best to look directly at the document that its writers infused with so petty and yet so deep-seated a sense of the deference due to the elected branch of England's national assembly.

The Apology begins by explaining to James why, despite his express readiness to believe in the goodwill of the House, the Members insist on rendering him an apology and satisfaction. They do it to clear from his mind the fog of misinformation with which misadvisers have filled it. He has been misinformed on three matters: (1) about the spirit in which his succession was received by the people – a spirit of joy; (2) about the 'rights and liberties of your subjects and the privileges of this House'; and (3) about several actions and speeches in the House with respect both to its privileges and to its agenda – union with Scotland, reform in the Church, and redress of grievances. The whole document is spent in spelling out the details under these three headings.

There is, however, no balance or equality among the items with which the Apology concerns itself. Taken together, the matter of James's accession, the Union, and the reform of the Church and States, including the legislative efforts on which the

---

[29] The King's prerogative to commandeer at set prices cartage and victuals for his court.

House had embarked early in the session, did not engage the attention of the authors of the Apology to the extent that 'the rights and liberties of your subjects and parliamentary privileges of this House' did.[30] Whatever the ordinary political preoccupation of the Members of James's first Parliament in its first session, the authors of the Apology were first and foremost concerned to clear up for the King what they saw as his serious and dangerous illusions about the freedom of his subjects and the privileges of Parliament. From their petty concerns with trivial affronts to the House we have already got the sense that on the matter of parliamentary privileges they may have been obsessive. The proportions of the whole Apology substantiate our previous impression. In the session of 1604 the House of Commons was above all intensely preoccupied with its own privileges.

In corporative bodies such a preoccupation is one of the commonplaces of social behaviour, its presence one of the givens of the most elementary social thought. Corporate 'persons' are as intensely self-regarding and self-protective as individual persons, and a good bit more narrowly so. Clergy, physicians, employers, lawyers, policemen, trade unionists all try to impose on society rules that serve the good of their particular group. Sometimes the rules that well serve a corporate person or 'interest group' are in actuality also beneficial to the larger society, sometimes they make little difference, often they are deleterious. However that may be, if the larger society is one that in the common view exists for the common good,[31] particular interest groups feel bound to pretend that whatever they seek for their particular good is also in the public interest, as if their privileges exist for the general welfare. To such allegations the usual and appropriate response is 'Oh, come on!' or 'Show me'.

The House of Commons dug deeper for its claim of privilege than do run-of-the-mill interest groups. Some of the privileges

---

[30] By line count, the proportion was about 48 to 52.

[31] In contrast to a society that explicitly exists for the exploitation of one group of its members by another (the south-east African society rooted in its exploitations of the Hutu by the Tutsi or the society of the Southern American States before the Civil War explicitly rooted in the exploitation of blacks by whites), or for the destruction of one group by another (the proletariat–bourgeois societies of communist lands), or for both (the Aryan–Jewish society of Nazi Germany).

it asserted for itself such as freedom from arrest were of course at least marginally advantageous to its Members or at any rate to those Members likely to be imprisoned for debt if they dared show their faces in London. Still, only a few Members of the House in their lifetime, much less in the few months of their lifetime that they spent in Parliament, stood in danger of arrest in London for debts or other private misdemeanours. Indeed, the House did not lay claim to any of the sorts of privilege that would have been most to the personal advantage of the Members – exemption, for example, from some part or all of the taxes it voted. Nor did the Members claim their privileges merely on the grounds that those privileges or liberties would do good to the people. That was the standard interest-group claim of all shady monopolists and favour-seekers. The Apology put the claim of the House to privilege, that is, to exemption from rules binding on other subjects, on a broader and more elevated base: it said that the privileges of Parliament *were* the liberties of the subject.

The King's most dreadful mistake, according to the Apology, the matter concerning which he had been most grossly misled by his misadvisers, concerned the source of the privileges of the House of Commons. Surrounded by those misadvisers, scarcely a week into the opening of Parliament, the King had been led by them to put on display before the House of Commons the rotten fruits of their ill-doing. In the unfortunate conference of 28 March between the House and the King, backed by the judges of the high courts, James had made a shocking claim which reflected all too clearly the view of the privileges of Parliament that the Chancellor and the judges had sustained during the last two decades of the reign of the lately deceased Queen. On that fateful day the King had said of the House of Commons that 'he had no purpose to impeach their privilege but since they derived all matters of privilege from him and by his grant, he expected they should not be turned against him'. Thus, in a sort of bland thunderclap, he had delivered an *obiter dictum* which impugned all the privileges of the House. It was, said the Apology, as if the King claimed 'that we held not our privileges of right, but of grace only, renewed every parliament', as a gift 'upon petition'.

The House of Commons immediately had given close attention to what the King had said to it on 28 March, but only in so far as it had to do with their immediate concern – 'freedom' of parliamentary elections, and the final jurisdiction of the House over election disputes. The Members had done nothing then, however, and had said nothing about James's general derogation of the privileges of the House; but, rather, had turned a deaf ear to it. On 20 June, almost three months later, a committee chosen for that purpose present to their fellow-Members a counter-claim in defence of the privileges of the House against the King's derogation of them – a statement and vindication of the judgement of the House as to the nature and source of its privileges. The King's 'assertions', the Apology says, tend 'directly . . . to the utter overthrow of the very fundamental privileges of our House *and therein of the rights and liberties of the whole commons* of your realm of England which they and their ancestors from time immemorial[32] have undoubtedly enjoyed under your Majesty's most noble progenitors'. Against the King's view of the privileges of the House and the liberties of the subject, the Apology declares in words to mark, 'we the knights, citizens, and burgesses of the House of Commons assembled in Parliament, and in the name of the whole commons of the realm of England, with uniform consent for ourselves and our posterity, do expressly protest'. Such a debasing of the privileges of the House is 'derogatory in the highest degree to the true dignity, liberty, and authority of your Majesty's High Court of Parliament, *and consequently to the rights of all your Majesty's said subjects* and the whole body of this your kingdom'. And, the Apology continues, we 'desire that this our protestation may be recorded to all posterity'.[33]

What have the authors of the Apology done in this bold and eloquent passage? First, to the King's claim to be the gracious granter of the privileges of the House they have counter-asserted that by such a claim he destroys those privileges and in so doing takes away the freedom of all his subjects.[34] The freedom imbedded in the privileges of the House belongs not merely to its

---

[32] *immemorial*, Petyt, p. 214; Tanner, p. 221, has *immemorable*.

[33] Tanner, p. 221; Petyt, pp. 213–14.

[34] Of all, that is, but the handful who were members of the Upper House, about a hundred in 1604, whose privileges are individually those of a peer and collectively those of the House of Lords.

Members; it belongs to all English commoners, to the whole English people, and it has been theirs from time immemorial. It is the condition of their liberty. To deny the privileges of the House of Commons, to allege that they depend on the King's will, is to deny all subjects their most important freedom. Against the wrongful claim of the King that his subjects hold their liberties by his grace and at his pleasure the Commons protest. They protest in the name of their ancestors, who were free men by virtue of those privileges, and on behalf of their posterity for whose benefit they want their protest to be a matter of permanent record.

The House and the people of England, for whom it speaks, the Apology continues, do not hold their 'privileges and liberties' by precarious tenure at the King's will. On the contrary, they 'are our right and due inheritance no less than our very lands and goods'.[35] At the dawn of the seventeenth century, the authors of the Apology already stood seized of the idea so firmly grasped by John Locke at the century's twilight that men have a property in their liberties, which puts those liberties beyond the reach of any lawful ruler. The Apology adds and insists that the privileges of the House of Commons are among the most important of the liberties of the subject, that, far from existing at the will of the King, they belong to the subjects of ancient right, and 'cannot be withheld from us, denied, or impaired but with apparent', that is, obvious, 'wrong', not only to the House itself but also 'to the whole state of the realm'.[36]

On this point a king like James, unfamiliar with English law and customs, might readily err and easily be misled. After all, at the outset of Parliament he had heard the Speaker petition him for the customary privileges of the House. He imagined, or by ill counsellors had been led to believe, 'that our making of request in the entrance of parliament to enjoy our privilege' meant that he was free to grant or withhold the privileges sued for. Not at all, says the Apology. That suit is 'an act only of manners'. It no more detracts from the right of the people to the privileges of the House than a subject's suit for his rightful estate in the King's

---

[35] Tanner, p. 221; Petyt, p. 215.

[36] ibid.

court leaves the King's judges free to dispose of the subject's estate as they will. To the contrary, if the estate is rightfully and lawfully his, the judges are bound to give it to the suitor. That a man must follow a course prescribed by law to get what is his does not render it any less his or make his right to it equivocal or precarious. In petitioning for what is his, a man is not begging for grace, he is calling for due process of law. So when through the Speaker of the House of Commons the Members sue or petition for the privileges of the House the King is bound to give his people what is theirs – the liberties or privileges of the representatives they have chosen.

What were the privileges of the House of Commons, or, as the Apology continued to press the identity of the two, 'the liberties of the Commons of England'? They consist chiefly in these three things.

> First, That the shires, cities, and boroughs of England, by representation to be present, have free choice of such persons as they shall put in trust to represent them.
> Secondly, That the persons chosen, during the time of the Parliament as also of their access and recess, be free from restraint, arrest, and imprisonment.
> Thirdly, That in Parliament they may speak freely their consciences without check and controlment, doing the same with due reverence to the Sovereign Court of Parliament, that is, to your Majesty and both the Houses, who all in this case make but one politic body whereof your Highness is the Head.[37]

The House, as we have seen, claimed these privileges as of time immemorial. Just how far back that was is not at all clear. The record of the proceedings of the Commons from the time that there was a Commons at or in Parliament until well after the middle of the sixteenth century is sparse indeed, so judgement on the extent of the privileges will depend on what the judge assumes. If he supposes that absence of a record establishes the absence of the liberty, then up to late in Elizabeth's reign the privileges of the House were exiguous; if he presumes on the other hand that silence implies consent, that persons, individual or corporate, might rightfully do whatever no explicit prior rule

[37] Tanner, pp. 223–4; Petyt, pp. 223–4.

on the surviving record forbade, then the fragmentary character of the evidence renders the extent of the privileges of the House wide indeed. In all likelihood, the most frequent situation was the one that James himself had perplexedly noted in March in the Buckinghamshire election case: 'No precedent did suit this case' – where 'this case' is almost every case of privilege – 'fully.'[38] The ill fit of precedent to case in part had to do with the lack of prior incidents and prior judgements on all fours with the current case. It also had to do with the defects of the records of the House of Commons in this as in all other matters – defects such that, had there been a truly covering case, the record of it would not exist in writing and would be blurred in the corporate memory of the House. In that normal course of legal change, which Maitland noted, from the vague and uncertain to the clear and certain, vagueness and uncertainty with respect to precedents that had to do with privileges surely survived to the beginning of the seventeenth century.

In 1604 the authors of the Apology were ready to go to the mat to assert the claim of the House to be final judge of elections. On this point the Apology is as unambiguous as feasible: 'The House of Commons is the proper judge of returns . . . of all . . . members . . . over which neither Chancery nor any other court ever had or ought to have any measure of jurisdiction.'

On the matter of freedom of speech, no such clarity exists. Everyone knows that unless there is some freedom of speech Parliament is nonsense: its very name designated it as a body for speaking. Not even the authors of the Apology – and they are not modest in their claims – are ready to assert that Members of the House can say whatever they please with impunity. The authors do not say what restraints 'due reverence . . . to your Majesty' imposes on the Members, nor who is or are to be the judge or judges of when such due reverence has been breached, nor what penalties for such a breach are appropriate. On those three cans of worms the Apology keeps the lids firmly clamped.

To vindicate freedom of elections, freedom from arrest, and freedom of speech for the Members the Apology inferred the privileges of the House of Commons from what the House was and what it was for. To say this does not imply that the writer

[38] CJ, 1, 159b.

himself claims to know what the House 'really' was in 1604, or even to know what the authors of the Apology really believed that it really was. What those authors had to be reasonably sure of was that the assumptions about the House of Commons on which they based their inferences were shared by the King and his advisers at least in their public avowals and by the House itself.[39] Otherwise the whole exercise of the Apology would have been futile: to try to satisfy the King of the rightness of the doings of the House on grounds drastically at odds with either the King's own view or the Members' view as to what the House of Commons was and was for would have evoked from one or the other a chilly or angry response, equivalent to 'Oh, nonsense!' Whatever the committee claimed in these matters had to lie close to assumptions shared by the King and the House.

That shared view was confirmed for the committee, not only by the trust of the House in reason and 'use' or custom, but also by explicit avowals of the King himself. As a 'member' or arm of Parliament the House was a part of both the highest court in the land and of the King's own most exalted council, or body of advisers. In itself it was representative of the English people; it spoke for them, was their voice. That the House of Commons was a 'member' of the High Court of Parliament and that the High Court of Parliament – King, Lords and Commons – was the highest court in the land was the least-disputed of political commonplaces about Parliament.[40] Its decrees, called statutes, were enforced in all other English courts. In so far as statutes ran counter to rules previously enforced in the courts, they superseded them. Contrariwise, no judgement or decree of any

---

[39] I think that this sort of thing may nowadays be called 'interpersonal knowledge' as contrasted with 'objective knowledge'. With no wish on my part at my age to plunge into the epistemological morass, it may be worth pointing out that interpersonally shared premises provide a sound basis for joint and agreed action whenever a dissonant actuality does not rudely intervene, but not when it does. Interpersonal agreement that the quickest way from room 1107 of the Plaza Hotel to a soda fountain on 58th Street is to exit from the room through the window, if acted on, would in a simple sense, since neither party would get there at all, turn out to be a double mistake.

[40] In 1600 even the most heterodox Englishmen from the standpoint of the ordinary subject would have agreed on this. Under the doctrine of the indirect power of the Pope a decision of the Papal Curia would be superior to and override a few – but by no means all – statutes in the eyes of an ultramontane Roman Catholic. No *English* court, however, surpassed the authority of Parliament.

other court superseded a statute, the decision of the High Court of Parliament.

The election proclamation of 11 January, in which James I announced his intention to summon a Parliament, assumes that the House of Commons represents the whole community of the realm. In that proclamation James expresses a concern similar to the concern of the House for the 'well choosing of knights and burgesses, who . . . *represent the body of the third estate*'.[41] Since they have to do in matters of commonwealth, it is essential that they 'come to that great and common council, with . . . public minds, sincere and void of any factious humour or dependency'. In that proclamation, too, the King describes Parliament as '*the highest Council of the Kingdom*'.[42] The assumption that the English people are representatively present in the House of Commons when Parliament assembles is explicitly part of the rationale for the rules that the King's election proclamation lays down for the conduct of the election and the proper return of the elected.

The privileges of the Members, the defence of which was the Apology's chief concern, followed from, and could be inferred from, the nature and function of the House of Commons on which both House and King were in agreement. If the House claimed free speech for its Members, so did every sovereign court for its judges. The deliberations of those judges were privileged; nothing was assumed – or, legally speaking, even known – of the *in camera* discussions of the members of the Court of Common Pleas, for example. All that was known as a matter of record were the actions of the court and the decisions handed down by it, its rulings, and such reasons for those rulings as the judges chose to make part of the record. Similarly – such was the conventional wisdom – with respect to counsellors; the value of a counsellor to his chief depended not only on the shrewdness of the counsellor, but also on his readiness to speak his mind fearlessly. To some degree this was true of all who counselled the King; it was especially true of the Members of the House, the counsellor-representatives of the commoners of England, who

---

[41] My italics.

[42] *Stuart Royal Proclamations, James I*, p. 67: my italics.

had chosen them as their spokesmen. As a qualification to provide the advice they were ordinarily called upon to give in the King's great council of Parliament, Members of the House were not assumed to be equipped with profound political experience, long observation of political affairs, or deep insight. About some things the novice serving in his first Parliament as representative of a backward constituency in one of the dark places of the land would know more and better than the cleverest member of the King's Privy Council, the longest experienced, or the most profound. He knew personally what those who chose him chose him for – to speak their grievances, and to support in the House the bills that accorded with their purposes and good, to grant taxes, levies on their property, only for ends that they could recognize as their own. How the men of the boroughs, towns and shires stood on such matters the men themselves knew better than anyone, and the Members they elected to the House of Commons were the men whom they chose to speak for them in the matters they knew best.

The House of Commons was thus the voice of the English commoners, of the people, and, said the Apology, 'the voice of the people . . . is said to be as the voice of God', not in all matters surely, but 'in the things of their knowledge'.[43] The 'things of their knowledge' were just what the King, any king, even that modern Solomon, James I, was ill-informed about. For, as the Apology noted, 'no human wisdom, how great soever can pierce into the particularities of the rights and customs of [the] people . . . but by tract of experience and faithful report of such as know them'.[44] This was a view of things that James shared with his faithful House of Commons. It has, said the Apology, 'pleased your Majesty's mouth to deliver' the view that the only trustworthy source of information on the customs of the people was the words of their spokesmen in the House. Particularly of their own griefs the people had infallible knowledge. In such matters, and such only, their voice was as the voice of God, inerrant; and it was to bring such matters to the King's attention that 'our countries, cities, and boroughs . . . sent us hither, not ignorant or

[43] Tanner, p. 230; Petyt, p. 239.
[44] Tanner, p. 218; Petyt, pp. 208–9.

uninstructed of their griefs, of their desires and hopes'.[45]

Because of these matters, in which great magnates and privy councillors could not advise the King as well as the humblest Member of the House of Commons could, the Lower House had its privileges – elections at the free choice of the electors, not at the command of the governors in Whitehall, liberty for the elected, the Members of the House of Commons, to speak their minds freely on the matters before the House, no bar to prevent any duly elected Member from taking his seat to speak and act in behalf of those who chose him. The privileges did not perfectly ensure that when the House of Commons acted it was as if the whole community of free Englishmen acted. They did make it more likely that this would be so, that when a Member of Parliament spoke he did so for the people in the country who sent him to Westminster. Were it not for the privileges of Parliament, the voices the King heard by report from the House of Commons would not be those of his people through their spokesmen; they would be the ordered and pre-arranged echo of the voices he heard every day, those of his privy councillors. A Parliament in the likeness of an assemblage of ventriloquist's dummies would be a fraudulent waste.[46] Neither for the people nor for the King would such a game be worth the candle.

In the eyes of the writers of the Apology, then, the privileges of the Members of the House were theirs because they were the King's counsellors. In matters that concerned the commonweal, the general welfare of his subjects, they were his chief counsellors. It was not that he looked to the Houses of Parliament for such counsel from day to day; he did not. He did look to Parliament for counsel in the most grave matters concerning the commonwealth, those requiring the most intimate knowledge of the deepest feelings of his people. And when he formally agreed to the advice Parliament gave him, then its counsel by way of

---

[45] Tanner, p. 220; Petyt, pp. 212–13.

[46] It is this trait that makes elected assemblies in communist countries a farce. Their members are not freely elected, they do not have freedom to speak their minds immune from punishment, nor are they immune from arrest at the will or the whim of the regime. Consequently, whatever they 'decide' shall be done is quite rightly read for what it reflects of the will of the Politburo, not for what it tells of the concerns of the people, for it tells nothing.

statute became the law of the land binding, until Parliament altered it, on King and subjects alike. If that counsel was to be the best, to reflect the freely given advice of the men freely chosen by the communities of the realm, then the Members of the House must freely consult with one another. They must not be inhibited by fears and intimations that what they said in their consultations and debates was displeasing to the King and might make them an object of royal wrath. Unless disburdened of such fears the Commons could not be expected to 'disclose unto your Majesty the truth of . . . matters concerning your subjects'.[47] In dread of him whose voice was as 'the roaring of a lion' they would say the things that they believed the King wanted to hear, not the things he needed to know. Thus they would join the ranks of his misadvisers, already too large. So to a King whom it judged misadvised the Apology asserted the inviolability of the privileges of the House of Commons as the rightful inheritance not only of the Members of the House but of the whole commons of the realm, and of the King, too.

King James, moreover, had chosen to hear the voices of his people through his House of Commons, not to hear a mere echo of his Privy Council; the very existence of the House of Commons showed that: it came into being only at the King's will, on his summons, to aid and advise him. Had he not wanted to hear the voices of those claiming to speak for, indeed representatively to *be*, the people he need not have summoned them to a meeting of Parliament at all in 1604. Much less did he need to do as he did in the election proclamation – acknowledge that the House is the representative body in which all English commoners are really present.[48] Nor did he need to – as he did – grant its Speaker's petition for its privileges as a matter of course, making no record of the sorts of reservations and restrictions that Elizabeth had got in the habit of expressing to qualify and limit her grant.[49] From early in the session James indeed had protested his good affection to the privileges of the House. He had, he said

[47] Tanner, p. 218; Petyt, p. 210.

[48] See above, p. 32.

[49] At least, no such reservations are recorded in any of the accounts of the opening days of the Parliament of 1604.

in March, 'no purpose to impeach their privilege'. On 5 April, although tangled with the Commons in a dispute over their privileges in elections, he protested 'by that love he bore to the House as his loving and loyal subjects, and by the faith he did . . . owe to God he had as great a desire to maintain their privileges as ever any prince had, or as they themselves had'.[50] In winding up an election dispute a week later he added that 'he would confirm and ratify all just privileges' and added that the whole contest had been a matter of 'private jealousies, without any kernel or substance', in which the privileges of House 'were not in question'.[51] And, on 5 June, James conveyed to the House through the Speaker his claim that, as to 'matters of privilege', he 'was as careful to preserve' them as the House itself.[52]

Yet despite the King's free and unsolicited recognition of the representative claims of the House and his avowal of good affection to its privileges nothing more deeply pervades the Apology than the uneasiness of its authors as to the government's intention towards the privileges of the House and about the King's unawareness of what a threat to those privileges signified for Englishmen. The cold fact of the matter was that the King had been advised that the House was not the correct forum for the examination of the return of election writs. He had been told that it was not a court of record, so *nothing* that it ordered could serve as a binding legal precedent for any purpose whatever. He had been told that its privileges did not belong to it 'of right, but of grace only'.[53] He had not only been told these things, he had taken this 'misinformation openly delivered to your Majesty' for the very truth[54] and, on 28 March and later, maintained it before its victims, the House of Commons.

On a close reading of the record of the first session of the King's first Parliament, the signals that James I gave off were ambiguous, and can reasonably be interpreted in divergent ways. This is

---

[50] CJ, I, 166a.

[51] CJ, I, 168b.

[52] CJ, I, 232.

[53] Tanner, p. 220; Petyt, p. 213.

[54] On 28 March the King asserts that all he said that day was on the advice of the judges of the sovereign courts, and the judges themselves avow the unanimity of their advice.

true not only 380 years after that Parliament assembled; it was true then, in 1604, while the Parliament sat, while members of the committee that wrote the Apology cast their minds back over their experience of the past three months in order to prepare the apologia that the House had asked them to write. His call on the House on 28 March to confer with the judges on an election case can be, and was, read as categorical by some, conditional by others. His reception of the Humble Answer in which the House vindicated its own intransigence in that same case can be read as a sign of honest perplexity or as a resolution to get his own way. His statements, reported on 11 April, on the scope of the jurisdiction of the House over elections seem contradictory, and his proposed resolution of the difficulty left the meaning of the settlement muddy.

The writers of the Apology were surely aware of these ambiguities in James's words and actions. They nevertheless interpreted every royal ambiguity as an assertion that the House derived its privileges from him. Further, they interpreted his meaning to be that the privileges of the Members were a free gift of royal grace not a due royal allowance to the subjects of what was theirs by right. Once the authors of the Apology, not absurdly but not of sheer necessity, either, made this construal of the King's statements their centrepiece, other evidence, even silly trifles, fell into place in a menacing pattern. The ineptitude of the Yeoman of the Guard and the Gentleman Usher, the Bishop of Bristol's sycophantic (or was it his sincere and proper) censure of the House for its hesitations about the royal proposals on union with Scotland, all became outward and visible signs of an inward and spiritual disdain for the House of Commons, too readily picked up by the lowly from the higher-ups on whose behaviour they modelled their own. Because this was the way the authors of the Apology interpreted their experience and that of the rest of the House they could say with conviction that in the present session '*the privileges of our House and therein the liberties and stability of the whole kingdom have been more unusually and dangerously impugned than ever . . . since the beginning of parliaments*'.[55]

---

[55] Tanner, p. 222; Petyt, p. 217.

Drawing only on what most present-day amateurs of the reign of the Virgin Queen know, and on what that mass of veterans of the late Parliaments of Elizabeth who sat in the first Parliament of James simply had to know, the sentence last quoted seems a victim of rhetorical overkill. Elizabeth did not suffer from an intense passion for the privileges of the House, nor did she suffer gladly fools who wasted time by excesses of adversary eloquence. She occasionally bashed them about a bit. We know this, and much more immediately most of the Members of James's first Parliament knew it. And they also knew that almost all the close advisers of the King knew it. Not to take this common knowledge into account was to shrink the credibility of the Apology.

So its authors took that knowledge into account in two ways. As to Elizabeth in her late years, they said, 'in regard of her sex and age . . . we had great cause to be tender'. They also trod lightly for political reasons, out of concern for James's own delicate political situation in Elizabeth's last years. They had striven 'to avoid all trouble which by wicked practice might have been drawn to impeach the quiet of your Majesty's right of succession'.[56] There had been, however, no grounds for general alarm in the Queen's day, no sense that the principles on which the privileges of Parliament rested were in any way threatened. 'For although it may be true that in the later times of Queen

---

[56] Tanner, p. 222; Petyt, p. 217. Historians lately have tended to minimize the sense of institutional continuity among the Members of the House under the last Tudor and the first two Stuarts on the grounds that no Member could think of himself as a career politician just because he had spent a few months every three to five years, if that, sitting in the House. He could spend no more because the House met no more. Politics was a profession of sorts among courtiers. It could not be a profession among Members of Parliament. There is surely something in this. There is also something in that 'we' who had 'great cause to be tender' in Elizabeth's last years. It can only refer to Members of Parliament in those years. The words, however, were from a committee of the House in the Parliament of 1604, and the casual identification of the Members of the House in 1604 with Parliaments of yesteryear is built into the syntax of the sentence. The sentence was written by Members of a new Parliament in the new reign. Yet in saying who did what in past Parliaments in an ended reign the pronoun 'we', not the pronoun 'they', is the one that came trippingly to the tongue or pen. Perhaps even more effectively than reaching back for precedents, this identification with past Members of Parliament by a shared first person plural reveals the unforced sense of linkage between successive Parliaments. Despite the rarity and brevity of the sessions of Parliaments under Elizabeth it requires us to think of the House of Commons as not just a casual and occasional assemblage, but as an institution as well, conscious of if not self-conscious about its continuity.

Elizabeth some one privilege were now and then by some particular act attempted against – not absolutely injured – yet was not the same ever by so public speech, nor by positions in general, denounced against our privilege',[57] as had been done of late. There is no mistaking the intended contrast here between Elizabeth and James I, who hardly a week into his first Parliament had already in all-too-public speech taken an all-too-general position dangerous to the privileges of the House.

In response the Apology itself moved quickly from the particulars to a general position. Bitterly it summed up the experience of the House since the beginning of the session:

> We have been subject to . . . extreme contempt . . . a jailer . . . obstinately . . . withstand[s] the decrees of our house, some of the higher clergy . . . write a book against us, even sitting the Parliament. The inferior clergy . . . inveigh against us in pulpits, yea, and publish their protestations tending to the impeachment of our most ancient and undoubted rights. . . .

With such things happening 'what cause we your poor commons have to watch over our privileges is manifest in itself to all men'. This is especially so in a world where '*the prerogatives of princes may easily and do daily grow; the privileges of the subject are for the most part at an everlasting stand*'.[58]

It was out. The authors of the Apology had done a thing rare indeed among representatives of commoners in Europe at the turn of the century. They had moved from particularized complaints about their situation to a theory about what was happening in history in their day. The theory went well beyond the particulars they had just previously set out.

What and who *did* the authors of the Apology have in mind when they wrote of the prerogatives of princes? Elizabeth? It hardly seems likely. Only a bit before they had taken special pains to exculpate her from any charge of *general* hostility to the privileges of Parliament, or to the liberties of the people. The

---

[57] Petyt, pp. 216–17. Without any marking in the printed text to warn the reader, Tanner has omitted this section from his reprinting of the Apology, where it should appear between (line 6) 'parliament' and (line 7) 'Besides'. In the interest of good sense I have not hesitated to clean up the punctuation of the quoted passage.

[58] Tanner, p. 222; Petyt, p. 218. My italics.

force of the contrast between the prerogatives of princes and the privileges of subjects, however, lies in its generality. Besides, for whatever it is worth as evidence, the Apology does not speak of *a* prince (much less a princess) in the singular, and it does not speak of what she *was* doing in the past, it speaks of the thing that is happening now to the prerogatives (in the plural) of princes (in the plural). Syntactically we are dealing not with a 'did', a static verb tensed in the past, but with a 'do', a processive verb tensed in the present, not a '*sein*' but a '*werden*'.

What princes, then, have prerogatives which have been and are now growing, and presumably will continue to grow? Henry IV of France? Philip III – in Castile? in Aragon? in Milan? in Naples? James's father-in-law, Frederick II of Denmark? Gustavus of Sweden? The authors of the Apology do not say, so we do not know. We do know that on the threshold of a historical generalization the authors of the Apology did not falter shyly and draw back but took it in their stride. We know that evidence to substantiate that generalization was conveniently and visibly scattered across the map of western Europe. In all the lands that Englishmen were likely to pay much attention to in 1604 except the Dutch Republic and Venice, the prerogatives of princes had recently grown and were currently growing further. And we know that in the present day most historians would find the words that the authors of the Apology used to make their point to King James remarkably apropos of the evidence of the growth of arbitrary power among Continental princes in the late sixteenth century.

The historians might not choose the exact phrasing that the authors of the Apology hit on. They have during the past century and a half made several stabs at finding the *mot juste* or, rather, the *adjectif juste* to convey their sense of what was going on politically on the Continent. They have spoken of absolute monarchy, of arbitrary power, of *monarchie administrative*, of despotism. For good reason they have never been entirely happy with the favourite of the moment. They might even want to retreat to the formulation of the Apology now nearly four centuries old. It catches a sense of continuing process missing from more recent phrasings.

Historians rightly take an unenthusiastic view of anachronism.

We are properly cautious lest we ascribe to people of an earlier time opinions and purposes which we find worthy but which they could not have held, which they would indeed have found quite revolting and vehemently repudiated. In this matter, however, undue caution is as foolish as carelessness. It is not an anachronism to say that some men in the early seventeenth century took a view of certain of the conditions of political freedom in the Europe of their day that approximately coincides with our view. Not to say so would be particularly foolish when their explicit though summary statement of the way things were coincides so neatly with our own view. Such caution becomes particularly stultifying in face of the palpable shrewdness of the men who so clearly perceived the increasing concentration of unbounded political power in the hands of European monarchs. Those same men had an equally sharp sense of the likely consequence of such concentration. The liberties of the people, they said, 'may be by good providence and care preserved; but being once lost are not recovered but with much disquiet'. On the Continent there was to be considerable disquiet of this sort in the ensuing four or five decades. The big disquiet did not come, however, for nearly two centuries, in 1789. When it came it rocked all Europe. Surely in the passage we quoted from the Apology there is more than a disengaged analysis of the historical situation in 1604. There is also a quiet but clear summons to those most deeply involved in that situation in England, the representatives of the people, to sit up and take notice, sit up and take action.

What the House of Commons did in June 1604 and what its committee did in producing the Apology contrast starkly with what the House had done in its first run-in with James three months earlier. That episode had emerged on the floor of the House on the first regular day of business in James's first Parliament. It was over an attempt by the King's government to reverse the result of an election duly certified as free in the sheriff's return of the elected Member. Throughout the affair of the Buckinghamshire election the House had narrowed the issues at stake as far as the meddling of the King and his advisers allowed it to. The most marked symptom of the resolution of the House to limit conflict is the way that it dealt at the time with James's assertion of 28 March that the Members held their privileges by grace only; it acted as if James had not made the assertion at all. It said and did nothing about it.

In June the very opposite thing happened. James provoked the House into responding to his repeated tongue lashings. When he woke up to the probable trouble that his exposure of the House to the rough side of his tongue was about to result in, he had sober second thoughts and tried to limit the damage that his verbal excesses threatened to cause. He partly failed; the House instructed its committee to continue its vindication of the course of action of the House and by necessary consequence its indictment not actually of James, but of the course of action he had been misled into pursuing. The committee charged with the task in June, as we have seen, got far enough to take up the challenge to the privileges of the House that three months before James had issued and the House had shut its ears to. It had further bound those privileges tight to English freedom and to the right of property, and had set the King's devaluation of parliamentary privilege into the context of the rise of arbitrary power and the decline of freedom in the European political universe in which England lived.

The House, we know, did not formally issue the challenge its committee had prepared. That challenge survived, however, in the memories of the Members of the House and even in the institutional memory or collective consciousness of that 'we' which was at once the House of Commons and representatively the commons of England. In the Parliament of 1621, Members of the House of Commons reached back to the Apology of 1604 to characterize what they regarded as a further stumble of their shaky-legged King in the direction of arbitrary rule. One Member of 1621, who had not been in Parliament in 1604, was nevertheless able to repeat nearly verbatim that echoing sentence about the privileges of princes. Still the Apology did not appear on the record, the Journal of the House, that record the status of which in this very session the House had so firmly asserted. So the last act in the drama of the Apology, before any epilogue, leaves us with awkward questions. What does the failure of the House to take official action on the Apology, positive or negative, signify? What does it tell about the collective state of mind of the House of Commons in June 1604? That last question raises another. What was the collective state of mind of the House *before* 1604? Was the vision of politics that the Apology so sharply reflects a vision generally shared by the House of Commons in the Parliaments of Elizabeth? What continuities of vision do we find? And what divergences of vision, if any? In short, when we examine the Apology are we just looking at more of the same, or does that effort bear marks or intimations of a *novus ordo seclorum*, a new order of things in the world. The Apology has already justified our asking these questions even though they assume a continuity in the collective consciousness of the House of Commons which extends forward and back from the particular incident that evoked the Apology itself. That assumption of continuity among the authors of the Apology is verifiable; assertions to the contrary are nonsense. The Apology itself refers firmly and seriously forward to a posterity for which the House of Commons will be a vital guarantor of freedom, or so it is assumed. Casually and unself-consciously, it refers backward to a 'we', which was the Elizabethan House of Commons.

The continuity of the men who wrote the Apology with the Elizabethan House of Commons was not just constitutional or notional or nostalgic. It is true that for a century the 'myth of Elizabeth' nourished men's propensity to view past times in rosy tints. Still the bridge of memory was not sustained by a long delicate filament in the Parliament of 1604. The old lady had died barely a year back. And the Jacobean House of Commons of 1604 was close to being the most Elizabethan House ever, the one with the most Members in it that had served before in a Parliament of Elizabeth. And the committee that wrote the Apology was even more Elizabethan than that. Only two or three of its Members, between five and ten per cent, were newcomers. When the authors of the Apology spoke of how Elizabeth got along with the House, they spoke with both knowledge and nuance.

A historical episode is like a Leibnitzian monad. Stare at it long enough and the whole universe will appear to be reflected in it. Shut your eyes quick enough and it will seem to reflect nothing at all. Or perhaps we should say that an episode in the past can be regarded as fitting into every historical context or into none at all. The first outlook is ultra-Whig, the second ultra-

Tory. They cancel each other out; if we took one or the other seriously in practice, we could write no history at all. Fortunately, in practice for most episodes, there are a few contexts into which they fit with ease – with historical grace, so to speak – and others into which they fit ill indeed. Into the struggle for sovereignty, the Apology does not fit at all. If we had enough information, we might be able to fit it into the clashes between court and country or between social classes. And we might not. Anyhow, it is most unlikely that the unexplored historical records hold enough evidence to warrant much hope on either score. On the other hand, into the process of the making of modern freedom the Apology – in its immediate context in place and time – makes an elegant fit. It is the first time on record that a cluster of Members of Parliament saw the actions of its ruler in the context of the political changes taking place in continental Europe, saw those actions as posing a general threat to the freedom of Englishmen, and 'blew the whistle' or sounded the alarm, both to their colleagues beside them and to the King above them. 'The prerogatives of princes. . . .'

AN ENGLISH *VALIDO*?

BUCKINGHAM AND JAMES I

Roger Lockyer

ENGLISH HISTORIANS have not been kindly disposed towards royal favourites, regarding them as at best contemptible and at worst dangerous. Macaulay expressed the prevailing view when he commented on James I that 'by his fondness for worthless minions, and by the sanction which he gave to their tyranny and rapacity, he kept discontent constantly alive'.[1] The authors of what was to become the standard repository of English folk history made the same point in a blunter fashion: 'James I slobbered at the mouth and had favourites; he was thus a Bad King.'[2] James was not, of course, the first English sovereign to have favourites. His immediate predecessor, the great Gloriana, had given her affections successively to Robert Dudley, Earl of Leicester, and Robert Devereux, Earl of Essex, while two and a half centuries earlier Edward II had made no secret of his love for Piers Gaveston. Yet the nineteenth-century historians who largely created the authorized version of English history assumed that there was something essentially un-English about favourites. This was because they thought in Whig terms of England's development from a monarchy into a parliamentary democracy being not only inevitable but morally right. Anything which ran counter to this manifest destiny was, by definition, an aberration.

In the early seventeenth century, however, there was no question of England developing naturally and inevitably into a parliamentary democracy. England was a monarchy ruled over by the King, and few of James's subjects wished to change this state of affairs or could conceive of any viable alternative. Even

---

[1] Thomas Babington Macaulay, *The History of England from the Accession of James II*, 5 vols (1849–61), vol. 1, p. 74.

[2] W. C. Sellar and R. J. Yeatman, *1066 and All That*, 34th edn (London, 1950), p. 61.

45

at the outbreak of the Civil War in 1642, Parliament proclaimed its desire 'to render unto your Majesty that subjection, obedience and service which we owe unto you' and it justified its action in raising an army on the grounds that this was intended to free the King from the stranglehold of the popish and ill-affected counsellors who surrounded him.[3] Far from wishing to destroy the monarchy the parliamentary opponents of Charles I were determined to restore it to its traditional position and create the conditions in which the King could resume his rightful role as head of the whole nation and not just the leader of a faction.

There was nothing hypocritical or falsely modest about Parliament's denial of any claim to share in the ruling function. Admittedly, events after 1642 were to show that Parliament could be a highly effective institution of government, capable not only of making policy but also of carrying it out, but this could hardly have been foreseen in the opening decades of the seventeenth century, when the House of Commons in particular seemed closer to the unruly grammar school of Sir Robert Cecil's description than to an assembly of grave and responsible counsellors.[4] James I did not hide his irritation with its Members over their failure to make an adequate response to his far-sighted scheme for a statutory union between England and Scotland. 'The greatest part of you were well affected,' he conceded, 'but where there is a like liberty the worst likely carries away the best. . . . There were wise men amongst you; so was there a roll of knavery. I do not think that any of you had seditious minds to overthrow and confound this monarchy, but out of divers humours and respects you were moved to curiosities.'[5] Given this jaundiced but justified view of the activities of the Commons it is hardly surprising that some years later James warned the assembled Members of both Houses 'that you do not meddle with the main points of government: that is my craft: *tractant fabrilia fabri* . . . I must not be taught my office'.[6]

[3] S. R. Gardiner (ed.), *The Constitutional Documents of the Puritan Revolution, 1625–1660*, 3rd edn, revised (Oxford, 1936), p. 263.

[4] G. R. Elton, *The Tudor Constitution, 1485–1603*, 2nd edn (Cambridge, 1982), p. 324.

[5] J. P. Kenyon, *The Stuart Constitution, 1603–1688* (Cambridge, 1966), p. 40.

[6] G. W. Prothero (ed.), *Select Statutes and Other Constitutional Documents*, 4th edn (Oxford, 1946), p. 294.

James's belief that government was solely a matter for kings was not based on any new-fangled notions of divine right. He was merely putting into words what had long been taken for granted throughout Christendom, and what had become increasingly self-evident in the course of the sixteenth century. For during this troubled period the cohesion of all European states was threatened by a potentially lethal combination of galloping inflation, population explosion and bitter religious divisions, and the only way in which to stop things falling apart was to reinforce the centre. This could have been done, in theory, by representative assemblies just as well as by monarchs, but in practice it was unlikely. Representative assemblies, as they had emerged from the Middle Ages, were primarily concerned with the preservation of sectional liberties that were an impediment to government rather than an aid. It is true that by the time James I ascended the English throne there was one country, the United Provinces, which was ruled by an Estates-General, but the Dutch constitution worked by default rather than by design, and in so far as it offered a model it was one that was not copied. The prevailing assumption in early seventeenth-century Europe was that the safety of the State depended upon exalting the authority of the royal ruler: in the words of the Duke of Alba, 'kings are born to do their will, and we, their vassals, are born to do their will likewise'.[7]

Where representative assemblies had managed to survive and had demonstrated their willingness and their ability to serve the sovereign, there was no point in getting rid of them. This accounted for the flourishing condition of the English Parliament under Elizabeth. With the advent of the Stuarts, however, harmony became more difficult to achieve, and as James's reign went on, and the bitterness created by the collapse of negotiations for the Great Contract was compounded by the sterile invectives of the Addled Parliament, it became an open question whether the difficulties that the King encountered during parliamentary sessions were worth what these assemblies had to offer in terms of money and prestige. If the answer was no, then England would follow the course already taken by other kingdoms. Nobody was

---

[7] Quoted in William S. Maltby, *Alba: A Biography of Fernando Alvarez de Toledo, Third Duke of Alba, 1507–1582* (Berkeley, Calif., 1984), p. 82.

47

more aware of the danger of this happening than Sir Dudley Carleton, who had spent long periods abroad as ambassador first to Venice and subsequently to Holland. Addressing the House of Commons in May 1626 he urged his fellow-Members not to trench upon the King's prerogatives 'lest you bring him out of love with Parliaments. . . . In all Christian kingdoms you know that Parliaments were in use anciently, by which their kingdoms were governed in a most flourishing manner, until the monarchs began to know their own strength, and, seeing the turbulent spirit of their Parliaments, at length they little by little began to stand upon their prerogatives, and at last overthrew the Parliaments throughout Christendom, except here only with us.'[8]

Kings, then, were the dominant figures in early modern Europe. They were chosen by God and invested by Him with responsibility for the well-being of their subjects. Yet the vagaries of the hereditary process meant that not all kings were fitted to rule. Placed in a position for which they might have few natural talents, yet compelled to remain there for the term of their natural lives, some monarchs eased their burden and their consciences by allowing the actual business of government to be carried out by persons in whom they had confidence. Louis XIII, for instance, entrusted the administration of his kingdom to Cardinal Richelieu, while his fellow-monarch, Philip IV of Spain, chose to rule through the agency of the Count-Duke of Olivares.[9] These men were not merely confidants of the sovereign, exercising their influence in a more or less underhand manner. Nor were they merely prime ministers, who had come to the fore by sheer administrative capacity or as leaders of interest groups or factions. As Francisco Valiente emphasizes, in his study of the Spanish *Valimiento* as an institution, the origins of their 'absoluto imperio' are to be traced 'en la voluntad del Rey y en el "manejo de los papeles" '.[10] In other words, although they were men of exceptional ability, the foundation

---

[8] Kenyon, *Stuart Constitution*, p. 50.

[9] The best recent study of these two favourites is J. H. Elliott's *Richelieu and Olivares* (Cambridge, 1984).

[10] Francisco Tomas Valiente, *Los Validos en la monarquia española del siglo XVII* (Madrid, 1963), p. 17.

of their authority was an arbitrary act of will on the part of the King. It followed from this that the actual amount of power that they exercised at any given moment depended upon the extent to which the sovereign was prepared to devolve his functions. The more capable the ruler, the less scope there was for a *Valido*.

In early Stuart England the most obvious example of a favourite was George Villiers, Duke of Buckingham. He first appeared on the scene in 1614 at a time when Robert Carr, Earl of Somerset, was in the ascendant, but by 1616 he had toppled Carr and established himself as supreme in the King's affections. Contemporary observers, whose opinion has coloured the later judgement of historians, assumed that over the course of the next two or three years Buckingham became in effect a *Valido*, the *de facto* source of authority in the English state. Such a development would only have been possible, however, if James had given up the reins of government, but there was never any question of this. James had been a king virtually since the day he was born, and he took it for granted that God had not only appointed him to rule but had also given him the capacity to do so. It was a trust he could not and would not relinquish.

Buckingham's role as James's favourite, and indeed the whole nature of his career, is best understood by distinguishing between various categories of favourite or, alternatively, various stages in the establishment of a *Valimiento*. There are at least three main categories, though the lines of division between them are not distinct, nor are they necessarily separate chronologically. First, there are the ruler's friends or, to use a more neutral term, Companions. These are men or women who engage the sovereign's affections, help him (or her) to while away the hours of boredom with which even monarchs are afflicted, and by way of recompense are showered with money and titles. The basis of Companionship in this sense is often overtly sexual, as in the case of Madame de Pompadour and the mistresses of Charles II. Yet it is not always or necessarily so. In 1518, for instance, Henry VIII established the new office of Gentlemen of the Privy Chamber and appointed to it a group of young men who were known as the 'minions', yet it seems unlikely that the relationship between these and the King was other than one of warm friend-

ship.[11] In general, Companions were of limited *political* significance, but this did not alter the fact that they were widely
thought to exercise a great deal of power behind the throne.

The second category is that of Political Favourites, which
includes those men (or, as in Louis XIV's France, women) whose
position derived from their hold on the monarch's affections but
who used this to build up an independent power-base. Two
obvious English examples of Political Favourites are the Earls of
Leicester and Essex in the reign of Elizabeth I. They came to
prominence in the first instance because the Queen found them
attractive, but they established themselves as power-brokers in
their own right and they embraced policies which – in the case of
Leicester's patronage of the Puritans, for instance, and Essex's
assault upon 'Cecil's Commonwealth' – ran counter to the
Queen's desires. Political Favourites occupied an ill-defined area
somewhere between a Companion and an ordinary minister.
Although they might establish a near-monopoly of the monarch's
affections, they never held a monopoly of power. Usually they
had to share this with men such as William Cecil, Lord Burghley,
who attained high office by virtue of their outstanding ability as
administrators.

The third and final category is that of *Valido* or 'Favourite'
tout court. The *Valido* does not depend upon the ruler's affections
in the way that the other two types do. Indeed, the key to this
particular relationship is the dependence not of the favourite but
of the monarch. Because the sovereign is, for one reason or
another, unable or unwilling to carry out the duties imposed
upon him by his high office, he delegates his authority to a
favourite who thereby becomes a viceroy or surrogate monarch.
The *Valido* is, in effect, the embodiment of specific aspects of the
royal authority, the agent who reconciles the theory of monarchical absolutism with the reality of monarchical incapacity.

Buckingham began his career as the King's Companion and,
although he subsequently acquired ministerial responsibilities,
he never abandoned this role during James's lifetime, for everything else depended upon it. As the King's Companion, personal

---

[11] David Starkey, 'From Feud to Faction', *History Today*, vol. 32 (1982), and the same
author's 'The King's Privy Chamber, 1487–1547' (unpublished PhD thesis, Cambridge
University, 1973).

service to James took precedence over all other considerations; even his wife and family had to accept second place, and Katherine Villiers was driven to declare that 'till you leave this life of a courtier – which you have been ever since I knew you – I shall ever think myself unhappy'. [12] James I liked nothing better than to escape from the press of suitors who made his life a misery by going into retreat in one of his many hunting lodges. As Bishop Goodman rightly observed, the King 'did love solitariness', [13] but not in the sense that he liked being alone. On the contrary, he surrounded himself in the country with young men who enjoyed the chase as much as he did and whose boisterous high spirits kept him young in heart if not in years. In the words of one anonymous versifier:

> At Royston and Newmarket
> He'll hunt till he be lean.
> But he hath merry boys
> That with masks and toys
> Can make him fat again. [14]

Buckingham became one of these 'merry boys', and a major reason why he kept his hold on the King's affections was that he made him laugh. James may seem a pathetic creature in twentieth-century eyes, but as far as his subjects were concerned he was the King, and they treated him with respect not untinged with awe. How refreshing, therefore, it must have been to James when he found in his young favourite someone who instinctively knew how to breach the wall of majesty when the occasion was opportune and to treat the sovereign like a human being. From time to time he adopted a bantering, mock-chiding tone that is best described as cheeky. When he was in Spain, for instance, in 1623, he reprimanded the King for being too mean in supplying his son with jewels, and gave his 'poor and saucy opinion what will be fittest more to send'. Then, in a postscript, he listed the animals which he was dispatching to James as a gift and promised to 'lay wait for all the rare colour birds that can be heard of'. But

---

[12] Public Record Office (hereafter PRO), SP 16, vol. 68.3.

[13] Geoffrey Goodman, *The Court of King James the First* (1839), p. 173.

[14] Bodleian Library, MS Malone 23, 20v.

the gift was not unconditional, for 'if you do not send your baby [Charles] jewels enough I'll stop all other presents. Therefore look to it!' There was always a risk, of course, in using such peremptory language to the King, but Buckingham knew his man. James was delighted and sent him hearty thanks for 'thy kind drolling letter'.[15] This shared sense of fun forged a bond between the King and his Companion that endured until James's death. Even as late as March 1625, Secretary Conway was thanking Buckingham on the King's behalf for 'your merry letter'. He added that James had 'commanded me to let you know he expects you here tomorrow, and that you make him laugh, according to your promise'.[16]

As long as James remained alive, Buckingham remained the King's Companion. But the first two stages in his career as favourite overlapped, for in January 1619 he was appointed Lord Admiral and thereby became a Political Favourite as well as a Companion. His interest in the navy had been aroused by his patronage of a group of men who were trying to reform the royal administration and thereby restore the crown to solvency. It might seem, on the face of it, that Buckingham was himself one of the main causes of the King's financial troubles, but although it is obviously true that James's lavish grants to his favourite made a bad situation worse, there is little relationship between the sort of sums that Buckingham was getting and the scale of royal indebtedness. James was burdened with an accumulated debt approaching £900,000, which was increasing at the rate of £250,000 a year.[17] Even if Buckingham's annual income – which amounted to at most £20,000, not all of it derived directly from royal bounty[18] – had been transferred to the exchequer it would have been a mere drop in the ocean. Buckingham was conscious of his good fortune in becoming James's favourite, but unlike his predecessors he wanted to show his gratitude in a practical

[15] British Library, Harleian MS 6987, 78, 80.

[16] PRO, SP 14, vol. 185.1.

[17] Frederick C. Dietz, *English Public Finance, 1558–1641*, 2nd edn (London, 1964), p. 172.

[18] Roger Lockyer, *Buckingham: The Life and Political Career of George Villiers, First Duke of Buckingham, 1592–1628* (London, 1981), p. 61.

way by helping restore the royal finances. He therefore took up where the Earl of Northampton had left off and gave his patronage to a number of reformers – most notably Lionel Cranfield and John Coke – who were engaged in the herculean task of cutting down on waste and corruption in the royal administration.

The first fruits of this alliance were seen in the outcome of the reform commission into the state of the navy, for the members found, to their astonishment and delight, that the new Lord Admiral was determined to break with precedent by seeing that their recommendations were carried into effect. Indeed, he went further by suspending the Navy Board and transferring responsibility for shipbuilding and supply to the commission, which was now established upon a permanent basis. The commissioners fulfilled their promise to build two new ships and repair two old ones every year at less cost to the exchequer than it had borne under the previous regime, and although the navy still suffered from serious defects, not least in the area of ship design, by the early 1620s it was in a far better state than it had been at any time since the 1580s.[19]

Another of Buckingham's political functions, though here he acted without any ministerial appointment, was to serve as the King's secretary. His job was to read incoming correspondence and digest it for the King, who hated reading long epistles. He also took note of James's directions on how to reply, and passed these on to the appropriate Secretary of State.[20] In the process of reading these letters, many of them from English representatives abroad, Buckingham acquired a good knowledge of the European situation. He also made a number of first-hand contacts, the most notorious of which was with the Spanish ambassador, Count Gondomar. But it was James's views which he transmitted, whether or not they coincided with his own. When he assured Gondomar of his devotion to the cause of friendship with Spain he was simply echoing James's sentiments. Similarly, in 1620, when he wrote to the ambassador to deny rumours that

---

[19] A. P. McGowan, *The Jacobean Commissions of Enquiry, 1608 and 1618* (London, 1971), and the same author's 'The Royal Navy under the First Duke of Buckingham, Lord High Admiral 1618–28' (unpublished PhD thesis, London University, 1967).

[20] Lockyer, *Buckingham*, pp. 37–8; *Documentos inéditos para la historia de España* (Madrid, 1936–45), vol. 2, pp. 272–4.

James was displeased with Spain for intervening in the Palatinate, he did so in response to James's explicit instructions.[21]

Because Buckingham was the King's favourite and because the range of his patronage was so great, he clearly played a major part in appointment to offices. Yet like all Political Favourites he was *primus inter pares*, not the monopolist that his enemies took him for. There were other powerful figures at court, not least the Lord Chamberlain, the Earl of Pembroke, who had their own clientage, even if it was smaller than Buckingham's, and constantly, and often successfully, advanced the claims of their protégés.[22] And there were always the King's wishes to be taken into account. In February 1619, James decided to appoint a new Secretary of State, and Buckingham had two candidates for the office whom he strongly supported. Neither of them was successful, however, for the King chose Sir George Calvert. All Buckingham could do when he realized the way the tide was flowing was to swim with it and switch his advocacy to Calvert.[23] Much the same happened in 1621 when a new Lord Keeper was needed to replace the fallen Bacon. Buckingham backed Cranfield, but although James had decided to break with the convention that only a lawyer could hold this office, he wanted a churchman, not a merchant-financier. His choice lighted on John Williams, Dean of Westminster and subsequently Bishop of Lincoln, and Buckingham had to save face by abandoning Cranfield and committing himself openly to Williams. It was, as a consequence, widely believed that Williams owed his appointment to the favourite's intervention. But the King made the choice; Buckingham merely acquiesced in it.[24]

The first indications that Buckingham was freeing himself from the King's tutelage came during the Palatinate crisis of

[21] Lockyer, *Buckingham*, p. 78; Bodleian Library, Tanner MS 290, 9.

[22] Lockyer, *Buckingham*, p. 36.

[23] PRO, SP 14, vol. 105.9, 104, 112; Berkshire Record Office, Trumbull Alphabetical MS, vol. 6.83; *The Letters of John Chamberlain*, ed. N. E. McClure, 2 vols (Philadelphia, Pa, 1939), vol. 2, p. 216.

[24] G. W. Thomas, 'James I, Equity and Lord Keeper John Williams', *English Historical Review*, vol. 91 (1976); *The Autobiography and Correspondence of Sir Simonds D'Ewes, Bart*, ed. J. O. Halliwell, 2 vols (1845), vol. 1, p. 188; *Calendar of State Papers, Venetian*, vol. 17, p. 88.

1621. Rumour had it that Buckingham and Prince Charles were in favour of active intervention on behalf of the Elector Palatine – who was married to James's daughter, Elizabeth – and were bringing pressure to bear upon the King to abandon his characteristically pacific stance.[25] It may have been as a consequence of this divergence of attitudes that Buckingham began to forge links with the Puritans. Sometime during 1621 he made the acquaintance of John Preston, a leading Puritan divine, and he was instrumental in having Preston appointed chaplain to the Prince and subsequently master of Emmanuel College, Cambridge.[26] James was no lover of Puritans, and it is therefore unlikely that the initiative for this *rapprochement* came from him. What seems more likely is that the scarcely veiled attacks upon Buckingham in the 1621 Parliament had shown the favourite that he must broaden the basis of his support, while the invasion of the Palatinate had given him a cause – that of restitution – which he shared not only with the Puritans but also with the nation at large.

Yet he was still a Political Favourite, the King's servant, not the King's master. And since James was more determined than ever to seek a solution of the Palatinate crisis by way of negotiation and through the Spanish marriage Buckingham had to acquiesce. There is no reason to assume that he seriously questioned James's judgement. James was, after all, an old and experienced king, while Buckingham was a novice in politics. It was the journey to Madrid in 1623 and his enforced stay in Spain that opened Buckingham's eyes and led to the completion of his political education at break-neck speed. He returned to England convinced that Spain was a dangerous enemy and that the creation of an alliance of anti-Habsburg states, built around an Anglo-French axis, was the only way in which to stop the House of Austria re-establishing its domination over Europe.

In other words, Buckingham, after his return to England in the autumn of 1623, was moving towards the final stage of his career as favourite, one which was far closer to that of Olivares

[25] *The Fortescue Papers*, ed. S. R. Gardiner (1871), p. 119; PRO, SP 14, vol. 112.93; PRO, 31/3, Baschet's Transcripts, bundle 53.79.

[26] *The Life of the Renowned Doctor Preston, Writ by His Pupil, Master Thomas Ball, DD*, ed. E. W. Harcourt (1885), pp. 66, 69, 84.

and Richelieu than anything that had yet been seen in England. But the essential precondition for the establishment of an English *Valimiento* was the withdrawal of the monarch from active politics, and James showed no sign of compliance. On the contrary, he used all his skills to thwart his favourite's designs. No wonder the Spanish ambassadors warned James that Buckingham planned to immure him in one of the royal hunting lodges and thereby reduce him to political impotence.[27] James and Buckingham were now moving rapidly apart, and it is not inconceivable that the King might have broken with him altogether, or at least connived at his fall. Buckingham had many powerful enemies, of whom the most dangerous was Pembroke, and although he had played his cards so well since his return that he was, for the only time in his life, a popular hero, 'St George on horseback', public opinion was highly volatile. If an alternative favourite had been available, or if the Prince had been less unwavering in his support for Buckingham, James might have taken the plunge. Yet the emotional ties that bound him to Buckingham were still very strong, and the favourite's serious illness in the spring of 1624 brought all James's love for him flooding back.[28]

From that moment onwards there was no question of Buckingham falling from favour. This did not mean, however, that the King slipped into the role of passive observer of events. James accepted the break with Spain, though he almost certainly regarded it as temporary and repairable, and went ahead with negotiations for a French marriage and alliance – though it may be that he nominated the Earl of Carlisle (a former favourite) as one of the envoys to Paris so that Carlisle could keep a wary eye on the activities of the Earl of Holland, who was known to be a confidant of Buckingham.[29] James's firm stand against any concessions to the English Catholics nearly torpedoed the negotiations, and although he eventually modified his position it was

[27] *Cabala, Sive Scrinia Sacra* (1691), pp. 13, 275–6; British Library, Harleian MS 6987, 196.

[28] *Scrinia Reserata: A Memorial Offer'd to the Great Deservings of John Williams, DD . . . by John Hacket* (1692), pt 1, p. 190; Lockyer, *Buckingham*, pp. 196–8; PRO, 31, Crisp Transcripts, 4/2.15.

[29] PRO, SP 78, vol. 72.83, vol. 73.65, 110; PRO, Baschet's Transcripts, bundle 60.222.

only on condition that the concessions should be contained in an
écrit particulier and not constitute a formal part of the marriage
treaty.[30] Similarly with the plans for military co-operation
between the two states, on which Buckingham was pinning his
hopes, James insisted that he would not commit himself to any
action which might lead to war with Spain unless the King of
France bound himself in writing to play a full part. James's
reservations were based on long experience of what he regarded
as French duplicity and may well have been justified, but the
effect of them was to destroy the fragile understanding that
Buckingham had established with Richelieu and to wreck whatever chance Mansfield's expedition had of succeeding.[31] If
Buckingham had really been a *Valido* the initial steps in his
campaign to build a common front against the Habsburgs would
not have been so faltering. It was because he was still a Political
Favourite, who had to deal with the King by persuasion, not
domination, that his ambitious plans failed of fulfilment.

It was only after the death of James and the accession of Prince
Charles to the throne in March 1625 that Buckingham became a
Valido, for the new King, at least in the opening years of his
reign, was content to play the passive role in political affairs that
James was temperamentally incapable of adopting. Yet, although
Buckingham now had full control over the making and imple-
mentation of policy, it was too late for him to throw off the accumulated encumbrances of the earlier stages of his career. As the
King's Companion he had provoked envy and anger among those
less fortunately placed to acquire money, titles and offices for
themselves, their kindred and clients. As Political Favourite he
had been held responsible for pro-Spanish and pro-Catholic
policies of which he was, in fact, the executant, not the framer.
The jealousy and suspicion that he had aroused in James's reign
clung to him in Charles's, and although the anti-Habsburg
strategy that he devised was in the best interests of England it was
interpreted as a subtle plot to cement his hold on power by

---

[30] ibid., bundle 59.197–206, 216–18, 246; PRO, SP 78, vol. 73, 113v–116, 171, 199, 250; British Library, King's MSS, vol. 134 ii.251; *Hardwicke State Papers, 1501–1726,* 2 vols (1778), vol. 1, pp. 546–9.

[31] PRO, SP 78, vol. 73.199v, 225, 354; PRO, Baschet's Transcripts, bundle 60.298.

destroying English liberties and the Protestant religion with which they were so closely linked.

One of the earliest historians of James's reign asserted that the King chose his favourites so that they should become odious to his people and thereby shield him from the unpopularity attendant upon his actions.[32] It may be doubted whether this was James's primary motivation, but it was a fact that the English system of government was based on trust in the King. The sovereign could do no wrong, at least in theory. If in practice he seemed to do so, this must be the fault of evil counsellors. The advantage of such an assumption was that while kings were not removable – except by God – counsellors were. The hostility shown towards Buckingham by James's subjects was therefore in large part an outlet for the frustration engendered in them by those aspects of James's rule of which they disapproved but over which they had no control. An anonymous versifier put the situation in a nutshell and provided a pithy and accurate summary of Buckingham's role as Companion and Political Favourite under James I:

> It is a destiny belongs to state.
> Him whom the Prince doth love, the people hate . . .
> Which wise kings know, and what it is to have
> A favourite, whose office is to save
> Their government from blame, as what's amiss,
> The fault be not their own, but counted his.[33]

---

[32] F. Osborne, 'Traditional Memoirs of the Reign of King James the First', in *Secret History of the Court of James the First*, 2 vols (1811), vol. i, p. 274.

[33] Bodleian Library, MS Malone 23, 123.

ENGLAND AND ITALY

THE MARRIAGE OF HENRY PRINCE OF WALES

Roy Strong

FEW PERIODS of European history contain more tragic monuments to lost hopes than the two decades which precede the outbreak of the Thirty Years War in 1618. They were an epoch in the aftermath of the terrible wars of religion of the late sixteenth century. In France the Huguenot Henri of Navarre became Catholic and thus reunited a divided people in loyalty to the *Rex Christianissimus*. In 1598 peace was made with Spain at the Treaty of Vervins. Across the Channel, James I had succeeded to the crown of England, thus re-creating the ancient legendary Empire of Great Britain. He, too, made peace with Spain. Even the long struggle in the Netherlands came to a halt in 1609 with the Twelve Years Truce. All over Europe lights began to be rekindled in the belief that some new resolution to the religious and political divide could be found, in which the domination of the Habsburgs might be broken and the extremes of post-Tridentine Catholicism held at bay. The aspirations took divergent and complex forms within the history of ideas: for example, in the messianic hopes which focused on rulers such as Henri IV, the Utopian visions of a Campanella, the revival of the encyclopaedic tradition and the resurgence of the shattered *respublica litterarum*. It is usually forgotten that dynastic marriages between partners of different faiths were one aspect of this attempt to achieve a *via media* before the holocaust. And James I was to be its prime exponent.

In this way the British Solomon revived the *politique* policy of Catherine de Medici, epitomized in the marriage of Henri of Navarre to Marguerite de Valois. That this ended in disaster seems in no way to have deterred him, for from the outset of his reign the policy of the twin marriages of his two eldest children to a Catholic and a Protestant remained constant. In this way he saw the *Ecclesia Anglicana*, being both Catholic and reformed, as a bridgehead to theological reconciliation. We know one part of his policy came off, the marriage of Elizabeth to Frederick V, Elector Palatine, the leader of the alliance of Protestant states within the Holy Roman Empire, an alliance that would end in catastrophe with the Bohemian venture. The second part James pursued in the Spanish match for his son Charles in the 1620s, eventually fulfilled when he married him to Henrietta Maria. What is forgotten is that Charles inherited a policy which had been initiated for his brother, Henry Prince of Wales. If Henry had not died on 6 November 1612, he would have married a daughter of Charles Emmanuel, Duke of Savoy. How different the course of history would have been had he lived and ascended the throne as Henry IX with a Catholic consort at his side it is still interesting to speculate.

The Prince himself was always to be a peripheral figure in the arrangements surrounding his marriage.[1] In 1610, at the age of sixteen, he was created Prince of Wales and given his own establishment. He proceeded to gather round him a brilliant court, vividly expressive of his own preoccupations and the antithesis of that of his father. Here was a prince who revelled in public appearances, who shone in tilt and masque, who was adept in the arts of horsemanship, who was passionate in his advocacy of the revival of England's naval strength, who supported colonial expansion and exploration, who was violently anti-Catholic and who embodied all the aspirations of the old Elizabethan war party. Taciturn and withdrawn, he presided over a household resembling a Protestant monastery where swearing was subject to fine and those absent from sermons had their food docked. And yet he collected books, pictures, bronzes, antique gems and medals as well as commissioning vast palace and garden projects, patronizing artists as varied as Inigo Jones, Robert Peake, Mierevelt and Constantino de'Servi. Above all he was a supporter and exponent of the 'arts mathematicall' and

---

[1] For the Prince, see my forthcoming book, *Henry Prince of Wales and England's Lost Renaissance*. The only previous biographies are Thomas Birch, *The Life of Henry Prince of Wales* (1760), and J. W. Williamson, *The Myth of the Conqueror. Prince Henry Stuart: A Study in Seventeenth Century Personation* (New York, 1978).

with his death the alliance of the monarchy and new developments in the sciences snapped, not to be reasserted until after 1660. And with regard to marriage every source agrees on two facts: the first his indifference to women; the second his deep-rooted dislike of any proposal to marry a Catholic.

For Henry this last, alas, was never taken into account as his father embarked on a series of negotiations to marry off his son to a Catholic bride. Although both France and Spain did figure on and off in James's plans, the two most significant sets of negotiations were those with Tuscany and Savoy. These form an almost forgotten episode in Anglo-Italian relations at the opening of the seventeenth century. They have, of course, their practical and political side but they also have their ideological aspect. Both were conducted with states which belonged to what was defined as *stati liberi*, those not directly aligned to either of the two major powers, and both were conducted within the immediate perspective of two events which had excited the whole of Europe. One was the quarrel of Venice with the Papacy in 1606 when the *Serenissima* was laid under interdict. In England it was followed with great interest as the ambassador, Sir Henry Wotton, used the embassy to propagate the Anglican theological position. The second, far more dramatic, was the mobilization of France in alliance with many of the *stati liberi* in the winter of 1609–10 as a preface to some huge anti-Habsburg conflict. That, owing to Henri IV's assassination, never happened.

Our best approach is through the correspondence of the Servite friar, Paolo Sarpi, official theologian to the Republic of Venice and a prime exponent of liberal ideals within a European context.[2] These inevitably rose once again as two Italian states, in the main subservient to Spain and the Pope, openly contemplated marriage with a heretic. For Sarpi, England with its reformed religion was the natural leader of the great crusade needed to crush the iron grip of Spain and stem the ideological extreme of Jesuit Catholicism. Alas, Sarpi was only too well aware that his hopes were founded in vain on a king who was *dottore* certainly but whose learning led only to chatter but avoided action. As early as 1609, however, he knew that James's

---

[2] See John L. Lievsay, 'Paolo Sarpi's Appraisal of James I', in Heinz Bluhm (ed.), *Essays in History and Literature* (Chicago, Ill., 1965), pp. 109–17.

son was of a far different calibre: '. . . from all sides one hears about the great *virtù* of the Prince, son of the King of England. But the world must wait a great while to benefit therefrom. . . .'³ Three years later Sarpi welcomed the splendid embassy that his old friend Sir Henry Wotton took to Turin even though he was sceptical that anything would come of it. Savoy, Wotton believed, was an ideal state into which to introduce Protestantism. On 4/14 August 1612, Sarpi wrote:

> In Italy there is no significant activity except the matrimonial bargaining of the dukes of Savoy and of Tuscany, the latter to wed off a sister, and the other a daughter to the Prince of Wales. The Tuscans, as if the marriage were already a sure thing, have sent to request licence for it of the Pope – of which [action], by those cognizant, two interpretations are being given: one that being certain to receive a negative reply from England, they wish rather to receive it from the Pope, for the sake of saving face publishing that all would have been completed had the pontiff assented. Others believe that, holding their own pretensions ruled out, they wish likewise to exclude the Duke of Savoy, receiving a refusal from the Pope to the end that it serve as a warning to him to proceed no further in the business, and that it would likewise force the Pope to do the same with Savoy, and to hold his position.⁴

Subsequent to the Prince's death he wrote as follows:

> Now the negotiations for the marriage will be abandoned, negotiations which, though they could only end in smoke, pleased me most highly because they served to domesticate affairs. And (chiefly) it was a great diminution of reputation for the Pope that papist princes should consider marriages with Protestants. But we ever seem to see die only those whose deaths will benefit Spain.⁵

Even although Sarpi, through long years of disillusionment with the inertia of James, viewed the matches with some degree of

---

³ Sarpi to Christoph von Dohna, 7 July 1609: Paolo Sarpi, *Lettere ai Protestanti*, ed. M. D. Busnelli (1931), vol. 2, p. 15.

⁴ Sarpi to De L'Isle, 14 August 1612: ibid., vol. 1, pp. 236–7.

⁵ Sarpi to De L'Isle, 4 December 1612: ibid., vol. 1, p. 253.

cynicism he cast them always in terms of liberal hopes. The last allusion to the Savoy marriage comes in January 1613:

> The King of England has favoured him [the Duke of Savoy], having given them an account of the death of the Prince of Wales, and has also written in the same way to his daughter Maria, whom it was negotiated to marry; from whence he will send an ambassador express to that King, without much pleasure to Rome, which does not approve such communications.[6]

And so a hope, European in its ideological dimensions, vanished. But for two years it was widely believed that one or the other would actually happen. And all the evidence supports that view, including the attitude of James, who would hardly have wished to be seen as going wholly into alliance with the Protestant north by the marriage of Elizabeth to Frederick V in the winter of 1612–13. The arrival of Frederick in October was to have been followed by the announcement of the Prince of Wales's Catholic bride, thus revealing to the whole of Europe James's *via media* dynastic policy of religious reconciliation. And, although the bride was eventually to be an infanta of Savoy, initially it was to have been a Medici princess.

I

The Tuscan state was a recent creation and its rulers, the Medici, were merchant bankers whose lack of antiquity of descent was constantly flung in the faces of those who promoted the match. Tuscany had been created in the aftermath of the Imperial subjection of Florence, when the Medici had been installed as dukes by Charles V. Cosimo de'Medici began the long process of consolidating the dynasty, achieved both by his continued support of the Imperial cause and by his establishment of one of the most administratively efficient states in Europe. Once more the population rose, commerce and agriculture began to flourish, an army and navy protected its land and sea frontiers, and the city attracted a new generation of artists and scholars which was to make Medici court style, which we now define by the word

---

[6] Sarpi to De L'Isle, 29 January 1613: ibid., vol. 1, p. 263.

'mannerist', the pattern for the northern courts. The treaty of
Câteau-Cambrésis in 1559 assured Habsburg hegemony and
confirmed the wisdom of Duke Cosimo's policies. In 1565 his
loyalty was rewarded by an Austrian archduchess as a bride for
his heir, Francesco, and in 1569 he was elevated by the Pope to
the status of Grand Duke.

The Medici–Stuart marriage, however, was prompted by
quite different motives. In 1587, Grand Duke Francesco was
succeeded by his brother, the Cardinal Ferdinand de'Medici.
Renouncing his cardinal's hat, the new Grand Duke initially
continued the traditional Medici pro-Habsburg policies. Indeed,
in 1588 he contributed a galleon to the mighty Armada that was
intended to subjugate Protestant England. Six years later, however, that inveterate traveller Fynes Moryson records that among
other treasures in the grand ducal collections 'I wondered to see
there the picture of Elizabeth our famous Queene: but the Duke
of Florence much esteemed her picture, for the admiration of her
vertues, howsoeuer the malitious Papists had long endevoured
to obscure her fame . . .'.[7] Within a few years Ferdinand had
successfully reversed policy, sensing that Spain had passed its
apogee. He cut off the perennial loans to Philip II, married a
French princess, Christina of Lorraine, in 1589, and during the
1590s supported the Huguenot Henri of Navarre with both arms
and money in his long struggle against the Catholic League. In
the aftermath of the French king's conversion to Catholicism he
was instrumental in his reconciliation with Rome and later occupied a central role in the negotiations resulting in the Treaty of
Vervins. Two years later his niece, Marie de'Medici, married
Henri IV. After 1600 his policies veered once more towards
Spain, particularly with the succession in mind and the need for
the reinvestiture of Siena, and in 1608 his son married another
Austrian archduchess. When Cosimo II succeeded his father the
year after, he inherited a well-organized state, with a powerful
navy, a port in Livorno which was a prime focus of Mediterranean
trade, besides presiding over one of the most splendid of courts.

Cosimo was only nineteen when he came to power, and the
dominant voices in the State were those of his mother and of his
father's secretary, Belisario Vinta. The policies, therefore, con-

---

[7] Fynes Moryson, *An Itinerary*, (Glasgow, 1907) vol. 1, p. 322.

tinued essentially to be those of Ferdinand: the preservation of peace in the peninsula and the maintenance of what was left of the independence of Italy. The latter objective they shared with their enemy Savoy, although, like Venice, they had stood to one side in the Julich-Cleve crisis of 1608 which had precipitated Henri IV's mobilization. But Florence was geographically in a far more exposed position, its frontiers actually bordering on the Papal States; compared with Savoy there was much less room for overt political manoeuvre and there was certainly no religious ambiguity. Florence was directly under the spell of the full flood of Tridentine Catholicism with its exclusion of lay participation, its renewed emphasis on the cult of saints and relics, its escalation of ceremonial and its promotion of new orders and forms of piety. When Marie de'Medici married Henri IV, God's message via the enraptured Maddalena de'Pazzi was that fruitfulness would only follow if she persuaded her husband to destroy the Huguenots and admit the Jesuits to France. From the point of view of Tuscany the Medici–Stuart match was always promoted *in spe conversionis*.

Unlike those with Savoy, relations between James I and Tuscany went back a long way.[8] Uncertainty about his likelihood of succeeding Elizabeth dominated the King's thoughts in the 1590s until, with the fall of Essex, a decisive alliance with Robert Cecil was formed. During the previous decade, however, James had looked to Henri of Navarre, also Protestant and likewise with a claim to a kingdom but who in the end was able to realize it only by becoming a Catholic (albeit of a moderate and ambiguous kind), one who protected the Huguenots but suppressed the Jesuits. James consequently courted Catholic rulers who had evaded the Habsburg net, and the Grand Duke Ferdinand was inevitably a key figure amongst them. Not only was James related to Ferdinand through his Guise grandmother but also, more to the point, the Grand Duke's role as an intermediator with Rome might prove useful. Between 1598 and 1604, Sir Michael Balfour was sent no less than four times to Florence. Ferdinand offered mediation with the Pope and, in 1601, James suggested Prince Henry as a husband for one of the Medici princesses, but his

[8] See J. D. Mackie, *Negotiations between King James VI and I and Ferdinand Grand Duke of Tuscany* (Oxford, 1927).

demand for a dowry in advance of 500,000 crowns and Ferdinand's insistence on papal approval held up the negotiations. Once James had gained Cecil's support the need became less pressing. What remained important was that the issues around which such a marriage revolved were already fixed. The Tuscan match was always purely for financial gain and reappeared with any seriousness only when crown finances tottered. On the Florentine side it was regarded as essential to obtain the Pope's approval and that, in the end, was to be the stumbling-block. That the project had begun in the 1590s was stated by the Prince's Chamberlain, Sir Thomas Chaloner, to Foscarini, the Venetian ambassador in England, at the height of the negotiations and, as late as 1623, the former Tuscan resident in London, Ottaviano Lotti, wrote a memorandum for the Dowager Grand Duchess Christina in which he stated that the marriage was to be in return for securing James's succession to the English throne and bringing with it some degree of toleration for Catholics.[9]

In 1603, Ferdinand sent an ambassador, Count Alfonso Montecuccoli, to congratulate him on his accession and once more renew the proposals of marriage. Nothing came of this, but the Grand Duke was henceforth represented in London by a member of the Count's train, Ottaviano Lotti. Lotti made a point of cultivating in particular Anne of Denmark, who had a taste for things Italian and who was taught the language by John Florio. His accomplishments also made him *persona grata* at the Prince's new court, for he played tennis with him and took part in chivalrous exercises in the tiltyard. Much centred on the personal charm of Lotti, whose ability to flatter and please was considerable. Nothing more is heard of the marriage for several years until the beginning of 1611.[10] On 18/28 January, Lotti describes a

[9] Dispatch of 2 March 1612: *Calendar of State Papers, Venetian, 1610–1613*, p. 300; and 6 April 1612: ibid., p. 327. For the 1623 account, see Anna Maria Crinò, *Fatti e Figure Seicento Anglo-Toscano* (Florence, 1957), pp. 263–4.

[10] The Medici match is dealt with in general in Jacopo Riguccio Galluzzi, *Istoria del Granducato di Toscano sotto il Governo della Casa Medici*, (Florence, 1781), vol. 3, pp. 316 ff.; G. S. Garganò, *Scapigliatura Italiana a Londra sotto Elisabetta e Giacomo I* (Florence, 1924), pp. 63 ff.; Mackie, *Negotiations*, pp. 71 ff. A large collection of transcripts from the Florentine archives is in the British Library (hereafter BL), Add. MS 40,079. These nearly all deal with the negotiations between Cosimo and the Pope, although some of the correspondence of Lotti and Cioli is also included. It runs from December 1611 to November 1612.

visit to Anne at Greenwich to present her with long-promised gifts from Florence, including dolls and portraits of the new Grand Duke and Duchess, Cosimo and Maddalena.[11] The Queen strolled in the gallery where she intended to hang the pictures. When she showed Lotti those of the Queen of Spain and the Infanta he said: 'I see that little princess Queen of England, if her youth does not impede it.' Anne replied that she saw no reason why it should because she was also considerably younger than the King herself. Lotti then moved on to refer to the imminent arrival of Marshal Laverdin with the offer of a French princess for the Prince of Wales.

'By God, that will never be. I would rather see my son damned.'
'Why, Madam?' I asked.
'Because it does not please me,' she replied, 'and because I do not wish to have children by one who has four wives.'

After this forthright allusion to the tangled *amours* of Henri IV she proceeded to indicate that she would much rather negotiate with the Grand Duke of Tuscany. Lotti was swift to respond with a lengthy eulogy of the Medici and an account of their marriages into the ruling dynasties of Europe.

After this initial overture little happened until early in March when Sir Edward Cecil, later Viscount Wimbledon, suddenly revealed himself to Lotti as the prime proponent of a Medici marriage.[12] Cecil told Lotti that he was upset at the imminent arrival of an embassy from Savoy and, suddenly seizing Lotti's hand, confided that he wished that the whole project for a Medici marriage be handled through him. Hitherto, he told him, the Prince had always intended to marry a subject and a beauty to avoid keeping a mistress. He had no intention of marrying into either France or Spain and was devoted to Tuscany. Portraits, he added, had to be secured as soon as possible of the available Medici princesses so that Cecil could produce them at the right moment. Lotti admitted that this would be difficult.

Throughout the marriage negotiations Sir Edward Cecil and, to a lesser extent, Sir Thomas Chaloner emerge as the key figures.

---

[11] Lotti to Vinta, 28 January 1610/11: Archivio di Stato, Florence (hereafter ASF), 4189.

[12] Lotti to Vinta, 3 March 1610/11: ibid.

The latter was the son of one of Lord Burghley's closest friends and had been educated under his aegis.[13] Chaloner is said to have visited Italy in the early 1580s and later he served under Leicester in the Low Countries. Through this he was drawn into the Essex circle, acting as the Earl's agent both in Florence and in France in the 1590s. Already, before the fall of Essex, he had returned to the Cecil fold and in the new reign occupied the key position of governor and subsequently chamberlain to Prince Henry. Cecil was a younger son of Thomas Cecil, Earl of Exeter and therefore Salisbury's nephew.[14] Nothing is known of his early life, but in 1594 at the age of twenty-two he was granted a licence together with his brother, Richard, to travel abroad. Florence was amongst the places that he visited, and the Grand Duke showed him 'extraordinary favour'; 'the duke gave him leave to ride his owne horse, and at his departure gave him gifts of price'. Subsequently he joined the English forces in the Low Countries and took part in the campaigns of Maurice of Nassau, who eventually gave him charge of the English horse. His relationship with his uncle was close and he acted as agent for him, sending reports from the Netherlands on the progress of the war. In June 1601 he married Theodosia Noel, daughter of Sir Andrew Noel of Dalby, Leicestershire, and in September he was knighted by Queen Elizabeth at Basing. In the same year he and his wife were staying with the Chaloners in the north. The link between the Cecils and the Chaloners went back to Lord Burghley, whose principal mourner, after a lifetime of friendship, had been old Sir Thomas Chaloner.

James I's reversal of the war policy in 1603, ending in the Twelve Years Truce in 1609, left Cecil unemployed. On his return to England he looked to his uncle, and the Prince was, of course, closely tied to the Cecils, having been brought up with Salisbury's son, William, Lord Cranborne. Salisbury probably regarded Edward Cecil as a good influence on his son through whom he must have been drawn into the orbit of the Prince. 'My

---

[13] For Chaloner, see P. W. Hasler (ed.), *The House of Commons, 1558–1603* (London, 1981), vol. I, pp. 588–9.

[14] For Cecil, see Charles Dalton, *Life and Times of Sir Edward Cecil, Viscount Wimbledon* (London, 1885).

Lord of Cranbourne used me well,' Chamberlain, the letter-writer, wrote to Carleton in November 1611, 'Sir Edward Cecil is continually about him, very much to my Lord Treasurer's liking.'[15] The relationship with the Prince had been cemented the year before when Cecil wrote him a series of letters describing the siege of Julich, which he was also to recount to him in person. Once more the fifteen-year-old Prince had attracted the older man: 'that grate and high favour which your Highness hath voutchsafed to cast upon me by your owne princely hand, that it hath given me a n[e]we life and incoragement to all my indevors'.[16] Although he never held an official post in the Prince's household, he was in constant attendance as one of his intimates. Cecil had all the characteristics that attracted the Prince. He was travelled and cultivated and, at the same time, he was a man-at-arms who not only fought on the battlefield but shone in the tiltyard.

What, however, prompted Cecil's sudden outburst? Although the Prince did have continuous and cordial communication with Salisbury, Edward Cecil, his favourite nephew, was the ideal go-between. Salisbury must have bestowed on him the role of sounding out what terms could be extracted for a Florentine marriage. In August portraits of the Grand Duke's sisters duly arrived and were taken to Richmond,[17] but it is difficult to believe that the Medici match was considered with any seriousness at all until September when James finally knew that he had been duped by Philip III of Spain, that the double marriage between France and Spain was a *fait accompli* and that the only Spanish Infanta available for Prince Henry was a child of six. Overtures by Cecil were then made to Lotti for the Princess Caterina. Freedom for the practice of the Catholic religion for her and her court was offered with vague hints of more. In the year of the sale of baronetcies and loans, money was the real focal point, and the dowry was to be the same as that paid with

---

[15] *The Letters of John Chamberlain*, ed. N. E. McClure, 2 vols (Philadelphia, Pa, 1939), vol. 1, p. 369.

[16] Cecil to Prince Henry, 21 August 1610: BL., Harleian MS 7007, fo. 398.

[17] Dispatch of 4 August 1612: *CSP, Ven., 1610–1613*, p. 192.

Marie de'Medici – 600,000 crowns. In October the Catholic party in the Council, led by the Earls of Northampton and Suffolk, began to say 'Behold our Prince turns to Tuscany for a bride', although there is no indication of a flicker of interest on his part.[18]

As a result of this Grand Duchess Christina sent her confessor to Rome to obtain papal assent. Paul V delegated the matter to a congregation of six cardinals before whom the case was argued, it was believed, with such conviction that the worst that could be expected was tacit approval. When this news was conveyed to Lotti early in January 1612 nothing seemed to stand in the way of the match proceeding. It soon became clear, however, that not everything was going according to plan in Rome, so that in February a grand-ducal secretary, Andrea Cioli, was dispatched to London to stand in for Lotti while the latter returned to Florence and proceeded to Rome carrying as much evidence as he could muster to persuade the Pope to allow the negotiations to continue. There was a letter from the Catholic lords in support of the match together with a surprising set of instructions and a letter from Anne of Denmark to the Pope admitting her Catholicism and signed 'humilissima et diligentissima figliuola et serva'.[19] In this she optimistically stated that the marriage would convert her son. In March, it was reported, both King and Council were still in favour, although the Prince was not, mainly on account of the presumption that his father would squander the dowry.[20]

Cioli arrived in England at the end of March. He began by lavishing praise on Lotti for all that he had achieved. Edward Cecil welcomed him with a splendid dinner at which the health of not only the Grand Duke was drunk but, covertly, also that of the future bride. He was taken to see the Prince from afar in the tiltyard and declared him a 'ben esperto cavaliero'. There followed formal visits of presentation to the King, Queen and Prince, and both were summoned before James and the Council to reaffirm that the Pope had not forbidden the match. Cioli

---

[18] Lotti to Vinta, 21 October 1611: ASF 4189.

[19] Copy of the Letter in ASF Miscellanea Medicea 293 inserto 29, no. 2.

[20] Dispatch of 2 March 1612: *CSP, Ven., 1610–1613*, p. 300.

seemed in a state of delirium at the prospect of 'quella vittoria' and off Lotti went to Italy.[21]

Before he left, however, one cloud had already crossed the horizon. Others were swiftly to follow. Salisbury was ill and had received them seated in a litter. His condition deteriorated rapidly and a month later he was dead. That was a blow.[22] More serious was Lotti's absence. His obvious magnetism and skill as a negotiator together with his knowledge of the court, bred by years in England, left Cioli by comparison in an increasingly isolated position. As weeks passed into months Cioli's laments reached a crescendo crying out for the return of Lotti. Things began to go badly.[23] The Prince publicly declared that he had no desire to be bought and sold and opposed the match, although, bypassing official channels, he sent his own messenger to Florence to ask the exiled Robert Dudley, Earl of Warwick to make overtures ensuring that if it did happen half the dowry should be specifically assigned to him.[24]

Cioli became progressively more and more exasperated as opposition appeared. The Earl of Arundel was regarded as particularly suspect in using his influence upon the Prince against the marriage.[25] The Savoy agent, Buglione, was busy pressing his master's claims and poisoning ministers against Florence.[26] By the middle of June, Cioli exploded, denouncing James as a weathercock, the Queen, 'tanto extravaganto cervello', as proud,

[21] Cioli to Vinta, 6 April 1612: ASF Miscellanea Medicea 295 inserto 26. For Cioli in England, see *CSP, Ven., 1610–1613*, pp. 318, 327, 332–3, 340. For report of the covert drinking of the future Princess of Wales's health, see Crinò, *Fatti e Figure*, p. 262.

[22] Cioli to the Grand Duke, 31 May 1612, specifically refers to Salisbury as its prime promoter: ASF Miscellanea Medicea 193 inserto 29. It is referred to again in Cioli to the Grand Duke, 1 June 1612: ibid., no. 18.

[23] For Cioli's correspondence, see: to the Grand Duke, 7 April, ASF Miscellanea Medicea 295 inserto 26; to the Grand Duke, 8, 12, 16 April, ibid.; and to the Grand Duchess Christina, ibid.

[24] Earl of Warwick and Leicester to the Grand Duchess Christina, 13 May 1612, and letter from Yates to the Earl, 27 March 1612 (Old Style), in ASF 4190, fos 33, 34.

[25] See letters of Cioli to the Grand Duke, 3 May and 12 June: ASF Miscellanea Medicea 293 inserto 29. In a later letter he describes Cecil asking him to reply to a list of objections to the marriage: Cioli to the Grand Duke, 10 May 1612, ibid., inserto no. 10.

[26] Cioli to the Grand Duke, 24 May 1612: ASF Miscellanea Medicea 293 inserto 29 no. 14.

vain, capricious, and spiteful, while the Prince, whom he admitted to be 'animo generoso et heroico', was also proud, haughty and pretentious in the extreme.[27] Poor man, he was in England, he believed, holding the fort waiting for news from Tuscany that would formally settle the matter. Instead he was faced with James entering into serious negotiations with Savoy as though no commitment had ever been given to Florence in the first place. What was more, Savoy outbid Florence by offering a dowry double the size.[28] On the day that Cioli at long last was escorted to Richmond Palace to present the Grand Duke's gift of bronzes by Giovanni da Bologna and meet the Prince again, Cecil tried to assure him that the Savoy match was by no means settled while Chaloner unfolded that Salisbury had been dealing with the Savoyards all along.[29]

More worrying was the lack of any news from Italy of what was going on in Rome.[30] There things also went from bad to worse because nothing had been more misleading than the impression that the Pope would acquiesce in the marriage. He proved immovable. The Grand Duke had sent his warrior uncle, Don Giovanni de'Medici, in an attempt to bludgeon Paul V into agreement. The Prince and his court would have been horrified by the arguments being advanced in favour of the match. One, calling himself a 'Politico-Catholico', listing off the precedents of the good fruits that invariably fell from Catholic brides, included the Massacre of St Bartholomew as one of the fortunate consequences of Marguerite de Valois's marriage to Henri of Navarre! James was billed as an anti-Calvinist (which was true) and a likely convert (which was certainly not).[31] Neither Spain

---

[27] Cioli to the Grand Duke, 16 June 1612: ibid., inserto 28, no. 20.

[28] Cioli to the Grand Duke, 22 June 1612: ibid., no. 21.

[29] Cioli to the Grand Duke, 27 June 1612: ibid., no. 22.

[30] For the proceedings in Rome, see Galluzzi, *Istoria*, and Mackie, *Negotiations*. BL Add. MS 40,079 contains a mass of material. For Lotti's mission to Rome, see the Grand Duke to Lotti, 19 April 1612: ASF Miscellanea Medicea 293 inserto 29 no. 7; Lotti to Cioli, 1 June 1612: ibid.; Lotti to Cioli, 9 June 1612: ibid., no. 19; Bartolini to Lotti, 19 July 1612: ASF Mediceo 78, fo. 64. There is a great deal in the Venetian dispatches on the Roman end which was watched closely in the light of their own experience in confronting the Papacy over Sarpi: *CSP, Ven., 1610–1613*, pp. 384–5, 385, 388–9, 413, 422, 423.

[31] Mackie, *Negotiations*, pp. 75 ff.; BL Add. MS 40,079, fos 70 ff.

nor France wanted the marriage and it was inevitable that the conservative cardinals, headed by James's arch-enemy, Bellarmine, got their way. The Pope forbade the marriage. This fact had already reached Foscarini, the Venetian ambassador, by the end of July. By the middle of August all the other ambassadors knew.[32] The only person who was never told was Cioli. No wonder by September he was 'in tanta confusione di mente'.[33]

Galluzzi, the historian of the grand dukes, who writes the only detailed account from the Tuscan side, records the Florentine rage at the decision. Paul V, fearing that Cosimo would proceed with the match anyway (which was precisely what Savoy was doing), sent Archbishop di Chieti as papal nuncio to Florence with a brief to denounce the alliance and call down the wrath of heaven on those who supported the marriage of a Medici to a heretic. These blasts were directed not at the Grand Duke at all but at his mother. Cosimo, on the advice of his council, acceded to the Pope's demands, but the nuncio went on to ask for a formal retraction, which so enraged him that he determined to proceed in spite of papal censure and the threat of interdict. The bride, it was decided, should be conveyed out of Italy to her Guise relatives in Lorraine beyond the reach of the Pope. There just such a Catholic–Protestant match had existed, for Henri IV's sister, a Huguenot, had married the Catholic Duke Charles. Lotti was sent with speed once more back to London.

Events in the meantime had not helped. James, in fact, was annoyed that he had been misled over the Pope's approval, although the match was still referred to as being alive in October, but only just. Flames were fanned from the dying embers by Lotti outbidding Savoy, which he did, offering a further 400,000 crowns in addition to the original 600,000, but for this there would have to be in return concessions on the toleration of Catholicism and a rewriting of the oath of allegiance so that it no longer offended the Pope. The dowry was to be paid over a period of three years and the Prince was to get half, so that his message had clearly been received. On 16/26 October the Venetian ambassador reported that James had appointed an envoy to

---

[32] Cioli to Vinta, 16 August 1612: ASF Miscellanea Medicea 293 inserto 28 no. 38.

[33] Cioli to Vinta, 6 September: ibid., no. 40.

Florence[34] and the last we hear of the matter comes in a letter written by Lord Roos on 25 November from Florence to David Murray before news of the Prince's death had reached Italy. In it he enclosed a *relazione* on Tuscany but wrote:

> I cannot omit to tell you, that the great Dutchess is now informed, that you are great a Puritan, that you are not only an endeavourer against this match, but also against all other matches, which are popish. . . . I pray God, that the Prince's Highness would match with one of his own religion, which would be best for him and our country. . . . The great Dutchess here is advertised, that Sir Charles Cornwallis is a great dissuader of the Prince from the marriage. Also, that Mr Sackfield hath done evil offices in the business.[35]

That Cornwallis, the Prince's treasurer, was against it we know because the Prince commanded that he compile arguments against it which survive.[36] Tuscany, it runs, is too remote to be of any practical use; its rulers owe their status to the Pope and are wholly in the embrace of England's foes; a Catholic bride would encourage Catholicism; any dowry would accrue to the King and not to the Prince; and the Medici were *nouveau*. For Cornwallis marriage into Germany was the only logical and proper course:

> Your conjunction with those of your owne Religion will demonstrate your clear, and undoubted resolution not to decline in the cause of GOD. This will fasten unto you throughout all *Christendom* the professors of the reformation, and make you dear to the subjects of this kingdom; out of whose loves you may expect a permanent and continual treasure, not to be equalled by many decrees greater than can be hoped; and whose contrary conceite upon a marriage is so high a degree distasteful unto them is likely to breed, and increase those obstructions which have lately been shewed upon the demands of supply in Parliament by the King your Father.

[34] *CSP, Ven., 1610–1613*, p. 438.

[35] Birch, *Life*, p. 321.

[36] Sir Charles Cornwallis, 'A Discourse Concerning the Marriage Propounded to Prince Henry with a Daughter of Florence', in John Gutch (ed.), *Collectanea Curiosa* (Oxford, 1781), pp. 156–60. A manuscript version is in the Public Record Office (hereafter PRO), SP 14/70, fos 160–2; see also *Calendar of State Papers, Domestic, 1611–1618*, p. 149.

What can we conclude about the Medici marriage? Certainly that the Prince was never seriously interested in it. He despised the Medici, and not one word ever fell from his lips to indicate other than disfavour. There is no doubt that the Tuscan match was first and foremost an idea of Salisbury's in the aftermath of the collapse of the negotiations with Spain. He knew that James was set on a Catholic match for his son, however distasteful to him; and, if this had to be, Salisbury no doubt thought to make it more palatable both to Prince and populace by looking for a Catholic state which fell within the Venetian definition of a *stato libero*, one of those still able to manage some degree of independence from the Habsburg hegemony. Tuscany fitted the bill exactly. The match already had a history which could be built upon. Tuscany (unlike Savoy) pursued peace and stability as prime objectives so that expensive international complications would be avoided. It already had important commercial links with England in the Mediterranean through the port of Livorno, to which merchants of all faiths were welcome; and, above all, the Grand Duke was rich. It was in short a characteristically ingenious solution, for it met James's desire for a Catholic marriage for his son with the minimum of dangerous overtones both at home and abroad, and simultaneously solved the King's financial problems. The agents for it were always those close within the Treasurer's circle, Edward Cecil and Thomas Chaloner, and with his death it lost its most potent advocate. The alternative was Savoy, an alliance with whose volatile and unpredictable Duke could have untold repercussions within Europe, and as long as Salisbury lived he did all he could to prevent it.

2

The key figure in all the negotiations for marriages with the House of Savoy was Sir Henry Wotton.[37] Seen through his eyes the proposals were a continuation of his belief that Protestantism

---

[37] For whom see Logan Pearsall Smith, *Life and Letters of Sir Henry Wotton* (Oxford, 1907); Frances A. Yates, 'Paolo Sarpi's "History of the Council of Trent" ', in *Renaissance and Reform: The Italian Contribution, Collected Essays*, 3 vols (London, 1983), vol. 2, pp. 195 ff.

could be introduced into Italy by way of one of the *stati liberi* in the same way that he had attempted in Venice, where he was ambassador, during the Sarpi affair. In this sense the projected marriages between the Princess Elizabeth and the Prince of Piedmont and Prince Henry and the Infanta Maria were variations of a single theme. How the Tuscan and Savoy matches were looked at in Italy was, of course, very different from how they were regarded in England, and the proponents at the English end were also different. In the case of Savoy it was Wotton and his brother, Lord Wotton, who were the key promoters, as in that of Tuscany it had been the Prince's Chamberlain, Sir Thomas Chaloner, and the soldier, Sir Edward Cecil.

Duke Charles Emmanuel I ruled over a country that geographically occupied a key position. To the east its frontier bordered on France and included the route taken by French armies over the Alps for over a century by way of Bresse, Bugey and the Pays de Gex. To the west lay the Spanish-occupied Milanese, key to the north–south axis for the Habsburg domination of Europe, the lifeline whereby troops were moved up through Italy over the Alps to the battlefields of Germany and the Low Countries. To the north stretched the Alps with the Swiss cantons and confederacies, including that bastion of the reformed faith, Geneva. To the south its coastline ran along the Mediterranean with the ports of Nice and Villefranche.

If Venice was the shield of the *stati liberi*, Savoy under Charles Emmanuel was its sword.[38] The Duke was warlike and chivalrous, but volatile and changeable, a man of fantasy whose dreams were about crowns. Obsessed by genealogy, there were no limits to his claims. Not only did he at one time nurse pretensions to the crown of France, he also at various periods of his life claimed to be King of England, King of Poland, King of Provence, Holy Roman Emperor, King of Cyprus, King of Morea, King of Albania, King of Sicily and King of Sardinia. And, although Catholic, assiduous in his cult of the Virgin and relics, at the

---

[38] On Charles Emmanuel, see Robert Bergadani, *Carlo Emanuel I* (Turin, 1926); Salvatore Foa, *Vittoria Amedeo I (1587–1637)* (Turin, 1930), chs 1 and 2; Andrea Griseri, 'L'Autumno del Manierismo alla Corte di Carlo Emanuele I e un arrivo "Caravaggesco" ', *Paragone*, vol. 12, no. 141 (1961), pp. 19–36.

same time he was liberal enough to receive fleeing Huguenots and protect the Waldenses in 'la vostra libertà religiosa'. He was also a patron of the arts and, although poor, ruled over a splendid court in which all the most avant-garde forms of late Renaissance theatre and spectacle were assiduously cultivated. Charles Emmanuel was also one of the earliest patrons of the *Caravaggisti*. Savoy was a typical late mannerist court, one which, apart from the fact that it was Catholic, had much in common with that of Stuart England. Both politically wished to keep clear of either of the major superpowers by a balancing act, but Charles Emmanuel, devoid of the encircling waters that guarded Great Britain, was in a much more difficult situation, sandwiched directly between the two protagonists.

In 1585 the Duke had been drawn into the Habsburg orbit by marriage to one of Philip II's daughters, the Infanta Catherine, but during the closing stages of the Wars of the Catholic League, in which he seized Saluzzo and aided Spain, he had been forced not only to accept Spanish garrisons but also to give his children as hostages to be educated in Madrid. In the Treaty of Vervins, Savoy was abandoned by Spain and, as a result, lost Bresse, Bugey, the Val-Romey and the Pays de Gex to France in the Treaty of Lyons (1601). The years following, however, led to a gradual *rapprochement* with the French. Charles Emmanuel's vision now became that of a league of Italian states that would eventually destroy the Spanish domination of the peninsula. In pursuance of this in 1608 his daughters became Duchess of Mantua and Duchess of Modena respectively. The year after followed a marriage treaty for his heir, Vittorio Amedeo, with France. By the Treaty of Brusola, Savoy became the only one of the Italian *stati liberi* to enter into direct alliance with Henri IV in the hostilities planned for 1610. French troops were to enter Italy and conquer the Milanese, which was to be annexed to Savoy. In the aftermath of the assassination of Henri IV in May 1610 the Italian campaign was abandoned and Charles Emmanuel found himself isolated as France courted peace with Spain in the negotiations leading up to the double marriage treaty of 1612.

Charles Emmanuel countered this by the surprising move of

marriage alliances with England.[39] Vittorio Amedeo, Prince of Piedmont, was twenty-four, a suitable match for the Princess Elizabeth. His third daughter, Maria, was exactly the same age as the Prince of Wales. The first match had been proposed before, in 1603, when, on the death of Elizabeth, diplomatic relations had been restored with England. Wotton's dream had always been of an aggressive anti-Spanish and anti-papal league achieved by the removal of either Venice or Savoy into the Protestant camp. Venice having for the moment failed, for the next two years Wotton's energies centred on achieving a Savoy marriage for either the Princess Elizabeth or Prince Henry. In both instances Wotton would have viewed this as a move whereby the reformed faith might gain a footing in the peninsula.

Although, as in the case of Tuscany, overtures had been made at the opening of the reign,[40] they were not revived until the close of 1610 immediately following the most appalling humiliation inflicted on one of the Duke's sons at the court of Philip III. Wotton, *en route* for England, changed his homeward course by way of Germany in order to stir up support for Venice by the German princes and instead went via Milan to Turin.[41] The ambassador arrived on 8 January 1611 and was splendidly welcomed by Duke Charles Emmanuel. At a fête on sledges Wotton's coach encountered the Duke's in which rode the daughter destined for Prince Henry. The coach stopped and the Infanta Maria adjusted her mask, thus revealing to Wotton the beauty intended for Princess of Wales. Later the prowess of the Duke's sons was displayed in a ceremonial joust and, the Venetian ambassador Gussoni reported to the Doge and Senate, Wotton was closeted no less than three hours with Charles Emmanuel. This was followed by the appointment of Claudio di Ruffia,

---

[39] See Domenico Carutti, *Storia diplomazia della corte de Savoia*, (Turin, 1876) vol. 2, pp. 106–9. For an account of the Savoy sources see Eugenio Passamonti, 'Relazione Anglo-Sapaude del 1603 al 1625', *Bulletino Storico Bibliografico Subalpino*, Turin, nos 5–6, 1934 pp. 264–317; 488–522.

[40] *Calendar of State Papers, Venetian, 1603–1607*, p. 189; Prince Henry to the Duke of Savoy: BL Harleian MS 7007, fo. 56; Pietro Orsi, 'Il carteggio di Carlo Emanuele I', in *Carlo Emanuele I, duca di Savoia* (Turin, 1891), p. 21, n. 1.

[41] Smith, *Wotton*, vol. 1, pp. 113–16.

Count of Cartignana as ambassador to England.[42] Within a month rumours were rife. On 15 February, Chamberlain wrote of 'matters of marriages',[43] while eleven days after Beaulieu wrote to Trumbull from Paris of the Count's journey with its offer of a match between the Duke's heir, the Prince of Piedmont, and the Princess Elizabeth, something unlikely to succeed 'considering the important Respects and *Difficulties* of *Religion, Remoteness*, and many other'.[44] By then talk had extended this to a double match between Savoy and England, parallel to the one which was shortly to be made public between France and Spain.

On 12 March, Cartignana arrived in London. News of a double marriage came as a complete surprise to Salisbury, and that of Prince Henry and the Infanta Maria was immediately dismissed. Salisbury wrote to Winwood pointing out the

> ... *Disparity*, both considering *the Fortune of our Prince and his Years* (which might give him leave to tarry) and the unlikelyhood to retain his mind within any such Circumscription, but that it was more probable he would affect (when time should be) his own Choice, though it were for *the greatest Match* in Europe....[45]

Any negotiations were henceforth to be limited to the Princess Elizabeth and the Prince of Piedmont, although Salisbury was against this, too,

> ... *as* Savoy *will never break with* Spaine, *so in contemplating of all the Circumstances of his* [the Duke's] *unquiet Nature, and poor Purse, his Fortune single would be but of small use to England, if* Spaine *and he were asunder.*[46]

That and religion summed up the opposition's arguments, which were shortly to be elaborated in written treatises by Sir Walter

---

[42] For Cartignana's first embassy, see Passamonti, 'Relazione. . . .', pp. 280–291; *CSP, Ven., 1610–1613*, pp. 119–20, 126, 130–1, 133, 172, 174, 180–1, 182; *CSP, Dom., 1611–1618*, p. 97, no. 83.

[43] Chamberlain to Winwood, 15 February 1611: *Letters*, vol. 1, p. 303.

[44] Beaulieu to Trumbull, 8 March 1611: E. Sawyer, *Memorials of Affairs of State . . . from the Original Papers of Sir Ralph Winwood* (London, 1725), vol. 3, pp. 265–6.

[45] Salisbury to Winwood, 3 April 1611: ibid., vol. 3, pp. 271–3.

[46] ibid.

Ralegh and Sir John Holles, Controller of the Prince's household. But although the ground was cut from under Cartignana's feet, as he had no authority to treat along these lines, the Savoy match was not without its supporters. There were the dreamers, Sir Henry Wotton and his brother, Lord Wotton, who saw the matches through, as it were, Sarpian eyes. There was also the Catholic party on the Council headed by Northampton, who wanted a Catholic bride for the Prince of Wales as a means of preventing further advances by the Puritan party and of eventually restoring Catholicism. There was the crypto-Catholic Queen, who showed favour, and there was a not unsympathetic James, who clung to his belief in mixed marriages for his children as a means to achieve concord in Christendom. The King actually went as far as saying that he had no objection to the Princess attending Catholic services, a concession that would have appalled his Protestant subjects, but Salisbury stated that his master would not agree to the abandonment of the free exercise of her religion, even if it made her Queen of the World. At the end of March, Cartignana left.

In the intervening months the Spanish ambassador countered by offering an Infanta for Henry and the German princes, headed by the envoys of the Prince Palatine, sought the Princess's hand. Early in September the Savoy match was referred to as 'almost dead', and it was not until November that Cartignana returned.[47] On 11 November he was received by James, Anne of Denmark and the princes, and this time he formally offered the Prince of Piedmont for Elizabeth. Subsequently he was referred to a committee of four of the Council headed by Salisbury, who surprisingly asked him whether he had any other proposals. Cartignana replied that as the match of Prince Henry and the Infanta Maria had previously been rejected he had not. Although Cartignana had come offering the private exercise of her religion

---

[47] Dispatch of 9 September 1611: *CSP, Ven., 1610–1613*, p. 208. For Cartignana's second embassy, see Passamonti, 'Relazione . . .', pp. 305–17; and *CSP, Ven., 1610–1613*; pp. 221, 232, 234, 238, 240, 241–2, 246–8, 255, 260, 263, 268–9, 270–1, 273–4; PRO, Savoy, 92/1, fos 60 ff.; transcripts from surviving documents in Turin are in BL Add. MS 32023A, fos 42, 43–50, 70–71v, 76–77v, 84, 99–100; Duke of Savoy to Prince Henry, November 1611; BL Harleian MS 7008, fo. 110; Prince Henry to the Duke of Savoy, December 1611: ibid., fo. 115; Chamberlain, *Letters*, vol. 1, pp. 313, 316, 319, 321, 325, 327.

for the Princess, the fact was the situation had changed. By the close of 1611, James had discovered that the offer of a Spanish infanta for Prince Henry had only been a ploy, for which he had naïvely fallen. Worse, the double marriage of the Dauphin and Anne of Austria and the Infante and Elizabeth of France was a *fait accompli.* England, like Savoy, was isolated facing a détente of the major powers. Simultaneously with Cartignana's visit the German Protestant Union had decided jointly to petition James for Elizabeth's hand for the seventeen-year-old Prince Palatine. Cartignana took offence at Savoy even being considered in tandem with the Palatinate. Although Cartignana lingered and was given 'but a cold answer' and was observed to be 'much fallen from his high hopes', James was evasive.[48] The fact was that he had already decided in favour of the Palatine match for Elizabeth and, devoid of a possible Catholic match for Henry with either Spain or France, was to reopen negotiations for the Infanta Maria of Savoy.

Sometime in the latter half of 1611, Sir Walter Ralegh, at the command of 'my lord the prince', compiled a series of arguments against the Savoy marriage.[49] And here speaks the voice of the Prince of Wales's party, anti-Catholic and anti-Spanish and militant. Nothing could come of this marriage, Ralegh wrote from the Tower. This was a remote country whose ruler reigned by the grace of either France or Spain, neither of which would ever countenance the English in Savoy. The Duke was in fact a pensioner of Spain, his country was weak and easily conquered, and there were not even trade advantages. The Prince's sister would find herself alone in a popish land living in isolation and she would be fated to see her children brought up as Catholics. Whom, the Prince of Wales asks, should his sister marry?

It is true that I have heard it that some overtures hath bene made for the *Princ Pallatine* of the *Rhine*, certenly he is as well borne as the *Duke* of *Savoy*, and as free a Prince as he is. The Nation is faithfull, he is of our Religion, and by him we shall greatly

---

[48] Chamberlain to Carleton, 27 November 1611: *Letters*, vol. 1, p. 319.

[49] For Ralegh on the Savoy marriage, see 'Concerning a Match Propounded by the Savoyan, between Lady Elizabeth and the Prince of Piedmont', in *Works*, (London, 1829), vol. 8, pp. 223–36. For two other memoranda against the match, see PRO, SP 14/70, fos 163–6; and that by Sir John Holles in *HMC Portland*, vol. 9, pp. 41–6.

fasten unto us the *Netherlandes* and for the litle Judgment that god hath givene me; I doe prize the alliance of the *Pallatine* of the *Rhine*, and of the house of *Nassaw*, more than I doe of the alliance of tenne *Dukes* of *Savoy*.

On 21 December, Cartignana had seen James and asked him whether perhaps the King was treating with other princes for the Princess and named the Palatine. Although clearly discomfited, James admitted that her hand had been sought but no treaty had been made and he promised to send an embassy to Savoy in the spring headed by an old favourite, Lord Hay.[50]

By 18 March, when the embassy departed, Sir Henry Wotton had succeeded Hay as the ambassador to Turin.[51] The arrangements were elaborate. Jewels were selected from the Tower, including a gold sword studded with diamonds, valued at £16,000. Ten horses with costly caparisons were shipped to meet the entourage at Lyons, which consisted of young aristocrats such as Sir Robert Rich, later Earl of Warwick, and Sir William Cavendish, later Duke of Newcastle.[52] It was a splendid embassy for such an initially negative response. Prince Henry, it was reiterated in the instructions, was to have 'the freedome of his owne choice'.[53] Over the Princess Elizabeth, James wished to know the attitude of Spain (which, in fact, he knew to be hostile). All in all Wotton was to decline the match on the grounds that France, Spain, the Protestant princes and the Pope were all against it.

None of Wotton's correspondence from this embassy survives, but the key event that changed its course was one in England: the death on 24 May of Salisbury. Vast honours were paid to Wotton and the whole of Italy was agog to see a Protestant embassy arrive in Turin treating of marriage.[54] Wotton was met at Rivoli by the Duke himself and, although the ambassador was

---

[50] Dispatch of 13 June 1612: *CSP, Ven., 1610–1613*, pp. 273–4.

[51] Dispatch of 20 January 1612: ibid., p. 277; Chamberlain to Carleton, 15 and 29 January, 11 March 1612: *Letters*, vol. 1, pp. 327, 331, 339.

[52] Smith, *Wotton*, vol. 1, p. 120.

[53] Instructions to Wotton, *HMC Hatfield*, vol. 21, pp. 343–5.

[54] For Wotton's embassy, see Smith, *Wotton*, vol. 1, pp. 121–2; Sarpi, *Lettere*, vol. 1, p. 231; *CSP, Ven., 1610–1613*, pp. 354–5, 362–3; Prince Henry to the Prince of Piedmont: BL Harleian MS 7008, fo. 142; to the Duke of Savoy: ibid., ms. 143.

prostrated by fever, Charles Emmanuel insisted on an interview the following day, 4 May. On the fifth Wotton made his entry into Turin, where a palace had been prepared hung with tapestries and gold embroidered velvet. There then followed a round of fêtes, concerts, dances and hunting parties at Mirafiore and the other ducal villas. Wotton, whose knowledge of Italian was complete, entranced the ladies of the court and especially the Infanta Maria, making them laugh and blush at his wit.

On 17 June, Chamberlain had heard that 'some new matter is abrewing in Savoy for that Infanta for our Prince, that our ambassador is so much made of and presented so richly'.[55] By then the treaty for the Palatine match was complete. More to the point, in the aftermath of Salisbury's death James was virtually offering his son to the highest bidder, either Florence or Savoy. A daughter meant a dowry, and the Palatine match was not only cheap but also popular, and it fulfilled the first stage of the King's plans for his children's marriages. Its implication was a Catholic bride for Henry. So desperate were the Stuart finances by the summer of 1612 that subsequent to Salisbury's death the treasury was put into the hands of commissioners. Spiralling royal debt, it was hoped, would be staved off by the enormous dowry that would come with the Prince of Wales's bride.

As in the case of Florence loyal theologians were recruited to argue the case for the marriage of a Catholic princess to a heretic prince.[56] The groundwork for that had been amply covered during the negotiations for the marriage of Elizabeth to the Prince of Piedmont, when the Savoyard theologians argued that this marriage did not only not incur mortal sin for the bridegroom but, because such a match was made *in spe conversionis*, on the contrary, was deserving of great merit. In this way Pope Paul V's envoy, Fra Paoloa da Cesena was given short shrift by the Duke. In the case of the marriage of Henry and Caterina the ingenious Fra Orazio produced a paper entitled 'Is it permissible for daughters to marry heretics?'. The Franciscan marshalled many Church Fathers in the cause and went on to enlist Aquinas as advocating such alliances. Through this match was to be seen

---

[55] Chamberlain to Carleton, 17 June 1612: *Letters*, vol. 1, p. 361.

[56] Passamonti, 'Relazione . . .', pp. 493–5.

the possible conversion of the Prince, of his children and of the kingdom.

Wotton returned to England early in August and this time the negotiations were conducted by way of a Savoyard banker resident in London, Gabaleone.[57] His brief from the Duke was to cancel out the Tuscans by outbidding them on the dowry and by pointing out the dynastic superiority of the house of Savoy to the *nouveau* Medici. Charles Emmanuel also acted in the knowledge of what had gone on in Rome, aware that in July the Pope had sent an envoy to Florence forbidding the match.

The situation had changed greatly from when he had left in March. Both James and Anne now wished to marry off the Prince as soon as possible 'as his Highness has begun to show a leaning to a certain lady of the court'.[58] Later sources suggest that this mysterious person was none other than the new favourite Rochester's mistress, the notorious Frances Howard, Countess of Essex. Wotton and Gabaleone pursued both the King and the Prince on progress to Belvoir Castle. Here Wotton presented the Savoy case in its most favourable light in such a way as to cast the competing Florentines into a role of being 'tutto spagnuolo'.[59] He spoke of the beauty of the Infanta and of the valour of her father. Assurances were given 'that she was so far from being superstitious as that she had always about her a lady of the Religion, and would desire them [i.e. Catholic services] only in her chamber as privately as could be wished, promising likewise to accompany the Queen to our sermons at times when she should be called'. To this surprising list he added that he had 'some hope of that duke's turning Huguenot upon such an occasion'! But the real issue was money. The Florentines had offered 700,000 soldi, James wanted a million. The French, the Prince said, had offered that with a second daughter but, he tartly added, he needed a wife he could sleep with and not the money. But a central part of the Prince's make-up was his total obedience in the last resort to his father. And everything during the autumn

[57] ibid., pp. 497ff.

[58] Dispatch of 19 August 1612: *CSP, Ven., 1610–1613*, p. 412.

[59] Smith, *Wotton*, vol. I, pp. 124–5.

of 1612 indicated that Henry would have to marry the Infanta Maria of Savoy. Throughout September references to the match continue and Gabaleone's hopes ran high.[60] On 7 September, Charles Emmanuel wrote to him confirming *carte blanche* as to the size of the dowry. Gabaleone received firm support from Anne of Denmark who pledged her support and influence with the King and Prince. Northampton wrote to Rochester that an ambassador would be sent as soon as needed and that any dowry would be paid.[61] On 10 October, Gabaleone went to Hampton Court and was summoned twice before the Council.[62] He promised that the Duke would not attack Geneva, he said that James could fix the dowry and that the Infanta would require only the practice of her religion with her suite in her rooms.[63] On 16 October, the very day that the Elector Palatine landed at Gravesend, Gabaleone went to Northampton for an answer but was told that he must await the King's return.[64]

On 18/28 October, Gabaleone wrote of how even the bitter opposition of the Archbishop of Canterbury and the clergy to the Savoy match had been overcome by the good will of the King, Prince and other allies at court working in its favour.[65] Eight days later the Council met to declare for the marriage. The day before Henry had taken to his bed and sent messages imploring the King to defer the matter until he had recovered.[66] That recovery was never to happen.

What would that answer have been? All the evidence on the King's side points to the affirmative. The Venetian ambassador states that James had decided in favour of the match.[67] The

---

[60] Dispatches of 21 and 23 September 1612: *CSP, Ven., 1610–1613*, pp. 427, 428.

[61] Northampton to Rochester, undated but annotated 26 September/6 October: PRO, SP 14/70, fos 156–157v.

[62] Dispatch of 20 October 1612: *CSP, Ven., 1610–1613*, p. 435.

[63] Biondi to Carleton, 9 October 1612: *Calendar of State Papers, Domestic, 1610–1613*, p. 435.

[64] *CSP, Ven., 1610–1613*, pp. 437–8.

[65] Passamonti, 'Relazione . . .', p. 517.

[66] Dispatch of 16 November 1612: ibid., p. 447.

[67] Dispatch of 6 December 1612: ibid., p. 457.

dowry had been fixed at 300,000 crowns down and 500,000 crowns to come over a period of four years. Sir Thomas Lake writing to Carleton in May 1613 refers casually to Gabaleone as the man 'who negotiated the late Prince's marriage' as though it had been a *fait accompli*.[68] James even knighted Gabaleone, and the King's apologetic explanations to the Council shortly after Henry's death of how restricted the Infanta's religious arrangements were to be is again an indication that the Prince, under pressure from his father, who needed money, was to marry a Catholic bride.[69]

The Venetian ambassador also records that if the Prince had appeared at the Council meeting on 26 October he would have argued against the match under the influence of Count Henry of Nassau, who was in England with the Elector Palatine, and at the instigation of Count Maurice.[70] And, as in the case of Elizabeth, Ralegh, amongst others, was called upon for advice.[71] After rehearsing most of what he had included in his earlier tract he wrote: 'what then remaines of profit to our prince by this alliance: a some of money, and a bewtefull Ladie'. And what matters the money from Savoy or Tuscany anyway, for if the Prince marries he will have princes and these, too, would have to be provided for – an event that should be avoided 'till his majestie have somwhat repaired his Estate'. Wait, wait, he urges, for a French match, for France alone in Europe is a power strong enough to vanquish Spain. And, as though in a prophetic vision, he anticipates the holocaust of 1618 and after:

> Seing therfor wee have nothinge yet in hande, seinge ther is nothinge moves, seinge the worlde is yet a slumber, And that this longe Calme will shortly breake out in to some terrible tempest, I would advise the Prince to keepe his owne grounde for a while and no waye to ingage or intangle himselfe. . . .

In this way Ralegh casts the Prince's marriage as a decisive move in the mighty anti-papal and anti-Habsburg battle shortly to come.

That the Prince had strong views as to his marriage we are

[68] Sir Thomas Lake to Carleton, 19 May 1613: *CSP, Dom., 1611–1618*, p. 185.

[69] Chamberlain to Carleton, 19 November 1612: *Letters*, vol. 1, p. 392.

[70] Dispatches of 23 and 30 November 1612: *CSP, Ven., 1610–1613*, pp. 450–4.

[71] For Ralegh's advice, see 'Touching a Marriage between Prince Henry of England and a Daughter o; Savoy', in *Works*, vol. 8, pp. 237–52.

left in no doubt, and that these were not coincidental with his father's is more than evident. He despised the ignominy of being auctioned off. His last masque, *Love Restored*, speaks to the King of his disgust at this:

> 'Tis that impostor Plutus, the god of money, who has stol'n Love's ensigns, and in his belied figure reigns i'the world, making friendships, contracts, marriages and almost religion. . . . 'Tis he that pretends to tie kingdoms. . . .[72]

His death removed overnight James's hopes of supply by way of a gigantic dowry and there was even talk of that last-ditch move, summoning Parliament. Henry is always on the periphery of all the marriage negotiations. His mood as far as we can catch it is one of frozen resignation to whatever was to be his fate, tempered by hints that brides could be converted. And there is no doubt that a Catholic bride was actually anathema to him. This view was decisively communicated by Isaac Wake in a letter to Carleton written after the Prince's death: 'He was resolved that two religions should never lie in his bed.'[73] The source for that statement was his secretary, Adam Newton, who was with him to the last and to whom the Prince conveyed vast vague schemes that included travelling with his sister to Germany and choosing a Protestant wife. These must have been final thoughts, prompted by the arrival of the Protestant chivalry of northern Europe in October to celebrate the great union of the Rhine and Thames, the marriage that was the apogee of his aggressive pan-Protestant policies, which must, under the influence of Maurice of Nassau, have quickened his desire for a reciprocal match in the same way that it quickened his father's for a Catholic one to emphasize his *via media* policy. Catholic queens were forever to be the curse of the Stuarts. Only when Henry's great-nephew, George I, ascended the throne was the tradition of marriages into Protestant northern Europe to become an accepted part of a family dynastic policy that was to last until well into the present century.

---

[72] *Ben Jonson: The Complete Masques*, ed. Stephen Orgel (New Haven, Conn., 1969), p. 193.

[73] Wake to Carleton, undated 1612, quoted in S. R. Gardiner, *History of England, 1603–1642*, (London, 1884), vol. 2, p. 57; Newton to Winwood, 17 November 1612: Sawyer, *Memorials*, vol. 3, p. 410.

PLATE I   Bishop Thornborough *Studio of Richard Lockey*
(*National Portrait Gallery*)

BISHOP THORNBOROUGH

A CLERICAL CAREERIST

A. L. Rowse

PERHAPS my title has a rather unfair inflexion, for everybody with any energy or initiative – or even without – was out to better himself in Elizabethan times, if not today. But John Thornborough's immensely long career – he must have had exceptional vitality to live to ninety – illustrates what could be done in the Church for a man of moderate ability with a good head for administration. Thornborough was a man of business, a useful beast of burden for the government, which used him up to the hilt for its various purposes, and rewarded him accordingly. This was not any different from the medieval Church, when the bishops may have been holier, but were often government officials, rewarded by appointment to sees for their work.

Thornborough never gave any trouble to the government, and he carried out its orders faithfully. Such men are indispensable to governments, and he proved his usefulness over and over. He seems to have been a jolly sort of man when young, and long retained his addiction to sport and games, bowling and cards. He was responsive to women, too – that, and the joys of family life, got him into some trouble later. In short, though a cleric, he was a normal enough specimen of *l'homme moyen sensuel*.

John Thornborough first receives notice upon the public scene in Simon Forman's now well-known Autobiography. Forman, a poor boy, was desperately keen to get himself an education; so he went to Oxford without any provision to serve a fellow-Wiltshireman at Magdalen College, who was provided for. This was Thornborough, son of a leading citizen of Salisbury, Giles Thornborough. Born in 1551, John was about twenty-two in this year of grace 1573, and became a bachelor of arts in that year, having matriculated as a demy in 1569. He proceeded Master of Arts in 1575, Bachelor of Divinity in 1582 – though not much of a divine. Everything came easily to him.

One hears the natural accents of envy and disapproval from poor Forman, who longed for learning and to whom nothing came without pain and trouble. 'Every day he went to the free school', i.e. the charming little grammar school within the gate at Magdalen, 'and followed his book hard always when he could have leisure. Now there were two bachelors of arts that were two of his chief benefactors. The one of them was Sir Thornborough, that after was bishop of Limerick, the other was Sir Pinckney, his cousin, of St Mary Hall. These two loved him nothing well, and many times would make Simon to go forth to Loes, the keeper of Shotover, for his hounds to go on hunting from morning to night. They never studied nor gave themselves to their books, but to go to schools of fencing, to the dancing schools, to steal deer and conies, to hunt the hare and to wooing of wenches.'[1]

In short, they were average normal humans; Simon not.

They frequented Dr Lawrence of Cowley, a Fellow of All Souls and Archdeacon of Wiltshire – 'for he had two fair daughters, Bess and Martha. Sir Thornborough, he wooed Bess; Sir Pinckney, he wooed Martha, and in the end he married her. But Thornborough, he deceived Bess – as the mayor's daughter of Brackley, of which Euphues writes, deceived him. There was their ordinary haunt always, and thither must Simon run with the bottle and the bag early and late.'

Thornborough's jilting of Dr Lawrence's daughter seems to have done him no harm in Wiltshire. With the patronage of the Earl of Pembroke, to whom he was chaplain, he got several valuable livings: rector of Orcheston St Mary in 1575, of Marnhull, Dorset, in 1577, and of Chilmark, Wiltshire, in 1578. Shortly after the Earl got him made chaplain in ordinary to the Queen, and in 1585 he was installed in a comfortable prebend in Salisbury Cathedral. In 1587 there was a spot of trouble at Marnhull, when he was forcibly dispossessed of the parsonage by the patron, whose servants killed Thornborough's hired

---

[1] cf. my *Simon Forman: Sex and Society in Shakespeare's Age* (London, 1974), pp. 277–8.

servant on the way going about his business – evidently collecting tithes, a frequent subject of dispute. The JPs of Dorset were instructed by the Privy Council to inquire into the matter; the dispute was to be tried at common law.

Whatever was the issue, it did not harm Thornborough, for shortly in 1589 he was made Dean of York. He was now a man of mark, and next got for himself the prebend of Tockerington in York Minster. For his useful government service over the next decade the rectories of Kirby Misperton and of Brandesburton were added unto him. These enabled him to support his dignity as Bishop of Limerick, to which he was elevated in 1593 but which can have brought him little in the way of revenue. A dean with a family – for he had of course married – needed support, and Thornborough was a man of business. In 1590 he was granted the privilege for seven years of refining sea-coals – this was probably leased out. He was going to lease Pickering Leath to Thomas Vavasour, a prominent Catholic doctor in York – perhaps for that reason the deal was held to be unsuitable; Vavasour was to have paid Thornborough £1500 for it, but the deal was off and the Dean was absolved of his promise of it to the doctor.

Thornborough had to perform the duty expected of him of pursuing recusants, who were numerous in the North, but he was not personally unfriendly to Catholics, as Topcliffe was. The Dean was no fanatic. Gossip in York reported that a priest had said that 'if his friend Mr Thornborough, the Queen's chaplain, holds his promise he hopes to go to Wisbech and remain there' (i.e. in Wisbech Castle, a convenient receptacle for priests and recusants, rather than a regular prison). 'Aye, for Mr Thornborough leans a little and he is upon being made lord bishop in Ireland. He will not forget, for I have promised to horse him as well as ever in his life and 100 marks to drink.' This was mere gossip, but it shows that Thornborough was thought to be what was called a good fellow.

This summer of 1593, Lord Keeper Puckering and Sir Thomas Heneage authorized the Dean to examine books and papers in the house at Denton. This was important, for this was the house of the Fairfaxes – of the later Parliamentarian family – and they had an openly Catholic wing. The North was peppered with

Catholic families; the Dean had an uphill struggle dealing with them and trying, often in vain, to enforce the laws. In March 1593 he was appointed to the Council of the North, with an eye specially to this unpopular and thankless task. Robert Cecil wrote down that they were 'to yield him such countenance as may be seeming for one of his sort', i.e. clerical status, without irony.

This was as well, for at the time he was in trouble about his second marriage, his first having foundered. Marriage of the clergy had its disadvantages as well as clerical celibacy. The Archbishop of York reported on the matter that he was 'willing to use the bishop of Limerick well by her Majesty's wish, not only because she has a gracious care of his well-doing, but for the common cause of religion, which has received some disgrace by his unfortunate marriages – especially by the last, which is flat contrary to her Majesty's ecclesiastical laws of this land and much misliked by most of the clergy of this realm. Yet I think that *pars innocens* by the law of God may marry. And albeit the presumptions are pregnant that this woman was with child by him at the time of his divorce, yet has he now protested to me that he was no offender with her or any other at the time of his divorce: which, if it be true, then in my judgement this his marriage is lawful.'

The poor Archbishop's mixed-up state of mind is evident in his language: what we can conclude from it is that Thornborough had divorced his first wife, presumably for adultery, leaving it not clear whether he had not consoled himself with the second in the interval.

From a long letter to Cecil in 1600 we see that Thornborough had used his time in Ireland to become well informed about the factions and feuds among the Irish. In this respect, too, his utility to the government was like Topcliffe's – he was a mine of information. The crisis of O'Neill's resistance was at last being effectively countered by Mountjoy, and the government were thinking of sending 'the Queen's Earl of Desmond' (or 'the Tower Earl') to rally Munster to him instead of falling to O'Neill. Thornborough volunteered his advice 'touching the Desmond here, wherewith I rather venture to trouble you than by silence to seem defective in duty'. The Bishop recalled events on the eve of the great Munster rebellion twenty years before, and the practice there had been for the escape of the then Earl from the Tower. He offered advice 'for better assurance of Desmond's faithfulness, and for less fear of Irish practice when he comes among them'. He recalled the Oath of Association which England had volunteered to defend the person of the Queen after the Babington Plot, and suggested that the Earl might 'voluntarily offer at Council table his oath of allegiance to her Highness. . . . In meantime I am verily persuaded that the rebel of Ireland who, upon Desmond's coming thither, doth not return to obedience will the more fear and less dare to trust Desmond or to practise to withdraw him. . . . I do conclude great hope of much good by this means.'

Alas for the good Bishop's hopes: Desmond was well received by his people, till he failed to go to Mass with them, when they turned their backs on him one and all. The olive-branch held out failed like everything else, except force – and the Irish went on to break the hearts of all who wished them well, as even Evelyn Waugh has said. Thornborough reported that the Irish rebels were buoyed up with the hope of Spanish assistance, and in this he was right, though they came in insufficient force and Mountjoy was able to defeat them at Kinsale. Thornborough suspected Ormond's loyalty: 'for my part, I was ever persuaded that he knew as much of the secrecies of the Irish rebel as any subject of Ireland, and more too. If my business had not called me from Court, I had entered into all his mind. Your wisdom may make use of him for her Majesty's service without revealing me to him.' This was likely enough, for as a quasi-independent power, half-Gaelic himself, Ormond was in an ambivalent position; still, he was never likely to rebel against his cousin the Queen, who trusted him.

The next we hear, in October, is that the Archbishop of Cashel would like the use of the Bishop's house at Limerick during his own absence: 'it shall be kept in better reparation than as I shall find it'. Thornborough replied to Cecil immediately, placing his house 'and all else he has at his commandment', and enclosing a warrant for the Archbishop to enter upon it. Thornborough was always amenable: this was the way to get on.

The poor state of the Bishop's house was a matter of common

knowledge from what gossipy John Harington tells us. Thornborough 'and his whole family had a miraculous escape in
Ireland. Lying in an old castle in a large room, partitioned but
with sheets or curtains, his wife, children and servants. . . . In the
dead time of the night, the floor overhead being earth and plaster
as in many places is used, over-charged with weight, fell wholly
down together and crushing all to pieces that was above two foot
high, rested at last upon certain chests, as God would have it, and
hurt no living creature.' All very Irish, we may say; Thornborough must have been glad to get back to the amenities of
York. Harington, who knew, paid tribute to his work: 'he did
many good services in Ireland for our Queen and state, for which
he was thought worthy of a better abode than in that Purgatory.
He hath very good understanding of that country, and if some
others had been as willing as he to have reported the diseases of
that country and the fittest cures, it may be it would not have
needed those desperate remedies.'

Harington, who knew Thornbury – as he calls him, and as the
name was probably pronounced – concludes 'whom I love more
than I praise, is not unfurnished of learning, of wisdom, of
courage and other as well episcopal as temporal *panoplia* or
furniture beseeming a gentleman, a dean, and a bishop'.

As a member of the Council of the North the Bishop was
active in a number of matters – we find him having to take ex-
aminations regarding the depredations of the Dunkirkers off
Hull – privateers, one must not say pirates, for the war was still
going, and they would have letters of marque to warrant them.
His activities must have meant a good deal of travel, to and from
Ireland, while he had to pay regular visits to London on business.
His main concern as a cleric was the stultifying business of
recusancy. Up in Westminster, where he was lodging by the
Woolstaple, he reported to Cecil on Catholic contacts with the
Spaniards in the Netherlands fighting under Spinola: 'I find it
an hell to deal with these men, for if I ask many questions they
are nice of answers.' I dare say the doctrine of equivocation
came in handy. Topcliffe explained how this worked in practice,
when he took prisoner someone entering the country from abroad,
who informed him that the Pope had hitherto enjoined priests
not to deny their profession; 'he hath now thought good to

license them to deny the same by word, so it be not in heart, thereby to clear themselves of the justices'. Similarly the Papal Bull of Deposition might be held to be suspended, or renewed, according to circumstances. On the Queen's Accession Day this year the Bishop of Limerick preached the sermon at Paul's Cross; John Chamberlain, a connoisseur of sermons, thought it a dull one. Decidedly Thornborough was no preacher: none of the intellectual excitements of Dean Donne at St Paul's, or the thrill the congregations at Cambridge experienced from the way that loud-mouthed Perkins uttered, with satisfaction, the word 'Damned!'

Oddly enough Thornborough's intellectual interests were, like Forman's, in alchemy and the pious uses of the physico-chemical arts of transmuting matter into gold, according to the long Greco-Latin title of the book he published in 1621. Bishop Kennet tells us that 'above all he was much commended for his great skill in chemistry, a study but seldom followed in his time. It is thought that by some helps from it it was that he attained to so great an age.'[2] It was more likely that he was exceedingly tough as well as flexible. John Dee's son, Arthur, paid tribute to his alchemical expertise.

Thornborough published his work proudly under his name as Bishop of Worcester at his old university of Oxford: *Litho-theorikos* [in Greek characters], *sive Nihil, Aliquid, Omnia Antiquorum Sapientium vivis coloribus depicta philosophico-theologice*, and so it goes on. Its dark meaning seems to indicate the Student of Stones and that Nothing, Something, Everything depicted in vivid colours philosophic-theologically by the Wise Men of old may be to the grace of those who practise transmuting into gold physico-chemically and piously. The book was dedicated to Ludovic Stuart, Duke of Lennox – the husband of Simon Forman's chief client, Frances Howard.[3] The reader is adjured, in a text from Holy Writ, that they who descend into the abyss shall see the marvels of God. The book showed that the Bishop could at least write in Latin, which is more than most of his detractors could do.

---

[2] Lansdowne MS 985.

[3] cf. my *Simon Forman*, ch. x.

It is stuffed with learning on his rebarbative subject, the philosopher's stone, the Nihil of the philosophers. Not only Aristotle, Cicero and Aquinas are cited, but Avicenna and Hermes Trismegistus of course – though a fraud, of great authority with these speculators. Naturally the Apocryphal Book of Esdras spoke specially to the Bishop, with its angelic revelations and crazy visions. More interesting it is to observe that he was well read in such Renaissance spirits as Marsilio Ficino, Paracelsus, Cardan and the admirable physician, Jean Fernel. Various more marginal authorities are brought in from the Middle Ages: Richardus Anglus, Trevisa, Raymond Lull. The conclusion is adumbrated that true philosophers can make the stone, caco-chemists not.

In book II, Christ is brought in – which was just as well for a bishop – and the conclusion reached that the transmuting of stone and metals may be coupled with the resurrection of the body according to Holy Writ.

It may be matter for surprise that so practical a man of business, so down-to-earth a spirit (he might consider that reflection corroborative), should have given his mind to such nonsense. But most of the speculative opinions that engage men's minds are, strictly speaking, non-sense; and Thornborough's were no worse nonsense than those of the theologians – only they wrangled more and killed each other for their mutually exclusive doctrines. At least the book – with its plate to illustrate the cosmos as he conceived it, the elements and their 'influences' – led to no controversy and did him no harm. His tomb in Worcester Cathedral was spattered with the Pythagorean symbols that evinced his interest in the mystique of numbers. Perhaps these occult interests offered a welcome contrast to the practical realism of daily chores, and the gathering pressures of family life.

A major interest of Thornborough's political mind was the theme of the Union with Scotland, for it forms the subject of three out of his five publications. In the first, *A Discourse plainly proving the evident Utility and urgent Necessity of the desired happy Union of England and Scotland*, he argued reasonably for the complete interchange of citizenship between English and Scots, which James I desired but his English Parliament denied.

Next year Thornborough came out with *The joyful and blessed reuniting the two mighty and famous Kingdoms of England and Scotland*. The argument of this, rather than its laboured eloquence, is thought to have had its influence in the development of the theme in Ben Jonson's *Masque of Union*. Thornborough returned to it yet once again, in the last year of his life, with *A Discourse showing the great Happiness that hath, and may still, accrue to His Majesty's Kingdoms of England and Scotland by reuniting them into one Great Britain*.

It was too late: the Civil War was foreshadowed by the rebellion of the covenanting Scots against Charles I. If a full union could have been achieved in time, it might have prevented the disastrous incursion of Scottish armies into England in the next decade, which left such a deplorable legacy. Thornborough's argument was too moderate and reasonable for contemporary humans, but then he was a moderate and reasonable man. When he died he left, among other manuscripts, a plea for Unity and Peace in the Church: *Pax Vobis*. He told King Charles I that he had 'outlived several that had expected to succeed him in the see, and now I am afraid I shall outlive my bishopric'.[4]

The advent of James I had meant no diminution of favour, for Cecil, shortly to become Earl of Salisbury, was all-powerful and he was Thornborough's patron. The Bishop was promoted to the see of Bristol, no great matter in itself, but he was given licence of non-residence, as too useful on the Council of the North to reside other than at York. James I would have liked a wider measure of toleration, if it could have worked, and both Catholics and Puritans – mutually exclusive as they were – had expectations. The Archbishop of York knew that it wouldn't work, and wrote to encourage Cecil: 'good my lord, let me put you in mind that you were born and brought up in true religion. Your worthy father was a worthy instrument to banish superstition, and to advance the gospel: imitate him in this service especially.'

Cecil replied: 'concerning the difference in our church I do subscribe *ex animo* to your grave and learned judgement, having always held it for a certain rule that the Papists were carried on

---

[4] Lansdowne MS 985.

the left hand with superstitious blindness; that the Puritans were transported on the right with unadvised zeal'. Each extreme was absolutely intolerant, incapable of seeing any good in the other: 'whosoever shall behold the Papists with Puritan spectacles, or the Puritan with Papistical, shall see no other certainty than the multiplication of false images'. Cecil was clear that the middle road was not only best (he was a true Anglican, less of a pure Protestant than his father) but the only practical way of holding the country together with something like a general consensus. Neither Rome nor Geneva could achieve that in England, and, if internal peace were to be preserved, uniformity had to be enforced.

The majority of Catholics and Puritans were loyal enough to the State, but each had an extreme wing which would not listen to reason. The Puritan extremists emigrated to set up their own church in Holland, and eventually to New England to inflict their brand of intolerance there. A small knot of Catholic desperadoes – Catesbys and Treshams had already been involved in the Essex rebellion – banded together in Gunpowder Plot to blow up James and Parliament at its opening on 5 November 1605. This proved the worst blow to Catholicism in England since Queen Mary's burnings, and Cecil emerged with increased prestige as the saviour of the State.

The Bishop of Bristol was not behindhand in his felicitations. A prebendary of Durham had brought home to a seminary priest in prison there that the Jesuit superior, Garnet – who had been allowed to carry on his work in England in peace for nearly twenty years – had known about the Plot and not discouraged or imparted it. The prebendary enforced upon the seminary priest that Garnet had been justly executed. The poor priest sighed and said: 'Then there is nothing for us but persecution. The Devil is in that Lord of Salisbury: all our undoing is his doing, and executing of Garnet is his only deed.' Thornborough reported to his master that the adherents of the dead Jesuits were 'enemies to the present flourishing state, and full of malice against Aristides surnamed Justus for his uprightness'. This was a new name for Cecil, but certainly he carried himself looking neither to the left hand nor the right.

Thornborough reported what difficulties there were in dealing with recusants in the wild North Country, so many pockets of Catholic gentry in their remote country houses who could not be brought to conformity. 'Those who are not upon bond are over-insolent and cannot be brought by friendly letters, ordinary process, attachments or excommunications to make appearance. Only their former bonds continue to keep them in a little awe' – 'bonds' meaning financial recognizance for attendance at church. He departed for London to follow up the cases against them depending in the Exchequer Court.

He had prepared the way by a memorandum to the Privy Council on the difficulties he found in collecting the government's fines imposed on the recusants. In one way to impose some fine was reasonable, since they were not supporting their parish churches; they were evading church rates and many of the burdens that fell upon the governing class – not pulling their weight in local society of which they should be leaders – as gentry, many of them with large houses and estates. They had opted out, forming their own little minority communities. The Elizabethan government's aim was not to destroy these people utterly, as Counter-Reformation Europe destroyed Protestants wherever it could. Burghley's express aim had been not to provoke them beyond endurance into rebellion, but to discourage, keep them within bounds as the diminishing minorities they formed.

The problem was especially difficult in the North, where there were more of them, harder to flush out, and had much sympathy from their neighbours. Thornborough's report said that recent sheriffs dealt leniently with neighbours, for all had Catholic relations or connections. Innumerable opportunities offered for fraudulent deals to evade the fines, agents were bribable, the returns engulfed in the expenses of collecting. At the other end, Sir Henry Spiller, the Exchequer receiver of recusants' fines, was himself a church-papist, i.e. attended church formally, while his wife remained a Catholic. One sees something of what Thornborough had to contend with.

He was followed by an amusingly angry letter from the President of the Council of the North, Lord Sheffield; who was afraid that Thornborough would accuse him of dragging his feet. Sheffield was a good enough Protestant, but as a Howard he had

Catholic connections and his wife was a Catholic – so Queen Elizabeth had refused to give him the office of Lord President, which he had wished for: he had to wait for the more easy-going James, with whom the Howards were in clover. Sheffield wrote to Salisbury: 'It has pleased the King to employ – upon extraordinary trust, as himself gives out – the unholy Bishop of Bristol in following his Exchequer causes against the recusants. He has followed it more industriously than belonged his place; for what time he could spare from bowling and carding he has spent in that service. As for preaching, he has not greatly troubled himself, having not filled the pulpit – though he see it every day in his Dean's seat – above once or twice in this whole year. For the success he has had in his employment, it will appear by the small profit he has brought in – which, I think, is not above £2000, the schedule out of the Exchequer of the names of recusants in this whole country [i.e. Yorkshire] amounting to £5000.'

One would have thought that this was a good argument for the Bishop to follow up the Exchequer cases, but the Lord President was afraid that he would delate him for letting off recusants – out of neighbourliness, the dislike of being unpopular, or whatever. Thornborough's was an unpleasant task, naturally incurring unpopularity – the fact that he was unpopular with the Lord President of the Council, of which he was a member, showed up some of the difficulties of government, particularly this intractable problem. Lord Sheffield went on: 'now this man has gone up to make his account to the King, to whom I know he will excuse himself by laying any false accusation upon others; for it was his course in the Queen's time, and has been in the King's, to insinuate himself into favour by seeking to disgrace other men's services. Therefore I, having been a hinderer of his unjust gains, and for that I have relieved many of the King's obedient subjects when they have made due proof of the wrongful taking of their goods, I know this evil spirit will seek to infuse into the King some ill conceit of me . . . the better to excuse his ill service.'

Apart from the personal abuse, one derives the impression from this that Sheffield had been impeding the Bishop in his task, by his leniency to recusants. He went on, 'consider how scandalous a thing it is to our Church that one of our bishops should leave the charge of his bishopric to follow his own courses, only for his own gain'. This was obviously unfair: the Bishop was given licence not to reside at Bristol – then an unimportant and poor see – in order to do his duty at York. He had been at work there long before Sheffield appeared on the scene. Lord Salisbury would know how to sum up the situation – and Thornborough eventually received the reward of his services. We learn, for instance, that Thornborough's commission eventually caught up with Richard Cholmley, who had evaded fines by retiring to remote Ingleton; while the conviction of Thomas Crathorne induced him to conform.

Thornborough did not get into any trouble for his government service – it was too useful; his troubles came from the joys of family life. In 1612, John Chamberlain reported that 'a son of the Bishop of Bristol's, of nineteen or twenty years old, killed himself with a knife to avoid the disgrace of breeching' – I suppose, being put back into breeches – 'which his mother or mother-in-law [i.e. step-mother] would needs have put him to, for losing his money at tennis'. He must have been a nitwit; his mother, a Suffolk Bayles, was certainly a character. She was next in trouble for her acquaintance with the wicked young Countess of Somerset, who poisoned Sir Thomas Overbury in the Tower.

This made the greatest scandal of James's reign. This Howard young lady was unhappily married to Essex's son, and in her passionate desire to compel the love of James's boyfriend, Robert Carr, she had resorted to Simon Forman for love-philtres, phallic figurines, what not. She – or they – succeeded, and she got him. The marriage was the grandest possible, the 'virgin' bride given away by her great-uncle, the old 'Lord Harry' of Elizabeth's reign, who belatedly made a large fortune as James's Lord Privy Seal. The King surpassed himself in extravagant presents to the happy couple – and Mrs Thornborough called attention to herself by the remarkable and ingenious bridal cake she made for the occasion.

Then the horrible truth about the bride's poisoning of Overbury in the Tower, to clear the way for her marriage, came out. The poor Bishop's wife was delated as 'a suspicious person in the affair. She is intimate with the Countess of Somerset and her mother [the Countess of Suffolk], and given to chemistry'. This meant 'Dr' Forman's kind of chemistry – who died before his young client's poisoning of Carr's friend. Mrs Thornborough was also a friend of Lady Walsingham, wife of Marlowe's former patron. Now the Bishop's wife was held at York House, under examination by the commissioners looking into the Overbury affair. It transpired that she had obtained some land in Yorkshire by means of the Countess, whom she had gratified with money. It is probable that this was the grant of 815 acres of waste in Knaresborough forest she obtained from the Forest Commissioners. She had brought the Countess at the Cockpit biscuits – not poisoned; evidently she prided herself on her cooking.

The Bishop's matrimonial troubles were common knowledge, for witty, punning John Harington comments, 'I would I could pluck out the Thorn of Dr Thornbury's first marriage out of every man's conscience that have taken a scandal of his second'. He excuses him on the score that 'it was the Bishop of Limerick in Ireland and not the Bishop of Bristol in England that thus married. Doth this lessen the scandal? I suppose it doth.'

Thornborough had no luck with his wives: perhaps a penance for jilting Dr Lawrence's daughter.

His unfortunate experience did not impede the good Bishop's career, and at last he received his reward for his protracted service – the goodly see of Worcester, with pleasant Hartlebury Castle to reside in. Here the troubles from his family pursued him. His son by his second wife, Thomas, abducted an underage heiress and carried her off to enjoy under the Bishop's roof. The Bishop submitted that he was impelled to marry them for fear of worse. Then the son consumed the wife's fortune, and the Bishop was forced to provide for her. In this he was not generous, but it seems that he maintained her and her children, up to the last year of his life. In 1640 the trouble surfaced and became public. Lady Thornborough – her husband was knighted in 1630 – left Hartlebury and Sir Thomas entered suit to make her cohabit again. She gave evidence that she had been spirited off to Hartlebury without her mother's knowledge at fifteen and, after six weeks, was married with the privity of the Bishop, though he at first denied it. He now refused to support the two grandchildren unless she returned to her husband – which she would do 'whenever he be reclaimed to an orderly and settled course of life that she might with safety live and cohabit with him'. She would obey the Bishop's directions, but meanwhile had no alimony.

Residing in one's diocese was not without its troubles – though it provided openings for one's family. A minister had preached against dancing on Sunday, evidently a Puritan sabbatarian who objected to the Sunday relaxation and fun allowed by the King's Book of Sports. This sourpuss had publicly 'prayed God to turn the King's heart from profaneness'. He had been now made to feel penitent; the Bishop wrote to the Archbishop to know whether he might restore him. The Attorney- and Solicitor-General handed the buck back to the Bishop.

Next he wanted to raise some provision for the widow of Dr Archbold, 'a special ornament of this church'. In return Mrs Archbold solicited Secretary of State Conway for the vicarage of Stoke for a Mr Thornborough; this turned out to be the Bishop's clerical son, Edward. The eldest, Benjamin, had been knighted by King James at Newmarket in 1618, which must have been gratifying. But there was trouble about the benefice of Hartlebury, which he had conferred upon 'an ancient grave preacher' – who next turned out to be his son-in-law. The King wanted it for a Dr Leslie, who sounds Scotch. The Bishop was sorry that the King was displeased, but he had promised the living three years ago.

The King replied to the Bishop that his excuses for not admitting Dr Leslie and Mr Woodford to the benefices of Hartlebury and Upton were insufficient. He required him to admit them at once; he would assist him to provide otherwise for his son-in-law and for his chaplain. The Bishop replied that he relied on the King's justice and clemency. All lawyers were weak reeds, his Majesty a staff of strength. He has complied and put Dr Leslie into Hartlebury, his son-in-law having resigned; Mr Woodford shall get Upton-upon-Severn. The Bishop explained to the Secretary of State that he would have mentioned that those benefices were in his own right to give, but he would rather lose twenty such than hazard the loss of his Majesty's favour. He came back with the thought that it was a retribution upon him for procuring two of his prebendaries' best benefices to please the King. The King thanked the Bishop for his dutiful conformity.

It was so characteristic an episode of time, place, and person – humanly and historically revealing.

The Bishop continued to be a beast of burden in secular affairs as much as clerical. As Bishop of Worcester he would be a Justice of the Peace for the county, and nominally a member of the Council of Wales, if not working regularly as for the Council of the North. In 1621 the Council of Wales asked him to be present one particular day to help in the business; while in 1623 the new Lord President, Sir John Scudamore, was sworn in in his presence.

Queens and kings might come and go, Thornborough seemed indestructible. From 1625 the young King Charles I and his intimate Buckingham idiotically involved the country in a war with both Spain and France. The Bishop was shortly back at his old job of returning and collecting the arms of recusants: the inventory of Lord Windsor's arms had been left at the Bishop's palace in Worcester; the Earl of Shrewsbury (the family had gone Catholic) had only ten brown bills for the defence of his house. The Bishop complained to Secretary Conway of poaching on his warren: 'ever since he was bishop he could not be master either of his fish or his conies'. People stole his conies and assaulted his keeper. In regard to the forced loans to which Charles I was reduced to meet the expenses of his superfluous war, the Bishop suggested sending a couple of pursuivants to the Commissioners for Worcestershire, to send up refractory persons refusing to contribute: it would bring in £1000 more than the King was like to have. Thornborough was an old hand in such matters.

So also in dealing with Jesuits. This year 1627 a Jesuit wished to confer with him, and he doubted not to win him to the Church of England. 'Otherwise, for his boldness in seeking to speak with a bishop, he would commit him to answer the law.' The King gave leave for private conference, but no public controversy. The Bishop was successful, as he had been in a number of cases in the North: he had got the Jesuit to subscribe the oaths of Supremacy and Allegiance; he had subscribed his conformity in the Bishop's book, among the many recusants he had converted. The King thereupon signified his pleasure that the Bishop's son, Giles, should have the first prebend that fell vacant in the cathedral.

The Bishop's business continued to be both secular and ecclesiastical, and to involve him in journeying to and from London. We find him in London taking part in the consecration of Lord Keeper Williams as Bishop of Lincoln in 1621. In 1629 he paid £50 for the confirmation of his see's liberties within the hundred of Oswaldslaw. He evidently possessed a knowledge of the law, as well as needed it. He was that year involved in settling a dispute between Mr Archbold and Mr Potter, the latter alleging a statute which 'puts the Bishop to a nonplus, his hands being bound by a writ of *ne admittas*'. He joined with Sir William Sandys, son of a previous bishop, in a contract with Sir Miles Fleetwood to convey to them a hundred acres of waste in Feckenham forest.

King Charles wrote to the Bishop, recommending Dr Fell to the archdeaconry of Worcester, 'knowing his care and zeal to promote men of worth'. But the Bishop had awarded the archdeaconry to his son, 'a learned divine and a good preacher'. He had very few preferments in his gift, and he recited the tale of yielding two to the late king. Nevertheless, if the King commands, the Bishop will command his son to submit, but he hopes not, 'being his natural son and without preferment'. Charles I was much more amenable to bishops than James I had been: Edward Thornborough became Archdeacon of Worcester.

Next year, 1630, the Bishop published his one theological work, *The Last Will and Testament of Jesus Christ* – the odd title bespeaks the Bishop's cast of mind – *touching the Blessed Sacrament of his Body and Blood*. This was the third of his publications to be published at Oxford; the other two in London. This one makes the Bishop sound more High Church than he actually was: was he moving with the times, with further preferment in mind? At his age, seventy-nine? One can hardly suppose so, his health was not good – though he lived for another twelve years. In his eighties he was treated by Dr John Hall, Shakespeare's son-in-law: Thornborough had been 'long tormented with a scorbutic wandering gout', and suffered from terrors in his sleep because of a sudden slaughter in his household, which afflicted him with melancholy. This accident would seem to have been among the servants; we do not learn otherwise, though in 1630 son Giles, prebendary of Salisbury, had been put to great trouble by the sudden loss of his mother. Dr Hall treated the Bishop with his special anti-scorbutic beer, boiled with scurvy grass, water-cress, fumitory, fennel, and juniper berries. It had cured Shakespeare's daughter, Susanna, of scurvy.

Stratford-upon-Avon was in the Worcester diocese and for some time past the Puritanical vicar Wilson had given Thornborough trouble: 'he laboured to shake the jurisdiction of the bishop and govern the people, as if he had been another Calvin or Beza at Geneva'. The Bishop had cited him upon certain articles before the Court of High Commission, and now had no complaint against him. A new spirit prevailed in the Church with Laud enthroned in the chair of St Augustine at Canterbury. His information from divers of quality living nearby was that Mr Wilson was conformable in nothing. (Was this man perhaps responsible for breaking the font in which Shakespeare was baptized?)

The appointment of a Laudian Dean at Worcester precipitated a dispute with the city authorities, who were supporting their own lecturer to preach in the cathedral, and the new Dean denied him the use of the pulpit. Everywhere all over the country city and town authorities were leaning to the intolerant, and intolerable, Puritanism which led to the Civil War. The poor old Bishop, who wanted nothing but peace, was brought into the dispute in his last years. He reported the divisions in a long letter to the Archbishop. The Dean's supporters among the prebendaries argued that the Bishop had nothing to do with the cathedral, that it was exempt from his jurisdiction. Ever since the Dissolution the decayed chapel over the charnel-house had been used for the bishops' hay. The Archbishop ordered the chapel to be delivered over to Prebendary Tomkins, 'the only incendiary between the Bishop and the Church'. The Bishop hoped to maintain his rights for his successors in the see, but 'fears that worldlings will clap their hands rejoicing to see altar against altar'.

The Bishop was in fact an old-fashioned Elizabethan Protestant. Puritan Richard Baxter, who was so hard to please, was content enough with him, for the Bishop always baptized without the sign of the cross, and such an ordinary Baxter at Kidderminster was pleased to follow, or – as he put it with his usual conceit – 'where the Ordinary thought as he did'.

Dean Potter, of course, wrote to Laud against his bishop, 'who hates Mr Tomkins and highly favours the City's beloved lecturers, one of whom called the choirmen "altar-mongers" '. This prebendary would have been Nathaniel Tomkins, of the brilliant Cornish family which contributed so much divine music to the Church – his brother Thomas, the famous composer, was organist of the cathedral who lived to see its organ smashed, and choir and music dispersed by the Philistine Puritans. Next, poor Laud was pestered by a long petition from the Mayor and corporation complaining that the Dean wants to enforce their attendance at choir services; they prayed for a pulpit of their own at the west end of the church. In this the Bishop supported them.

Dean Potter riposted with an enormously long letter, filled with trivial details, complaining of 'our weak and silly Bishop and these silly weak ones of my company', i.e. the prebendaries who supported him. The Dean was very rude about gratifying them 'with their own beloved old place, till that mistress of fools, their own experience, show them the vanity of their own desires and the wisdom of your direction and choice for them'. No doubt it was all very silly, for such are humans.

The King and Archbishop handed down a reasonable compromise: the Mayor and corporation should have their pulpit, with movable seats, at the west end.

The dangerous spirit boiling up on the Puritan side is vividly brought home to us by one Nehemiah Wharton who reported, after the capture of the city in 1642, that the new bishop and 'other Popish priests are all run away; the city is so vile and the country so base, so papistical, and atheistical, and abominable, that it resembles Sodom and is the very emblem of Gomorrah'.

Bishop Thornborough was well out of it. He had died the previous year, having prepared for himself a grand tomb, a columned four-poster, himself in effigy lying in scarlet robes within. The monument was decorated with the mottoes and astrological symbols that expressed his inner life. 'Denarius Philosophorum, Dum Spiro, Spero.' 'In Uno 20, 30, 4 or 10 Spirans Sperabo.' All very odd for a bishop, but it serves to bring him close to his still odder servant, Simon Forman, in his gay bachelor days at Oxford. Perhaps he would have done better after all to marry Dr Lawrence's daughter.

One sees what stuff the Puritans were made of when one goes to Worcester and looks at his tomb, defaced and hacked about, the damage visible today.

Sources

Calendars of State Papers, Domestic; *Acts of the Privy Council*; *Historical Manuscripts Commission, Salisbury Manuscripts*; E. Lodge, *Illustrations of British History*; T. Wright, *Queen Elizabeth and Her Times*; Hugh Aveling, *Northern Catholics, 1558–1790*; Sir John Harington, *Nugae Antiquae*.

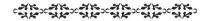

STRAFFORD AND VAN DYCK
Oliver Millar

OF THE PORTRAITS Van Dyck painted in London in the years when he was in the service of Charles I, none are more compelling or magnificent than those he painted of the Earl of Strafford. Students of the period will often have been tantalized by the extracts from the Wentworth Woodhouse Muniments which have been quoted by biographers of Strafford, such as Lady Burghclere (1931) and Dame Veronica Wedgwood (1935 and 1961); an extensive selection from the papers had been published as *The Earl of Strafford's Letters and Despatches* in two large volumes by William Knowler in 1739; but it may be of service to present, in honour of a historian who has done so much to bring alive the age of Charles I, and who has herself so keen and affectionate an eye for the visual evidence from that period, transcripts (with the briefest of commentary) of those passages in the papers, formerly at Wentworth Woodhouse, which tell us something of Strafford's dealings with Van Dyck and the characteristic care he bestowed on the pictures which he had commissioned.[1]

Viscount Wentworth was appointed Lord Deputy General of Ireland in January 1632. Not until January 1640 did he become

---

[1] In 1949 the papers were deposited by the 9th Earl Fitzwilliam in the Central Library in Sheffield. I am very grateful to Miss Ruth Harman, Senior Assistant Archivist, and Dr David Postles, the Archivist, in the Central Library for their kindness in making the examination of the muniments so enjoyable a task. Miss Harman was so kind as to check this article in proof for me. The documents are quoted by kind permission of Olive, Countess Fitzwilliam's Wentworth Settlement, Trustees of the Fitzwilliam Estates and the Director of the Libraries. I would also like to acknowledge the kindly interest of Lady Juliet de Chair, the present owner of the portraits and her son, and to recall the unfailing kindness with which the 9th Earl answered inquiries about his pictures and muniments. Dates have been given, in the extracts printed, in the New Style. The abbreviation WWM is used for the muniments. I am profoundly grateful to my wife for helping in the search through this material.

Lord Lieutenant and Earl of Strafford. The King had granted to Wentworth vice-regal powers which had not been exercised by any of his predecessors in Ireland. The authority with which he was invested was a symbol of the King's policy, in England as well as in Ireland, and of the personal trust with which the King was prepared to honour his great servant. This note of royal confidence is struck in a letter, dated 29 October 1633, from the Earl of Carlisle to Wentworth, in which he described 'how well the King is satisfyed wth yor noble and wise proceeding, and what it is, hee expects from you, yor lor.^{p} will best understand by a lr̄e from his owne hand'; or, from the same correspondent on 13 January 1634: '. . . you will receave therewth an expression of as great love and affection as your sellf can desire from a most gratious and wise master, whose excellent iudgment knows how to sett a true price and value upon so worthy and faythfull a servant as yor lor.^{p} '.[2] As evidence of this love and affection, Wentworth received from the King, it is presumed, the full-length of the King in Garter robes by Daniel Mytens, signed and dated 1633, and a version of Le Sueur's bronze bust of him. More surprisingly, the King presented him with a portrait by Van Dyck: 'the Picture of o:^{r} dearest Consort the Queene by him made', for which the artist was paid £40 from the King's Exchequer on 21 October 1633.[3] These three royal portraits are still in the collection; the last is a version of Van Dyck's lovely image of the Queen in hunting costume, with the dwarf Jeffery Hudson, which lacks the sparkle of the presumed original in Washington. According to the list (printed below) of portraits in the family collection, Wentworth himself had been painted at length as a young man by Mytens.

Van Dyck's first portrait of Wentworth himself, the great full-length in armour, over crimson breeches, with a baton in his left hand and an Irish wolfhound under his right (Plate 2), should probably be dated between Strafford's appointment and his departure for Dublin in July 1633. From possible references to

[2] WMM, Str. P 13, 80a, 163.

[3] O. Ter Kuile, 'Daniel Mÿtens', *Nederlands Kunsthistorisch Jaarboek*, vol. 20 (Weesp, 1969), pp. 61–2; C. Avery, 'Hubert Le Sueur, "the unworthy Praxiteles of King Charles I" ', *Walpole Society*, vol. 48 (1982), pp. 156, 182; W. Hookham Carpenter, *Pictorial Notices . . . a Memoir of Sir Anthony Van Dyck . . .* (1844), p. 73.

PLATE 2   Thomas Wentworth, 1st Earl of Strafford
Sir Anthony van Dyck (Coll. Lady Juliet de Chair)

PLATE 3   Thomas Wentworth, 1st Earl of Strafford
Sir Anthony van Dyck (H.M. Treasury and the National Trust)

it in the later letters it may always have been intended to hang at
Wentworth Woodhouse. In this superbly painted portrait, one
of the masterpieces of portrait painting in this country, the more
impressive for the nervous touch and for the tensions which
underlie both characterization and brushwork, Van Dyck con-
jures up for us, in Dame Veronica's words, 'the image of a strong
and resolute man, of great practical ability, of powerful intellect,

of tireless energy; over-confident in his own opinions; over-certain of his own rectitude; not always scrupulous in the pursuit of public power and personal advantage; but a man of generous vision and unswerving loyalty'.[4] It is interesting to note that, although the three images, or 'types', which Van Dyck created for Strafford are so closely related to celebrated Renaissance compositions which the artist and his patron would have seen at Whitehall and in the other chief collections in London, there is no evidence that Strafford himself was interested in acquiring any pictures other than portraits.

Early in June 1636, Wentworth came back to London, where he was warmly welcomed by the King. Later in the summer he went up to Yorkshire. On 17 July he was writing from Gawthorp ('a poore house I have'), and a letter dated 5 October was written from Wentworth Woodhouse. By the end of November, Wentworth was once more in Dublin. It was presumably in the weeks immediately after he arrived in London that he sat once more, at Eltham, to Van Dyck and commissioned the portraits referred to in the letters which follow; but allusions in them to 'my originall that is at lengthe' (from which the miniaturist John Hoskins was to make copies of the head), 'the first originall of my Picture at large' and 'that great picture wch is for woodhouse' may be to the full-length with the hound which Wentworth may not have had time, before he departed from London in July 1633, to put in the place where he intended it should hang.

On 17 August 1636, Wentworth wrote from Gawthorp to William Railton (or Raylton), whom he had appointed as his personal agent in London:

> . . . you will have a note inclosed what pictures you are to have of S.ʳ Anthony Vandike, and how they are to be disposed of. the halfe pictures must stande me inn 30ˡⁱ a peece and thos at lengthe in 50.ˡⁱ a peece, but me thinks that 20.ˡⁱ a peece for the Coppy of the shortt, and 35ˡⁱ for the lardger were sufficient, espetially taking soe many from him at once and in a deade time allsoe. but gett them as cheape as you can. I pray you gett Hauskins to take my picture in little from my originall that is at lengthe, and to make it sumthing lesse then that he last drew, and desire S.ʳ

---

[4] C. V. Wedgwood, *Thomas Wentworth, First Earl of Strafford, 1598–1641* (London, 1961), p. 397; Oliver Millar, *Van Dyck in England* (London, 1982–3), no. 15.

Anthony from me to helpe him wth his direction. and soe I
rest. . . . (WWM, Str. P 21, 151)

The 'halfe pictures' to which Wentworth refers were presumably the original, replicas and copies of the searching three-
quarter-length in armour, of which the version at Petworth
(Plate 3) is the finest example: the portrait which has the look
of Macaulay's 'lost Archangel' and so vividly illustrates Sir
Philip Warwick's description of this formidable man: '. . . of a
tall stature, but stooped much in the neck. His countenance was
cloudy, whilst he moved or sat thinking; but when he spake,
either seriously or facetiously, he had a lightsom and a very
pleasant ayre.'[5]

On 5 September 1636 Wentworth wrote to Railton from
Wentworth Woodhouse. At least one of Hoskins's miniature
copies was by now ready to be put in its gold enamelled case; and
the instructions for packing and transporting a big picture have
a modern ring:

> . . . For the Pictures, yo^w had my note of direccon howe they were
> to be disposed, onely this more, I would have yo^w send the first
> originall of my Picture at large hither to Woodhouse, soe soone
> as may be, But in [anie] Condicon, let speciall care be taken, that
> it be verie well put up, soe close, as that neither the wett spoile it,
> or that it be anie way hurt or bruised in the Cariage. Send alsoe
> hither to me, the little Picture, soe soone as yo^w can get it from
> Mr Hoskins, but before it be sent, let it be set in a goulden Case,
> inamelled wth azure, lyke to the last. . . . (WWM, Str. P 21, 156)

In his letter to Wentworth of 14 September 1636, written from
Fulham, Railton refers, in an addendum written on the following
day, to another miniaturist, whom Van Dyck obviously preferred
to Hoskins, who appears not to have produced a very satisfactory
work:

> . . . I shall observe your Lo^{ps} directions about the Pictures, having
> written to Sr Anthony Vandyke to know if he be ready wth the
> Cases and Frames, and then I purpose to ryde . having also in
> my letter intimated unto him the doing of the little Picture as he
> shall thinke fitting, now that I see, your Lo^p affects not the other

[5] ibid., no. 23; Sir Philip Warwick, *Memoires of the Reigne of King Charles I* . . . (1701), p. 112.

man; And I presume, seing that seing Sr Anthony recomends this man, he will contribute more, of his advise and Judgement to him then he will doe to Hoskins; who in my eye, did not shew any Masterpeece in that wch he drew for your Lo^p at first. . . . (WWM, Str. P 16, 58)

On 15 November 1636 Wentworth wrote to Railton from Lichfield, not long before he crossed to Ireland:

Will. Raylton. for the pictures bespoken before my going downe into the Northe you have my directions allready, thos that are for Irelande I pray you lett them be made up wthall care to preventt taking of wette, and sent over by the first conveniencye by long sea, if you cannot lighte of an opertunitye sooner, you may soe provide as to lett them cum by the Swallowe this next spring, itt will be necessary Beverley Newcomen should be ther to receave his chardge of Admirall, who will be carefull to see them brought to Dublin, for if they should cum by lande to Chester, ther would be sum mischeefe or other dun to the paintings, or frames, or both. that great picture wch is for woodhouse, I would should rest at your house till summer, and then choosing sum faire season, it may be sentt thether, wth directions that soe soon as it cums thether itt be taken carefully forth of the case and sett up in one of the places in the Gallorye ther. for thos tow wch weare last drawen at my being at Eltam; the shortt one is for my Ladye of Carlile, and this you must see to be carefully sett to the frame wch I appointed for itt, and soe lett it stande with Sr Anthonye till you have waited upon her Lap and knowen her pleasure wher shee will have it delivered wch you will see dun according her La^p direction. The other at lengthe is for my Lo. Newcastle, this I would have you to take home to you, and in summer when you send the other to woodhouse take a course that this may be delivered att wellbecke, and minde Sr Anthonye that he will take good paines upon the perfecting of this picture wth his owne pensell. you will likwise remember my Lady of Carlile that shee hath promised me her picture allsoe, wch may be sent me wth the rest into Irelande. . . .

For the Picture in little you must call to Hauskins for it, gett it sett in a case, and sent over as soon as may be. . . . (WWM, Str. P 21, 163)

This important letter reveals that the 'great picture' for Wentworth Woodhouse was still in London and that, of versions

PLATE 4   Thomas Wentworth, 1st Earl of Strafford
Sir Anthony van Dyck (From a Private Collection)

of the new portrait, the 'shortt one' was for Lady Carlisle and the version (or variant) at length (Plate 4) was for the Earl of Newcastle and was in due course to be delivered at Welbeck, where it still hangs. The picture for Lady Carlisle is presumed to be the version at Petworth, which she may have given to her brother, the Earl of Northumberland. There was a warm friendship between Wentworth and Newcastle at this time: 'It is impossible I should Conceive to ye disadvantage of yor lo:^{ps} Noble friendship, and kindnesse in any sort wch l esteeme soe highly of, and shall wth all Care p^{r}serve my selfe Capable to inioye ye Contentment I have allwayes received by it' (Wentworth to Newcastle, 10 December 1638: WWM, Str. P 10(*a*), 235). The most interesting part of the letter, however, is Wentworth's instruction that Van Dyck was to perfect the full-length variant of the new portrait with his own brush: a request that must have been carried out as the head in this portrait is almost as finely painted as that in the more familiar three-quarter-length.[6]

After he had returned to Dublin, Wentworth continued to issue instructions to Railton. On 21 January 1637 he wrote:

. . . For the Pictures such as are for Irelande you will take order wth Sr Beverley Newcomen they say ther is a waggon goes weekly betwixt London and Portchmouthe soe that if his shipp be ther, yet your convenience willbe good of sending them thether. you will remember my Ladye of Carlile shee was pleased to promise me hers. for thos other tow greate pictures, the one for my Lo. of Newcastle the other for me, I have allready writt how you might dispose of the former, and for the other sin[c]e you have not a roome for itt, desire S.^{r} An: Vandike it may rest wher itt is till after Whitsuntide, and then itt may be sentt to woodhouse. for the moneys you will set downe upon every picture what they cost, and soe I shall knowe how to call for my money of M.^{r} vicetreasorour &c. for the 60^{li} unpaid, in truthe considering soe many of them ar coppies, he hath had allready as much as they are worthe, the rather in regarde it was in a long vacation and a plague time when he had had small store of worke wthout them, deale wth him aswell as you can, ther being few things I affectt soe little as wragling towards the end of an agreement, as soe [iust?] contrary to old Arthure [i.e., Ingram] that makes sure

---

[6] G. Glück, *Klassiker der Kunst* (Stuttgart, 1931), no. 436; exhibited at Nottingham University Art Gallery, 1960, no. 17.

to keep sumthing backe upon the parting, that of my Lo. of Clevelands you may still say you have noe directions for itt. . . . (WWM, Str. P 21, 167)

The reference to Lord Cleveland is obscure and may not be to a portrait, although Cleveland certainly sat to Van Dyck at this period. The full-length for Wentworth Woodhouse was still apparently with Van Dyck, or at least in his care. There is a second reference to the portrait of herself which Lady Carlisle had promised to Wentworth. In the previous summer the friendship between Wentworth and this beautiful, intelligent and dangerous *politique* had been very close. It is probably to the promised portrait of her that Sir Beverley Newcomen, who commanded one of the King's ships off the Irish coast, referred in his letter to Wentworth from London, 20 February 1637: '. . . Wandyke, is now in hand wth the Picture yor Lop: desires and the Party setts very Constantly. though it be very could; and frosty wether . . .' (WWM, Str. P 16, 125). If it was Lady Carlisle who endured such discomfort in order to gratify her admirer, the result was the full-length of the Countess (Plate 5) which is still in the collection.[7]

The copies Van Dyck was producing for Wentworth, under some duress, of the new portrait in armour were perhaps by now being promised or delivered to friends. On 21 August 1636 Wentworth's brother George wrote to his brother from Dublin: '. . . my wife presents her humble service to your L^p, and her intreaties, are more earnest than ever, to receave your promised picture, it will I thinke save her longinge . . .' (WWM, Str. P 16, 48); and, on 18 January 1637, Archbishop Laud wrote to Wentworth: '. . . I humbly thank your L.^d for y^r Picture, I shall god willing keep it while I live. It is now come safe to me, and yet I hope you think I shall not need y^r Picture much to keep you in memory (WWM, Str. P 7, p. 13). That Wentworth had been 'so often' with Van Dyck was well known at court; and, in an amusing letter of 22 January 1637, Lord Conway assumed that he had known of the artist's 'Gallanterye for ye love of' Lady Stanhope; 'but hee is come of wth a Coglioneria, for hee disputed wth her

[7] A second version (Glück, *Klassiker der Kunst*, no. 447) was in the collection of Lord Wharton. It last appeared at Sotheby's, 19 April 1967 (99). In restoration being carried out at this moment the characteristic Strafford inscription, identifying the sitter as Lady Carlisle, which had been painted out, has been revealed.

PLATE 5   Lucy, Countess of Carlisle *Sir Anthony van Dyck*
(*Coll. Lady Juliet de Chair*)

about y^e price of her picture and sent her word that if shee would not give y^e price hee demanded hee would sell it to another y^t would give more'.[8]

Unfortunately, nothing has emerged so far in the muniments about the later portraits Van Dyck painted for Strafford, notably the portrait with his secretary, Sir Philip Mainwaring, the portrait in armour which may have preceded it, or the group of Wentworth's three children from his second marriage.[9] It is significant that the group does not figure in the list of pictures attached to the will, dated 9 September 1695, of Strafford's son, the second Earl. Nor does the full-length of Lady Carlisle. The attainder on the fallen Strafford was reversed in 1662. His son had obtained all his father's titles in 1641. He was obviously a devoted guardian of the portraits his father had assembled with such care and he himself augmented the collection. It was probably he who caused a distinctive type of identifying inscription to be written on the portraits. The second Earl had no son, and Wentworth Woodhouse and the bulk of his estates passed to his nephew, the Honourable Thomas Watson, son of his oldest sister, Anne. Thomas Watson assumed the additional name of Wentworth. His son, the sixth Lord Rockingham, was created a marquess in 1746. On the death of the second Marquess the estates passed into the Fitzwilliam family; the first Earl Fitzwilliam had married the sister of the second Marquess. The list of pictures which the second Earl caused to be made is printed below (WWM, D. 1493; the pictures appear in two sections but with the same heading, which is not repeated below; numbers have been added for ease of reference).

A Schedule of such goods as shall be left at Woodhouse for heir loomes to be Continued with the House and the Estate.

[1] King Charles the first in brass a Statue to the Wast
[2] King Charles the first by Mitten
[3] The Queene his Consorts picture at length by Vandike
[4] Queen Anne Bullen a head said to be Holbens

---

[8] *The Earl of Strafford's Letters and Despatches*, ed. William Knowler, 2 vols (1739), vol. 2, p. 48.

[9] Millar, *Van Dyck in England*, nos 57 and 32.

[5] My Lady Derby my Mother in Law and the princess of Aurange Her Aunt in one peece to the Knees by Hunthurst

[6] My said Lady Derbys picture like Pallas by Hunthurst to the Waste

[7] My said Lady Derby to the Knees in mourning with an Urne before her by Lilly

[8] My Wifes to the Wast by Vandike at Seaven yeares Old

[9] Another of my Wifes when A Child of Nine monthes Old

[10] My ffathers Picture at length by Vandike

[11] Another of my Fathers with S.ʳ Philip Manwaring by Vandicke

[12] Another in Armour to the Knees by Vandicke

[13] Another of my Father to the knees in Armour Copied by Lilly from Vandicke

[14] My Mothers picture to the Wast by Johnson

[15] The Two last Earles of Cumberland at length by Mitten

[16] My Lord Baltimore at length a great freind of my ffathers and Secretary of State to King James the first by Mitten

[17] My Lord Henry Earle of Derby

[18] My Lord Edward Earle of Derby

[19] My Lord William Earle of Derby

[20] My Lord Derby my Father in Law &

[21] S.ʳ William Stanley all these pictures are Copies from peices att Knowsly by Henry Heskett to the knees

[22] My Lord Derby my Nephew by Knellor

[23] My Grandfathers picture and my Grandmothers picture to the knees

[24] My Great Grandfather and great grandmothers together

[25] My Sister Margrett by Lilly to the Waste

[26] My Lady Marquess of Dorchester to the Waste by Lilly

[27] The Dutchesse of Tremoile my Ladys Sister

[28] And Mademoiselle de la Tremoille her daughter with Diamonds 2 little pictures about a foot broad and a foot and halfe long

[29] My brother Edward Stanley to the Waste by Lilly

[30] The Countess of Richmond & Derby – The Chevalier Sans reproach

[31] The Dutchesse de Tremoille my Wifes Grandmother all Copies from Knowsley Copyed by Henry Hesket to the Waste

[32] The Earle of Clare my Grandfather to the Waste Copyed by Lilly

[33] Arch Bishop Laud by Vandicke to the Knees

[34] My Sister in Law my Lady Marquess of Dorchester at length by Walker

[35] The Prince of Aurange my Ladys Unckle

[36] another of his Son the late Prince to the Waste

[37] The Princes of Aurange in a Chaire with a Parrott A Copy of Hesketts to the knees

[38] The Magdalane thought to be by Leonardo Vincentio and worth 100£.

[39] The picture of our Saviour & the blessed Virgin an old Peece

[40] and a Peece of Perspective these three pictures are painted upon boards and were my wifes given her by my Lord her Father

[41] The Prince of Bohemia to the waste drown'd in Holland

[42] William de Nassau Prince of Aurange to the Waste & Copied by Heskett

[43] The King then Prince of Aurange A Child –

[44] The Douchesse of Bovillion my wifes great Aunt to the Waste

[45] The young Douchess of Bovillion her daughter in Law to the Waste Coppies by Heskett

[46] Margrett Clifforde Countesse of Derby to the Waste Coppyed by Heskett

[47] My Aunt Countesse of Tyrconnell to the Waste

[48] My two Sisters the Lady Rockingham and the Lady Arabella in one peece by Lilly to the Knees

[49] The Earle of Oxford my wifes great Grandfather at length

[50] The Earle of Derby my Father in Laws Picture to the Waste Copied by Henry Heskett

[51] James Marquess of Mountross to the Waste

[52] The Earle of Southampton Ld Treasurer by Lilly to the Waste

[53] My Lord Deputy Wandsfords

[54] My Fathers picture at length when he was a young man by Mitten

[55] My Lady Margrett Clifford my Fathers first Wife A bad picture but I have noe other of her

[56] Sr Stanhope my great Grandfather to the Wast

[57] Sr John Atkinson my great Unckle by Lilly to the Wast

[58] My Lord Cottington Copied by Henry Heskett to the Wast The two great Bedds of my Wifes and a Suite of Hangings in Eight peeces being the History of Sampson all given by my Lady Derby her Mother to my wife at her marriage.

The fflat Capp Hangings old ones I found here the Same with a suite at Knowsley taken in Richard the 3.ds Tent in Bosworth field

[59] D.r William Spenser to the Waste by M.rs Beale[10]

[10] Of the pictures listed in this 'Schedule' the following can still be identified in the collection: nos 1, 2, 3, 5, 8, 9, 10, 11, 16, 18, 19, 21, 22, 23, 25, 26, 29, 35, 36, 37, 42, 48, 51, 52, 53, 57.

No. 6 was sold at Christie's, 26 October 1984 (31). Either no. 12 or no. 13 could be identified with the respectable copy, in the collection, of Van Dyck's three-quarter-length of Strafford at Petworth, but it does not seem to have been done by Lely. As for nos 20 and 50, there are three copies in the collection of portraits of the 7th Earl of Derby. No. 33: there are now two versions in the collection of Van Dyck's portrait of Laud. No. 59: this could be one of the two late portraits in the collection by Mary Beale.

The 'Schedule' can be compared with the list of pictures at Wentworth Woodhouse which was sent to Vertue (*Notebooks*, vol. 5, *Walpole Society*, vol. 26 (1938), p. 79).

A WEDDING
AT ST MARGARET'S
Richard Ollard

PRIME MINISTERS, or potential prime ministers, whose marriages take place at St Margaret's, Westminster, hardly belong to that period of English history that Veronica Wedgwood has illuminated with the sympathy of her perception and the breadth of her learning. Yet Edward Hyde, first Earl of Clarendon, for all that he stoutly resisted what he considered a frenchified description of his office, strangely enough blazed the matrimonial trail followed by so many eminent politicians. All of them were married there because they were Members of the House of Commons. Yet when the future architect of Charles II's Restoration, the friend of Selden and Whitelocke, the Chairman of Committees in the Long Parliament, the great articulator of Royalism as a parliamentary and legal position, led his bride down the aisle on 10 July 1634 he was not and had not ever been a Member of Parliament, for the good reason that since he reached the qualifying age of twenty-one there had been no Parliaments for him to be a Member of.

Why, then, was he married at St Margaret's? His father-in-law, Sir Thomas Aylesbury, a courtier of some importance, Master of the Mint and Master of the Court of Requests, had a house (in which the young couple were to lodge) in Dean's Yard.[1] The bridegroom's father and mother did not attend the wedding. Henry Hyde had been a great traveller in his youth, but his son tells us with pride that 'from the death of Queen Elizabeth, he never was in London though he lived above thirty years after . . . the wisdom and frugality of that time being such that few gentle-

---

[1] *Life*, Oxford, 1857, 1, 22; Clarendon MSS 20, 1505/11.

men made journeys to London, or any other expensive journeys, but upon important business, and their wives never'.[2] In fact Henry Hyde was probably too frail to face the journey. He had already decided to leave his country house at Purton for Salisbury so that he could attend the daily offices in the cathedral in which he wished to be buried. The young couple came down to see him in the Long Vacation and found him active and in good spirits in spite of his ailments. During their visit, on Michaelmas Day 1634, he was carried off by a sudden attack, apparently of some circulatory disease.

With a characteristic contempt for mere figures Clarendon in his autobiography misdates these two landmarks in his personal life, his marriage to Frances Aylesbury and the death of his father, by two years, placing them in 1632. He has been followed in this by Lister and all his subsequent biographers with the exception of Sir Charles Firth in his article in the *Dictionary of National Biography*, which cites the evidence of the Westminster Abbey register. Oddly, Firth himself seems to have forgotten this, or not to have noticed the discrepancy, when he came to give his tercentenary lecture on Clarendon in 1909 in which he falls into the same error.[3] The misdating is confirmed by the date of Henry Hyde's will and of its probate cited in the article by J. Jones in a recent volume of the *History of Parliament* edited by P. W. Hasler.[4] Clarendon's attitude towards mensuration was in the fullest sense cavalier. Readers of Macray's edition of the *History of the Rebellion* can hardly fail to notice his wild inaccuracy about distances even when they are crucial to his narrative. He belonged to the generation that immediately preceded the foundation of the Royal Society for all that its Charter passed the Seal during his Lord Chancellorship. Indeed, had he lived at a later date his temperament would surely have led him to sympathize with Burke's views of sophisters, economists and calculators.

What Clarendon was good at was people. The portrait studies in his published works have been too often praised by historians and men of letters alike for there to be any doubt of his powers

[2] *Life*, 1, 5.

[3] C. H. Firth, *Essays, Historical and Literary* (Oxford, 1938), p. 116.

[4] P. W. Hasler (ed.), *The House of Commons, 1558–1603* (London, 1981), pp. 11, 361.

not only of delineating and analysing characters but also of bringing them to life. The brilliance of his intelligence was fuelled by warmth of heart, a warmth that sometimes led him into injustice and often into injudicious conduct but never into emptiness or insipidity. Readers of the *History* and the *Life* can see this for themselves. But how much can they see of these qualities as they affected the domestic and family life of a man to whom they can hardly have been unimportant?

About Henry Hyde, the Lord Chancellor's father, there is no obscurity. Clarendon praises him in the highest and most affectionate terms: '. . . not only . . . the best father, but the best friend and the best companion he ever had or could have . . . whom he did in truth believe to be the wisest man he had ever known'.[5] These words, written in 1668, when their author was passing in review a career that had brought him into contact with the first men of his time, are the more telling for their perspective. His mother, though generously and affectionately remembered, is not distinguished by particular recollection – 'he did not value any honour he had so much as the being the son of such a father and mother'. Her death passes unnoticed in his reminiscence. In fact she lived to witness her son's triumphant return and, presumably, came up to London to live with him since she was buried in Westminster Abbey on 28 December 1661.[6] Did Clarendon, steeped as he was in the literature and in the moral and social ideas of Periclean Athens and of the Roman Republic, feel that the highest compliment that could be paid to any woman was that she should not be mentioned in public? Perhaps. But as the *Life* was avowedly written only for the perusal of his own immediate family and, conceivably, their descendants[7] this is not an entirely satisfactory explanation.

In any case, if such a principle be postulated, he compromises over his two marriages and departs from it altogether in the highly emotional and transparently candid account he gives of his reaction to the news of his daughter Anne's liaison with the Duke of York. From his first marriage to Anne, daughter of Sir George

[5] *Life*, 1, 17.

[6] J. L. Chester (ed.), *Westminster Abbey Registers* (London, 1876), p. 155.

[7] *Continuation*, 1245.

Ayliffe, in 1632 we catch a glimpse of the ardent nature that the author seems at pains to camouflage under prudent maxims and conventional wisdom.[8] He embarked on the marriage, he implies, in order to reinforce his professional concentration, 'to call home all straggling and wandering appetites, which naturally produce irresolution and inconstancy in the mind'. His father approved both the plan and the lady selected to forward it. But at this point romance enters a somewhat *terre à terre* transaction. She was 'a young lady very fair and beautiful' and when after a few months she caught the smallpox, miscarried and died the young widower was inconsolable. 'He bore her loss with so great passion and confusion of spirit, that it shook all the frame of his resolutions, and nothing but his entire duty and reverence to his father [he was the eldest surviving son and thus heir to the Purton estate] kept him from giving over all thoughts of books, and transporting himself beyond the seas to enjoy his own melancholy: nor could any persuasion or importunity from his friends prevail with him in some years to think of another marriage.'[9] It was, as we have seen, in fact two years.

Again the motives he adduces for marrying his second wife Frances Aylesbury were professional and filial: '. . . he knew it would be the most grateful thing to his father (for whom he had always an infinite reverence) he could do'. It would bind him closer to his practice at the Bar and help to keep off thoughts of travel after which he still hankered.[10] The prudence of the marriage, as Sir Charles Firth points out,[11] was enhanced by the fact that his new father-in-law was the judge in whose court he practised. Foreshadowings of *Trial by Jury*! But perhaps in this particular Firth has adopted too easily the representation of him-

---

[8] Erroneously dated 1629 by his first biographer, T. H. Lister (1838), who deduced it from Clarendon's own misdating of his second marriage (see below), which, he claimed, had followed the death of his first wife after an interval of 'near three years' (*Life*, 1, 5). Lister's dating has been accepted by all subsequent writers, including the editor of the *Life and Continuation* (1857). I am indebted to Mr Sidney Ball for drawing to my attention two separate and conclusive pieces of evidence: a parish register entry of the marriage (4 February 1632) and a mural tablet giving the date of Anne's death (2 July 1632). I shall print details of these in my forthcoming book on Clarendon and his friends.

[9] *Life*, 1, 13.

[10] ibid., 15.

[11] Firth, *Essays*, p. 116.

self that Clarendon was concerned to establish and in so doing has transmitted it to those writers who have followed him. We know from several passages in Clarendon's *Life* – the most famous example is the wager between Falkland and Charles I – that he prided himself on his ability to disguise his thoughts and his literary style. He is not – who is? – always to be taken at his face value.

Firth glosses Clarendon's statements in the *Life* thus: 'It proved a very happy marriage: with this wife "he lived very comfortably in the most uncomfortable times, and very joyfully in those times when matter of joy was administered". Some critics have complained of this lack of sentiment in Clarendon's character, and of a certain materialism in his nature. He would not have denied the charge, but would have taken it as a tribute to his worldly wisdom, and as one of the causes of his success.'[12] 'He would not have denied the charge.' Precisely. It was exactly the impression he wished to convey in his persona as historian alike of his times and of his own life. But is it a wholly faithful representation of what he really felt and thought? There is other evidence to be considered, not least his letters to his wife. But before we turn to them it is worth remembering the other instances already cited of the passion that was surely a much more conspicuous feature of Clarendon's temperament than his materialism, a characteristic which Firth so strangely finds predominant. His grief over the death of his young wife, his agony of shame at what he considered the inexcusable misconduct of his favourite child were not kept within the bounds that Firth's interpretation predicates. And Firth himself in a fine passage does the fullest justice to what he describes as 'that incomparable portrait of Falkland', the friend whose loss Clarendon still felt in old age as the worst blow inflicted on him by the Civil War.

There are, so far as I know, no letters to Frances Hyde among the mass of Clarendon manuscripts in the Bodleian Library, with one single exception, never sent, which he wrote in Jersey when a Parliamentarian assault appeared imminent, in which he took an affectionate farewell and gave her directions as to pro-

---

[12] ibid.

viding for their children. Since he made file copies of the most trivial letters of civility it might be inferred either that he wrote none or that he thought them too intimate for the eyes of even the most confidential secretary. We know the first inference to be untrue: the second may perhaps be correct. Though they were often separated for long periods both during the Civil War itself and in the earlier years of Charles II's exile, it is from the summer of 1649 to the spring of 1651, when Clarendon had been at Cottington's request joined with him in Charles II's embassy to Madrid, that the surviving letters come. The bulk of them are to be found in the Marquis of Bath's manuscripts at Longleat and have been printed *in extenso* with scrupulous accuracy in the second volume of the Calendar published by the Historical Manuscripts Commission in 1907. Such others as survive, some of them torn or incomplete, are in the Department of Manuscripts in the British Library (Add. MS 34727).

The earliest, written from Brussels whither he had gone for an official audience with the Governor of the Spanish Netherlands, is dated 7 June 1649. The tenderness and intimacy of the correspondence is at once evident:

My deere little Rogue

I have forborne to write to thee since I left thee because I knew thou didst not so much desyre to heare that I was heare (of which thou couldst not be ignorant) as that I was ready to returne to thee. . . .

His audience had been delayed by one of the many religious festivals that encouraged the Spanish talent for procrastination, but he expects to be back with her in Antwerp within the week before setting out for Paris on his way to Spain. This would be the last they would see of each other for what they both knew would be a long time. The exiguous means at the disposal of an ambassador whose main function was to beg would not allow him to bring his wife and children. After a little gossip and some family messages the letter ends: 'God blesse thee and all thy cattle, and me, as I am, my deere, thy owne most affectionate husband.'[13]

---

[13] *Calendar of Bath Manuscripts*, vol. 2, p. 80.

The next letter was written about a month later from Peronne where Clarendon and Cottington had paused on their way to Paris, relieved to have passed safely through the territory in which the French and Spanish armies were campaigning. Again the letter is natural, easy, affectionate and humorous, the outward and visible sign of a marriage in which each loved the other and knew themselves beloved.

> If thou desyrest I should prosper, and have any happynesse in the world thou wilt remember all that I have sayd to thee concerninge thyselfe, and not suffer a melancholique thought to enter into thy hearte, and I have no doubte but God will so blesse us, as to bring us quickly agayne to each other's company; which believe me I desyre as much as I do to lyve, and the last only to enjoy the blessinge of the first.[14]

A month later he is at St Germains receiving his final instructions from the King. His opening words betray his anxiety at not having heard from her since he left Brussels.[15] By 3 September he is really alarmed:

> My dear little Rogue
>
> I beshrew thee for putting mee in so much trouble and apprehension with not hearing from thee. Heare is now another post past and no letter from thee. I pray thee amend this fault. It is now three weeks since I writt to thee. . . .[16]

He was anxious both about her health and the precarious dribble of funds for her and the children's support. But it is the effect of their renewed separation that is his chief worry. In a torn, undated letter from Brussels, probably written only a day or two after they had parted he warns her of the danger – 'I do from my hearte thank thee for thy great affection. I must likewise chyde thee for the passion of it' – but admits his own reliance on her: '. . . the hope of living hereafter happily together does so absolutely and solely support me in this affliction of our separation . . .'.[17] Perhaps suspecting that this is likely to last longer

[14] ibid., p. 82.

[15] ibid.

[16] British Library, Add. MS 34727, fo. 74.

[17] ibid., fo. 75.

than he has so far allowed her to imagine, he urges her in the same letter to bring over her father and mother from England.

On 11 September, 'at last, and just as I was begynninge a grumblinge letter to thee for so longe silence', he receives a letter of hers written on the third. It seems that this devoted couple wrote to each other by every post but that his letters had better luck than hers. On the twenty-fourth, on the eve of setting out for Spain, his anxiety has returned:

> . . . another post come and no letter from thee, which I wonder exceedingly at, for I have never fayled of hearinge once a week from Bruxells, and sure from Antwerp the conveyance is as safe. . . . Well, wee are of good cheer and infallably on Wensday next begynn our journy. After that tyme I believe I shall heare seldome from thee till I come into Spayne, but I will not fayle to write to thee once a weeke. By this tyme I hope our friends of the Forrest [her parents had a house in Windsor Forest: oblique rather than direct reference to people still living under the enemy regime had become second nature to him by this time] are arryved with you, and then it is not possible but the joy and kindnesse amongst yourselves, will supply all other wantes; in earnest I could live with greate content with you together with breade and water. . . .[18]

Enough has been quoted from this most attractive correspondence to justify a difference in opinion from Firth and others who have relied perhaps too implicitly on Clarendon's own low-key statements in the *Life*. Reading the letters in their entirety leaves a sense of warmth and vivacity, of wholeness and humour, of balance and awareness of little things as well as great, in short of those qualities that make Clarendon's biographical sketches at once so satisfying and so suggestive. As he travels through France and Spain he shares his stream of consciousness with his wife. He tells her about his health and the hazard of the journey: he comments adversely on the food and drink, he wonders about their friends in England, he speculates about the likely initiatives of Commonwealth policy, he worries about her (not his) finances. Most of all he worries about their means of communication: 'The truth is, every letter from thee revives my hearte so much, that I am the better for it for many dayes. I perceive some of myne have

[18] *Bath MSS*, vol. 2, p. 84.

layne longe in the way, yet at last they have come to thee, which is a comforte, and whilst wee are at this distance, wee must be contented with those accidents.'[19] How important he thought this element in a happy marriage is clear from a letter written from Madrid in May 1650. Frances has told him that she is suffering from 'her old disease of her foreheade'. Her husband urges her to see the doctor but does not disguise his fear that the ailment may be psychosomatic:

> . . . I would have thee very carefull to watch this humour, that it gett not too much grounde. If it were possible, I would be very gladd to prevent any indisposition, and that thou mightest be without cause of the least melancholique thought to perplex thee, but since it were madnesse to expect such a degree of happynesse, ther is no reason it would make thee unwillinge to communicate the worst of it to me, for ther is some ease in the very communicating it, and thou and I together are likelier to finde some ease or remedy, then thou arte by thyselfe; at least it is a burthen fitt for us to beare togither.[20]

Clarendon was, on abundant evidence, deeply loved and respected by his sons. The courage and frankness with which both Henry and Laurence, rising and ambitious politicians, championed their father at his fall brighten that sad and shuffling story. Laurence kept the first anniversary of his father's death as a solemn day of thanksgiving and private prayer.[21] Clarendon's letters to his wife show time and again what care he took to involve her in any decisions affecting the children and how much he valued and admired her upbringing of them. An example of this may be found in a letter from Madrid:

> I thanke thee for the children, that thou hast provyded them people to teach them French: I thinke it is very fitt and I hope we shall bee able to pay them: it is a greate blessing (little Rogue) that they are good and dutifull, and therefore lett us make all possible shift to supply them in point of education, and then if

[19] ibid., p. 88.

[20] ibid., p. 91.

[21] *Correspondence of Henry Hyde, Earl of Clarendon and of His Brother Laurence Hyde, Earl of Rochester*, ed. Singer, vol. 1, pp. 645–7.

we can leave them nothing else, it will not be oure faulte, and I have an opinion that good education is as cheape a thing as badd.[22]

In the early summer of 1651 this loving pair were reunited. In December they were parted again when Charles II summoned Clarendon to Paris to become his chief adviser. During the long separation that followed Henrietta Maria indicated to Clarendon that if he would sponsor her policies in the King's Council she would accommodate his wife and family in one of the Parisian palaces. Needless to say the offer was rejected. However, Cromwell's alliance with Mazarin brought their separation to an end. For the rest of their married life, with some intervals when the minister had to follow the travels of the exiled court, they were together.

At the Restoration, Frances Hyde behaved with her usual good sense and decorum. In that supremely malicious, factious age of English politics no one accused her of interfering in public affairs or pursuing personal interest. Her presence on the stage of court life was only felt by virtue of her husband's refusal to allow her to meet Lady Castlemaine, an assertion of the decencies of married life that the King felt to be tiresome and ill-bred. She died in the middle of August 1667,[23] only days before her husband's dismissal. One of his colleagues told Clarendon's old friend Ormonde that he believed she had died of grief.[24] Clarendon himself simply records that, though she had made an unsuccessful journey to Tunbridge Wells, the doctors believed her in no danger. To him the political nightmare that followed was a distraction from 'that more insupportable misfortune'.[25] Charles II paid him a visit of condolence. Ten days later he was being jeered by Lady Castlemaine, Bab May and Arlington as he left Whitehall after his last interview with the master he had served for more than twenty years. Perhaps he was grateful that his wife was spared so vile a humiliation.

[22] British Library, Add. MSS 34727, fo. 84.

[23] She was buried on 17 August: *Westminster Abbey Registers*, p. 167.

[24] Keith Feiling, *British Foreign Policy, 1660–72* (London, 1930), p. 229.

[25] *Continuation*, 1133.

THE WORD 'REVOLUTION' IN SEVENTEENTH-CENTURY ENGLAND
Christopher Hill

There is nothing so hard to discover in the
past as that which has subsequently become familiar.

Joyce Appleby, *Capitalism and a New Social Order:*
The Republican Vision of the 1790s (New York, 1984), p. 5

'The revolution in trade brought about
a revolution in the nature of things.'

Daniel Defoe, *Robinson Crusoe*

CONVENTIONAL WISDOM has it that the word 'revolution' acquired its modern political meaning only after 1688. Previously it had been an astronomical and astrological term limited to the revolution of the heavens, or to any completed circular motion. This has received the stamp of approval from Braudel, though on the rather shaky authority of Hannah Arendt. Peter Laslett in 1956 dated the new meaning to the political literature of 1688–9, though he himself shows Locke using it in 1679–81.[1] V. F. Snow in 1962 appeared to accept a date after 1688, despite himself giving many earlier examples.[2] Melvin Lasky, whilst attributing to 'English lexicographers' a date after

---

[1] Peter Laslett, 'The English Revolution and Locke's Two Treatises of Government', *Cambridge Historical Journal*, vol. 12 (1956), p. 55. By 'the English Revolution' he means the revolution of 1688. Cf. F. Braudel, *Civilisation Matérielle, Economie et Capitalisme* (Paris, 1979) vol. 3, p. 465.

[2] V. F. Snow, 'The Concept of Revolution in Seventeenth Century England', *Historical Journal*, vol. 5 (1962), pp. 168–70.

1688, recognized that the changed application from astronomy to politics was a consequence of the mid-seventeenth-century English Revolution.[3] I wish to suggest that the transition to the modern sense occurred considerably before 1688.

Since the stars were believed to influence events on earth there is clearly much room for ambiguity in a shift from 'the revolution of the heavens' to a political revolution on earth. But one characteristic of the earlier sense is that a revolution is circular, returning to its starting-point: the historical process is cyclical. The modern idea of a revolution suggests a break in continuity. One important factor in bringing about the change of meaning, I believe, was the decline of cyclical history after the decisive break of the Reformation. Protestants proposed to return to the primitive church, it is true; but many radicals hoped for continuous reformation until God's kingdom had been established on earth. Millenarianism was widely preached in England after the liberation of press and pulpit in 1640. The millennium is a once-for-all occurrence: it means the end of cyclical history. And it is reached by a series of revolutions – the wars of Armageddon, the defeat of Turkish power, the raging and ultimate overthrow of Antichrist. None of these is likely to recur, because they signify the approaching end of history.

Another radical concept, that of a third age, the age of the spirit, whether or not derived from Joachim of Fiore, also pointed in the direction of linear history. The last age would be an improvement on what had gone before, not a reversion to the past. As Winstanley put it, 'the ministration of Christ in one single person is to be silent and draw back' once Christ has risen in sons and daughters.[4] John Reeve believed that his commission replaced that of Christ and the Apostles, as their commission had ended Moses's.[5] 'We look for a new earth as well as a new heaven,' the Quaker Edward Burrough told Parliament in 1659, echoing what William Erbery had written earlier.[6] Millenarianism and

---

[3] Melvin Lasky, *Utopia and Revolution* (1976), p. 246.

[4] *The Works of Gerrard Winstanley*, ed. G. H. Sabine (New York, 1941), p. 162.

[5] *Remains . . . being a Collection of Several Treatises by John Reeve* (1706), pp. 64–8.

[6] Edward Burrough, *To the Parliament of the Commonwealth of England* (1659), p. 3; *The Testimony of William Erbery* (1658), pp. 207–8.

the concept of the third age thus cut across the circularity of the historical process: God's revolutions might move in a straight or a wavy line, but they did advance along a line.

Seventeenth-century lexicographers adhered firmly to the old meaning of the word throughout the seventeenth century. Three things need to be said here. First, post-dating is a normal tendency in lexicographers: anyone who has tried to use *The Oxford English Dictionary* as a guide to the chronological origins of words is aware of this.[7] Second, lexicographers copy from one another, and therefore are slow to spot changes in usage. Third, seventeenth-century lexicographers were mostly scholarly men, to whom Latin was as familiar as English: this helped to fix the idea of 'return to a starting position' in defining the word 'revolution'.

To illustrate these points, consider the word 'absolute', another word which was acquiring a political sense in the seventeenth century. Mr Daly suggests that there was a shift in meaning from about 1640, after which the original sense of 'complete', 'perfect' receded and the modern sense of 'legally unlimited', 'arbitrary' began to emerge.[8] We could date the shift considerably earlier. In the 1590s Hooker spoke of 'an absolute monarch' who 'commandeth . . . that which seemeth good in his own discretion';[9] and the Earl of Essex suggested that Elizabeth was seeking 'an infinite absoluteness'.[10] Fulke Greville referred to 'absolute princes', with 'an absoluteness dangerous to their subjects' freedom', and feared lest 'our moderate form of monarchy' might be transformed into 'a precipitate absoluteness'.[11] Christopher Brooke in 1614 contrasted 'lawful power' with

[7] See my *Milton and the English Revolution* (1977), p. 226 n.; and *Change and Continuity in Seventeenth-Century England* (1974), pp. 103–5.

[8] J. Daly, 'The Idea of Absolute Monarchy in Seventeenth-Century England', *Historical Journal*, vol. 21 (1978), pp. 227–50.

[9] Richard Hooker, *The Laws of Ecclesiastical Polity*, 2 vols, Everyman's Library (London, 1925), vol. 1, p. 194.

[10] W. B. Devereux, *Lives and Letters of the Devereux, Earls of Essex*, 2 vols (1853), vol. 1, pp. 501–2. Cf. S. B. Chrimes, 'Constitutional Ideas of Dr. John Cowell'. *English Historical Review LXIV* (1949) p. 481.

[11] Fulke Greville, *Life of Sir Philip Sidney* (Oxford, 1907), pp. 48, 52, 54. First published 1652, written *c*.1610–12.

'absolute power';[12] and Simonds D'Ewes in 1622 believed that all James I's 'actions did tend to an absolute monarchy'.[13] The *OED* cites Bacon in 1625: 'a King more absolute but less safe'. All these examples approach the modern sense, yet seventeenth-century lexicographers do not notice the change. Robert Cawdrey's *A Table Alphabeticall* (1604, 1613) defines 'absolute' as 'perfect or upright'. Randle Cotgrave's *French–English Dictionary* from 1611 to 1673 translates 'absolute' as 'absolu, parfait'. J. Bullokar's *An English Expositor* retained the definition 'perfect, accomplished' from 1616 to 1680. Henry Cockeram's *The English Dictionarie* (1623) has simply 'perfect', expanded to 'perfect, accomplished' in his 1642 edition. Edward Philips, Milton's nephew, in *The New World of Words* (1658), defined absolute as 'perfect'; by 1671 this had been expanded only to 'perfect; as it were finished'. Elisha Coles had 'perfect' as his only definition in *An English Dictionary* (1676, unchanged to 1708). Even John Kersey, who by 1702 had caught up with the new meaning of 'revolution', still defined absolute as 'perfect; or not depending' in his *New English Dictionary*.

So it is not surprising to find that lexicographers were equally slow to note changes in the meaning of 'revolution'. Cawdrey and Bullokar define it as 'a wandering or turning about, especially in the course of time'. Cotgrave's *A Table Alphabeticall* has 'turning back to the same place'. In his *French–English Dictionary* the French 'révolution' was translated as 'a revolution, a full compassing, rounding, turning back to the first place or point: the accomplishment of a circular course'. This sense survived down to 1677, despite James Howell's helping hand in later editions. Cockeram in 1623 only slightly modified Cawdrey and Bullokar: 'a winding or turning about, especially in the course of time'. This was repeated down to 1642. Thomas Blount in *Glossographia* had 'a returning back to the first place or point, the accomplishment of a circular course' (1656, unchanged down to 1681). Edward Philips was even more restrictive in *The New World of Words*: 'a rolling back of celestial bodies to their first

[12] *Wentworth Papers, 1597–1628,* ed. J. P. Cooper, Camden Society, 4th Series (1973), p. 67.

[13] *The Diary of Sir Simonds D'Ewes, 1622–1624,* ed. E. Bourcier (Paris, n.d. [?1975]), p. 59.

point, and finishing their circular course' (unchanged 1658–78). Elisha Coles's *An English Dictionary* has 'a turning round to the first point' in editions from 1676 to 1708. His English–Latin dictionary of 1677 distinguished between 'the revolution of heaven' = 'coeli cursus' and 'revolution' = 'revolutio', 'a revolution, a turning quite round'. The first definitely political definition which I have found comes in John Kersey's *New English Dictionary* of 1702: 'whirling about, a certain course of the planets, time, &c.; or a change of government'.

The Oxford English Dictionary clearly establishes that there were other meanings than 'a turning back to the first point' before the middle of the century. Under the definition 'alteration, change, mutation' it cites *Hamlet* as he looks at a skull: 'Here's fine revolution, an we had the trick to see't' (V, 1, 98), and Tourneur, 'The self-same course/Of revolution, both in man and beast', referring to 'birth, growth, decay and death' (*The Atheist's Tragedy*, 1611, I, 1). Under the heading 'great change or alteration, in affairs or in some particular thing' *OED* cites Fynes Morison, 'every important revolution of our business . . .' and a translation by H. Cogan in 1663, 'How great the revolutions of time and fortune are'.

These senses were well established in seventeenth-century England, though contemporary lexicographers ignored them. Antony's remark in *Antony and Cleopatra*:

> the present pleasure,
> By revolution lowering, does become
> The opposite of itself (I, 11)

like the passage from *Hamlet* quoted above, does not seem to imply circularity, though 'the revolution of the times' in *2 Henry IV*, III, 1, may.[14] Ben Jonson in *The Fortunate Isles* (1625) has

> That point of revolution being come
> When all the Fortunate Islands should be joined.[15]

[14] In *The Birth of Merlin* (possibly *c*.1622), one of the plays occasionally attributed to Shakespeare, Merlin refers, more traditionally, to 'revolutions, rise and fall of nations', which are 'figured yonder in that star' (IV, v).

[15] Ben Jonson, *Works*, ed. C. H. Herford, P. and E. Simpson, vol. 7 (Oxford, 1941), p. 722.

Edward Bolton in *Hypercritica* (*c.*1618) speaks of the 'five hundred and fifty years between the Norman Conquest till the Union under King James' as 'the English Revolution'.[16] This period could hardly be thought of as a return to an earlier state: though equally it is not 'a change of government'.

A third definition given by *OED* approximates to the modern sense: 'A complete overthrow of the established government in any country or state by those who were previously subject to it; a forcible substitution of a new ruler or form of government.' Surprisingly, *OED* cites Edward Blount in 1600: 'assuring those quarters from all revolutions that might be feared'; and, less surprisingly, George Monck in 1660 (not 1655, as *OED*), explaining that Sir Arthur Haslerig, just before the Restoration, had been 'very jealous of the intended revolution of government to his Majesty's advantage'. *OED* also cites examples from 1674 onwards of 'the revolution' signifying 'the overthrow of the Rump' of the Long Parliament in 1660.

J. Hatto and V. F. Snow rightly draw our attention to influences from romance languages, which seem to have preceded England in adopting the modern meaning. Upheavals in Florence of 1494, 1512 and 1527 were called 'revoluzioni' by those who witnessed them. Guicciardini (1508–12) described constitutional changes as 'revolutions'. Montaigne wrote 'many worse revolutions have been seen'. A. Giraffi's *Le Revolutioni di Napoli* (1647), describing Masaniello's rebellion, was translated in 1650–2 by James Howell as *An Exact historie of the late revolutions in Naples*. By then this sense was common. Howell himself had already in 1646 spoken of 'the strangest revolutions', apparently referring to political and social changes.[17]

Already the sense of change, of a significant transformation in personal or political circumstances, is present in the word: revolutions do not always have to be circular. The profound political changes of the 1640s influenced this shift. The Five Dissenting Brethren in their *Apologeticall Narration* of 1644

---

[16] Edward Bolton, *Hypercritica, or a rule of judgment for writing or reading our historys*, in *Critical Essays of the Seventeenth Century*, ed. J. E. Spingarn, 3 vols (Oxford, 1908), vol. 1 (*1605–1650*), p. 102.

[17] J. Hatto, ' "Revolution": An Enquiry into the Usefulness of an Historical Term', *Mind*, vol. 58 (1949), pp. 502–3; Snow, 'Concept of Revolution', pp. 169–70.

spoke of 'these revolutions of the times', in which 'it pleased God to bring us his poor exiles back again'. The words contain the idea of restoration, but the Brethren were hardly thinking of a recurrent process.[18] Fast Sermons preached before Parliament illustrate the point. In February 1644, Thomas Young was wholly traditional: 'after the revolution of so many solemn fasts'.[19] So was Humphrey Hardwick four months later: 'after the revolutions of many thoughts'.[20] John Owen, two years later, used the word to describe a transformation that is not circular: 'all revolutions here below . . . are carried along according to the eternally fixed purposes of God', and so are historically inevitable.[21] Nicholas Lockyer in the same year opposed the idea of cyclical history, whilst using 'revolution' in its traditional sense: 'an impatient man thinks that the revolution of all times should be of the same aspect: that the present times should be as full of trade, as full of friends, as full of peace and plenty, as former times'.[22] But in Matthew Barker's Fast Sermon of 25 October 1648 a more ominous and more modern note is struck: 'The Lord knows what revolutions and changes we may see before the next monthly fast.'[23]

One way of describing what was happening in the 1640s was to speak of 'the world turned upside down'. That is half a revolution, and perhaps use of the phrase by conservatives implied a hope that the revolution would be completed by a return to normality. But some way of describing one-directional political change was needed, since it was happening. Just as today we might speak of 'revolutions of the heavenly bodies' to distinguish the astronomical use of the word, so in the seventeenth century men came to speak of 'revolutions and changes' to distinguish

---

[18] *Op. cit.*, p. 22; in *Tracts on Liberty in the Puritan Revolution, 1638–1647*, ed. W. Haller, 3 vols (New York, 1933), vol. 2.

[19] Thomas Young, *Hopes Incouragement* (1644), p. 1.

[20] Humphrey Hardwick, *The Difficulties of Sions Deliverance and Reformation* (1644), p. 4.

[21] John Owen, *A Vision of Unchangeable free Mercy* (1646), p. 3.

[22] Nicholas Lockyer, *A Sermon Preached before the House of Commons* (18 October 1646), p. 16.

[23] Matthew Barker, *A Christian Standing & Moving Upon the true Foundation* (1648), p. 49.

political revolutions, a break in continuity, from traditional circular revolutions.

The experience of the winter of 1648–9 seems to have expedited adoption of the new meaning. Thus in March 1649 an unknown 'D.P.' wrote: 'We need not wonder at the revolutions and changes of government.'[24] Antony Ascham published in 1648 *A Discourse wherein is examined What is particularly lawfull during the Confusions and Revolutions of Government.* It was expanded next year as *Of the Confusions and Revolutions of Governments.* Ascham saw 'confusions and revolutions of government' in the Wars of the Roses, when power shifted backwards and forwards from one group to another until Henry VII's *de facto* law 'concluded these contradictions and revolutions'.[25] Robert Heath in *Clarastella* (1650) has a phrase which perhaps sounds more modern than he intended:

> Nothing but fair Utopian worlds i' the moon
> Must be new formed by revolution.[26]

Robert Boyle in 1651 seems to think of revolution (in the singular) as a sudden change: 'I do with some confidence expect a revolution, whereby Divinity will be much a loser and real Philosophy flourish, perhaps beyond men's hopes.'[27] There is no suggestion here of turning back to the first point. The Ranter Joseph Salmon in the same year also uses 'revolution' more in the modern sense, though he is referring to events in his private life. There 'happened a sudden terrible, dreadful revolution, a most strange vicissitude'.[28] An anonymous radical pamphlet, also of 1651, likewise had the modern sense: 'all revolutions and

[24] D. P., *The True Primitive State of Civill and Ecclesiasticall Government* (1648[–9]), p. 3.

[25] *A Discourse*, Sig. ᵡ3, p. 93; *Of the Confusions and Revolutions*, Sig. A 2v, p. 103.

[26] Quoted by Marjorie Nicolson, 'English Almanacs and the "New Astronomy" ', *Annals of Science*, vol. 4 (1939), p. 21. Milton is old-fashioned: see *Complete Prose Works*, ed. D. M. Wolfe, 8 vols (New Haven, Conn., 1953–82), vol. 2, p. 539, vol. 5, p. 403, his second Hobson poem and *Paradise Lost*, bk II, ll. 596–8, bk VIII, l. 31, and bk X, ll. 813–15.

[27] Quoted by J. R. Jacob, *Robert Boyle and the English Revolution* (New York, 1977), p. 97. Cf. Boyle, *Occasional Reflections* (1665), pp. 13–14.

[28] Joseph Salmon, *Heights in Depths and Depths in Heights* (1651), in *A Collection of Ranter Writings*, ed. N: Smith (1983), p. 212.

changes . . . are for the perfecting of this glorious work'.[29] Arise
Evans in 1653 used similar words: 'these revolutions and changes
came to pass even to fulfil the words and promises of God'.[30]
John Hull in New England slipped from the sublime to the
ridiculous when the grand phrase 'it is best willing to submit to
the governing hand of the greatest Governor of all the greater
and lesser revolutions that we poor sons of men are involved in'
led on without any punctuation to 'by the invoice you see the
whole amounteth to £405.16.3'.[31] *Mercurius Politicus* in March
1652/3 used the word 'revolution' to signify recurrent change:
'as in the governments of the people the successive revolution of
authority by their consent hath been the only bank against
inundations of arbitrary power and tyranny'.[32]

From 1653, the year which saw the dissolution of the Rump,
the rule and abdication of Barebone's Parliament and the proclamation of the Protectorate, we find a cluster of examples. Henry
Newcome wrote, apropos the expulsion of the Rump: 'I had
upon thoughts of this revolution, amongst others, this Scripture
brought to hand, Isaiah 29. 14–17.'[33] George Wither resolved:

> Let not the revolutions or the changes
> Or the prevarication which now ranges
> Throughout the world, me from my station carry,
> Or cause me from good principles to vary.[34]

The millenarian John Canne predicted for 1655 'great changes
and revolutions, in respect both of persons and things', for at

---

[29] [Anon.], *A Cry for a Right Improvement* (1651), p. 7. I owe this reference to J. P.
Laydon's 'The Kingdom of Christ and the Powers of the Earth: The Political Uses of
Apocalyptic and Millenarian Ideas in England, 1640–1653' (unpublished Ph.D. thesis,
Cambridge University, 1976), p. 150.

[30] Arise Evans, *Admonitions to all the People of this Kingdom*, in *The Bloudy Vision of
John Farley* (1653), p. 23.

[31] L. Ziff, *Puritanism in America: New Culture in a New World* (New York, 1973), p. 150.

[32] *Mercurius Politicus*, no. 91 (26 February–4 March 1652[–3]), p. 1442.

[33] Henry Newcome, *Autobiography*, ed. R. Parkinson, Chetham Society (1852), p. 44.

[34] George Wither, *Westrow Revived* (1653), p. 63, in *Miscellaneous Works*, Spenser
Society, vol. 3 (1874).

that time the Lord will 'most eminently appear, shaking the earth and overthrowing the thrones of kingdoms everywhere in Europe'.[35] A translation of Lieuwe van Aitzema published in 1653 was entitled *Notable Revolutions: Being a True Relation of What Happened in the United Provinces.*

Ralph Josselin in January 1654, looking backwards, noted in his diary that 'this year hath brought forth notable revolutions at home in dissolving Parliament and declaring Cromwell Protector'.[36] Here 'revolution' clearly involved innovation. Twenty-five years later Josselin had adopted the singular: 'some threat as the greatest revolution we ever saw were at the door'.[37] At the beginning of 1654, Whitehall messengers' salaries were twelve months and more in arrears, 'which hath been mainly occasioned by the uncertainty of the times through the many revolutions of government'.[38] Here again the reference is to specific change, not to turning back to the first point. A very clear instance of the modern sense comes in Christopher Feake's *The New Non-conformist* (1654), where (like the Five Dissenting Brethren) he speaks of émigrés who had returned to England 'from New England and from Holland at the beginning of the late great revolution'.[39]

Matthew Wren wrote (probably in the 1650s) but did not publish *Of the Origin and Progress of the Revolutions in England.* The title might have been added by Gutch, who published it in 1781: but in the text Wren refers to 'those strange revolutions we have seen' and – even more to our purpose – said that 'a pack of discontented noblemen and gentlemen . . . were engaged to labour a revolution of affairs'.[40] The use of the singular is significant.

[35] J. Canne, *A Voice from the Temple to the Higher Powers* (1653), pp. 29–30.

[36] Ralph Josselin, *Diary, 1616–1683*, ed. A. Macfarlane (Oxford, 1976), p. 316.

[37] ibid., p. 616: 8 December 1678.

[38] G. E. Aylmer, *The State's Servants: The Civil Service of the English Republic, 1649–1660* (1973), pp. 121–2.

[39] *op. cit.*, Sig. A 3v.

[40] *Collectanea Curiosa*, ed. J. A. Gutch, 2 vols (1781), vol. 1, pp. 228–53. The passages cited are on pp. 242 and 238 respectively.

The most striking example of the new usage, appropriately enough, comes from Oliver Cromwell himself, in his speech at the dissolution of his first Parliament on 22 January 1655. 'Let men take heed,' he warned, 'how they call his revolutions, the things of God and his working of things from one period to another, how . . . they call them necessities of men's creations.' To deny that 'those mighty things God hath wrought in the midst of us' have been 'the revolutions of Christ himself' was to deny God's sovereignty. 'Take heed, again I say, how you judge of his revolutions as the products of men's inventions'. 'The Lord hath done such things amongst us as have not been known in the world these thousand years.'[41] Though still using the word in the plural, Cromwell seems to employ it in its modern sense. His 'working of things from one period to another' recalls Marvell's view of Cromwell himself as 'the force of angry Heaven's flame', who 'cast the kingdom old/Into another mold'. By 1657, Cromwell could use the word casually in a letter to Blake – 'all these late revolutions'.[42]

In 1656, William Howard, on behalf of a group of former Levellers and Anabaptists, wrote to Charles Stuart in exile, referring to 'the many changings, turnings and overturnings of governors and governments which in the revolutions of a few years have been produced'.[43] Here 'revolutions' could simply mean 'successions of years'; but the singular would seem more appropriate if that was the sense intended.

After Ascham, James Harrington is the political theorist who comes nearest to using the word in its modern sense in print before 1660. In *The Prerogative of Popular Government* (1658) he wrote: 'Property comes to have a being before empire or government two ways, either by natural or violent revolution. Natural revolution happeneth from within, or by commerce, as when a government erected upon one balance, that for example of a nobility or a clergy . . . comes to alter to another balance. . . .

[41] *Writings and Speeches of Oliver Cromwell*, ed. W. C. Abbott, 4 vols (New Haven, Conn., 1937–47), vol. 3, pp. 590–3.

[42] ibid., vol. 4, p. 549. Cf. *Calendar of State Papers (Domestic) 1656–7*, p. 272, *1657–8*, p. 48.

[43] Clarendon, *History of the Rebellion*, ed. W. D. Macray, 6 vols (1888), vol. 6, p. 68.

Violent revolution happeneth from without, or by arms.' The English Revolution, as Harrington explained elsewhere, was a 'natural revolution': 'the dissolution of this government caused the [civil] war, not the war the dissolution of this government'.[44]

Various publications of 1659 refer to 'our late revolutions' – George Bishop's *Mene Tekel*,[45] R. Fitz-Brian's *The Good Old Cause Dressed in its Primitive Lustre*.[46] Rushworth, in the preface to the first volume of his *Historical Collections* (1659), gave as his object 'to learn the true causes, the rises and growths of our late miseries, the strange alterations and revolutions'. The former radical William Sedgwick used the plural in his *Inquisition for the Blood of our late Sovereign* (1660): 'in these times when there are so great and notorious revolutions'; 'these strange revolutions', 'the great revolutions of this kingdom'.[47]

The Restoration should have offered an opportunity for applying the word 'revolution' to politics in its sense of return to a first position. Professor McKeon says that for Dryden's contemporaries the word meant restoration or renovation, return to a former state. One example which he gives is clear enough: 'Revolution! Revolution! Our King proclaimed! restored!'[48] But it is, I think, at least possible that Henry Bold (in the passage just cited) was being deliberately provocative in appropriating the word to this conservative purpose: recall Cromwell's 'the revolutions of Christ'. Dryden in *Absalom and Achitophel* and elsewhere does not always use the word to mean restoration.[49]

---

[44] *The Political Works of James Harrington*, ed. J. G. A. Pocock (Cambridge, 1977), pp. 405–6, 198.

[45] George Bishop, *Mene Tekel: Or, The Council of the Officers of the Army Against The Declarations &c. of the Army* (1659), p. 5.

[46] *op. cit.*, p. 1 (rightly p. 2).

[47] *op. cit.*, pp. 63, 155, 259.

[48] Henry Bold, *St. Georges Day* (1661), pp. 1–2, quoted by M. McKeon, *Politics and Poetry in Restoration England* (New Haven, Conn., 1975), pp. 237, 262–4.

[49] *Absalom and Achitophel*, ll. 252–3: 'Heaven has to all allotted, soon or late, Some lucky revolution of their fate'; cf. Dryden's translation of Juvenal's sixth satire, ll. 56–7: 'What revolution can appear so strange/As such a lecher, such a life to change?' See also his translation of Virgil's ninth eclogue, ll. 4–6, and *On the Marriage of the Fair and Virtuous Lady, Mrs Anastasia Stafford*, ll. 53–4.

The Matchless Orinda, Katherine Philips, puns on the two senses of the word:

> Why should changes here below surprise,
> When the whole world its revolution tries?[50]

One wonders how often apparent ambiguity in use of the word is, as here, a deliberate pun.

By 1665, Edward Waterhouse is consciously looking back to the experience of the 1640s and 1650s when he writes that money buys men 'in all revolutions': wisdom 'little avails in worldly revolutions without it'.[51] Sprat in 1667 spoke of 'those dreadful revolutions'.[52] When two old Cromwellians, Thomas Povey and Samuel Pepys, discussed politics in 1668, the former 'thinks there will be great revolutions', in consequence of which 'a man of the old strain . . . will now be up again'.[53] Sir William Temple in 1672 referred to the 'fatal revolutions' of the crown and nation between 1646 and 1660, 'the revolution of England in the year 1660'. In the Netherlands there had been 'some unavoidable revolutions', 'revolutions unparalleled in any story'.[54]

Henry Stubbe, former radical Parliamentarian, used the word 'revolution' in the singular: 'From the apostolic and primitive times to the revolution under Constantine'.[55] As J. R. Jacob points out, Stubbe regularly employs the word in its modern sense, especially in that very modern work, *The History of the Rise and Progress of Mahometanism*. Mahomet's 'prosperous revolution' was directed against 'the ostentation and abuse' of 'arbitrary power'.[56] Stubbe's friend Charles Blount spoke of

---

[50] 'Submission', in *The Caroline Poets*, ed. G. Saintsbury, 3 vols (Oxford, 1905), vol. 1, p. 568. Mrs Philips died in 1664, the year in which her poems were posthumously published.

[51] Edward Waterhouse, *The Gentleman's Monitor* (1665), in Joan Thirsk, *The Restoration* (1976), p. 92.

[52] Thomas Sprat, *History of the Royal Society of London* (1667), p. 58.

[53] Samuel Pepys, *Diary*, 20 June 1668.

[54] Sir William Temple, *Essay on Popular Discontents* and *Observations upon the United Provinces*, in *Works*, 3 vols (1757), vol. 3, pp. 32–66, vol. 1, pp. 56, 59.

[55] Henry Stubbe, *Legends no Histories* (1670), p. 121.

[56] Stubbe, *op. cit.* (1911), p. 128; cf. p. 49: 'such great revolutions': J. R. Jacob, *Henry Stubbe: Radical Protestantism and the Early Enlightenment* (Cambridge, 1983), p. 66.

'those revolutions which (otherwise) no human sagacity or courage could have accomplished'; 'all revolutions whatever, both in church and state . . . must still be seconded by some private temporal interest'.[57]

Andrew Marvell, another former Parliamentarian, was using the word in an entirely modern sense when he wrote in 1677 of 'the tendency of all affairs and counsels in this nation towards a revolution'.[58] So was Samuel Butler, when he saw an analogy between 'revelations and revolutions'.[59] Locke, as Laslett showed, was using the word in the modern sense in 1679–81. Hobbes's *Behemoth* was not published until 1679, having been previously prohibited by Charles II. But it was probably completed not later than 1668. In it Hobbes wrote: 'I have seen in this revolution a circular motion of the sovereign power.' Monarchy – sedition – republic – sedition – monarchy: here Hobbes, like the Matchless Orinda, seems to be punning on the old and new meanings of the word.[60]

In 1685, Evelyn had referred to Titus Oates's reversal of fortune as 'a strange revolution' – the traditional usage. But in 1688 he spoke of 'a sad revolution' threatening 'this sinful nation'; and in December he said, 'It looks like a revolution,'[61] just as Louis XVI in 1789 was told that what was happening in France was a revolution, not a revolt. 'The very Papists,' Halifax had assured William of Orange in April 1688, 'have . . . an eye to what may happen in a revolution.'[62] Professor Kenyon's bland note here on the word 'revolution' – 'any change of government; not "revolution" in our sense' – seems to me to beg most of the questions I have been trying to raise. How could governments

[57] *Letters of John Wilmot, Earl of Rochester*, ed. J. Treglown (Oxford, 1980), pp. 208, 213–14.

[58] Andrew Marvell, *An Account of the Growth of Popery and Arbitrary Government in England*, in *Works*, ed. Captain Edward Thompson 3 vols (1776), vol. 1, p. 645. Marvell appears to refer to a revolution in religion.

[59] Samuel Butler, *Prose Observations*, ed. H. de Quehen (Oxford, 1979), p. 246.

[60] Thomas Hobbes, *Behemoth*, ed. F. Tonnies (1889), p. 204.

[61] *Diary of John Evelyn*, ed. E. S. de Beer, 6 vols (Oxford, 1955), vol. 4, pp. 445, 603, 609.

[62] Marquess of Halifax, *Complete Works*, ed. J. P. Kenyon (Harmondsworth, 1969), p. 338.

be changed in seventeenth-century England (really changed, as governments were changed in 1640–2, 1649, 1653, 1659–60 and 1688: not the sort of cosmetic shuffle tried – unsuccessfully – by Charles I in 1641 and – successfully – by Charles II in 1679)? There was no His Majesty's Opposition standing patiently in the wings waiting for its cue. The 'complete overthrow of the established government . . . by those who were previously subject to it',[63] to which Ascham, Feake, Cromwell, Harrington, Pepys, Marvell and Evelyn referred, was as different from a twentieth-century 'change of government' as that is from the lexicographers' 'change of position'. The shift from circular motion to a one-way 'change of government' is decisive for our theme. For such a change could happen only if politics passed out of the control of those holding government office.

The word 'revolution' may have become more acceptable after 1688. Edward Howard's *Caroloriades* was in its first edition of 1689 subtitled *or the Rebellion of 1641*. The second edition, in 1695, was called *Caroloriades Redivivus, or the Wars and Revolutions in the Time of King Charles I*. Burnet said that Lady Ranelagh, sister of Roger and Robert Boyle, had cut 'the greatest figure in all these revolutions of three kingdoms for above fifty years of any woman of her age'. Lord Wharton was said in 1696 to have 'behaved himself with honour in all the revolutions that happened in his time'.[64] Locke in his *Second Treatise* (published 1690) spoke quite casually of 'the many revolutions which have been seen in this kingdom in this and former ages'. 'Such revolutions', he added, 'happen not upon every mismanagement in public affairs.'[65] By 1710 a pamphlet could be published entitled *The True English Revolutionist*.

The idea of revolution as a significant political transformation thus appears to have emerged during the Interregnum. The concept of a revolution which God had brought about precluded the idea of such an event being 'a necessity of men's creations', a

---

[63] See p. 139 above.

[64] J. Kent Clark, *Goodwin Wharton* (Oxford, 1984), p. 369. A play called *The Late Revolution* was staged in 1688.

[65] John Locke, *Two Treatises of Government*, ed. P. Laslett (Cambridge, 1960), pp. 432–3. Laslett here appears to date these passages to 1679–82 (ibid., p. 424).

conspiratorial *putsch* or a revolt in blind reaction to localized grievances. Men might co-operate with God in His 'working of things from one period to another'; they could not initiate a revolution. Such an event had deep roots in God's purposes for His people.

Professor Pocock once said 'men cannot do what they have no means of saying they have done'.[66] I find this surprising. Men and women committed suicide before Sir Thomas Browne used the word in the 1630s.[67] There were pantheists before Toland invented that word in 1705. Men presumably were 'civilized' before they began to say they were; and it is unlikely that the word 'urbanity' preceded the thing. Nor would men think of the word 'suburb' before building one.[68] The word 'feminism', Barbara Taylor reminds us, did not appear until the late nineteenth century, but there had been people whom we can call feminists for at least a century before that.[69] Jonathan Dollimore points out that ideology existed long before the word which describes it.[70] The disease rickets came to notice a generation before it was given a name. Things precede words. Men and women find words to say what they have done or experienced in the process of doing it, or after they have experienced it. It is difficult to see how it could have been otherwise. Especially when we are dealing with terms of analysis like 'ideology' and 'revolution'.

During the Revolution, Sprat thought, the English language 'was enlarged by many sound and necessary forms and idioms which before it wanted'.[71] New words were needed because new things happened, or old concepts forced themselves anew upon popular attention. Fuller thought 'malignant', 'plunder' and

---

[66] Pocock, 'Virtue and Commerce in the Eighteenth Century', *Journal of Interdisciplinary History*, vol. 3 (1972), p. 122; cf. J. S. Morrill, *Seventeenth-Century Britain, 1603–1714* (Folkestone, 1980), pp. 108–9.

[67] *OED*.

[68] J. M. Roberts, *The Pelican History of the World* (London, 1976), p. 525.

[69] Barbara Taylor, *Eve and the New Jerusalem* (1976).

[70] Jonathan Dollimore, *Radical Tragedy: Religion, Ideology and Power in the Drama of Shakespeare and His Contemporaries* (1984), p. 18.

[71] T. Sprat, *History of the Royal Society of London* (1667), p. 42.

'fanatic' were new in his time.[72] Keith Thomas identified many
new words dealing with change – 'epoch', 'synchronize', 'out-
of-date', 'anachronism'.[73] Other new words which clearly relate
to the events of the Revolution are 'anarchism' (*OED* 1642,
though 'anarchy' had appeared earlier),[74] 'antinomianism'
(1643), 'superstructure' (1641).[75]

The words 'nature' and 'natural' underwent a transformation
in the seventeenth century. We make romantic assumptions about
'nature', but for early Protestants 'natural man' was sinful man.
The word 'class', too, begins to assume its modern sense. In
1624 the deputy lieutenants of Essex referred to 'some of the
better classes setting a very ill example'.[76] This will displease
historians who argue that there could have been no classes in
seventeenth-century England because the word was not used in
its modern sense: a false conclusion from a false premise.

Many words change their meaning in the seventeenth century.
C. L. Barber wrote a fascinating book on changing concepts of
'honour';[77] I looked briefly at new senses of 'liberty' and
'reason'.[78] Quentin Skinner has pointed out that 'obsequious'
becomes pejorative, and words like 'gentle', 'generous' widen
their connotations. 'Frugality', 'squandering' and 'spendthrift'
are new: 'commodity' and 'honesty' narrow their meanings, and
'purchase' changes its reference.[79] So do 'value', 'worth',

---

[72] T. Fuller, *Church History of Britain*, 3 vols (1842), vol. 3, p. 443; *Mixed Contemplations in Better Times* (1660), in *Good Thoughts in Bad Times* (1830), pp. 294–5; cf. P. Styles, *Studies in Seventeenth Century West Midland History* (Kineton, 1978), p. 20.

[73] Keith Thomas, *Religion and the Decline of Magic* (London, 1971), p. 429.

[74] Milton used 'anarchy' as well as 'anarch' in *Paradise Lost* (bk x, l. 283, bk ii, l. 988).

[75] 'Superstructure' was used by Harrington (*Political Works*, pp. 202, 609–10); cf. John Philips, in *Early Lives of Milton*, ed. H. Darbishire (1932), p. 24.

[76] William Hunt, *The Puritan Moment: The Coming of Revolution in an English County* (Cambridge, Mass., 1983), p. 184. Blount's *Glossographia* (1656) defines class as 'an order or distinction of people according to their several degrees'. I am indebted to Penelope Corfield for this reference.

[77] C. L. Barber, *The Idea of Honour in the English Drama, 1591–1700* (Göteborg, 1957).

[78] My *Change and Continuity in Seventeenth Century England*, ch. 4; for 'liberty', see Appleby, *Capitalism*, pp. 16–22, 62. For 'reason', see her *Economic Thought and Ideology in Seventeenth-Century England* (Princeton, NJ, 1978), p. 62 and passim.

[79] Quentin Skinner, 'Some Problems in the Analysis of Political Thought and Action', *Political Theory* (August 1974), pp. 296–8; 'Language and Social Change', in L. Michaels

'credit'.[80] 'Society' and 'community' acquire new senses.[81] Joyce Appleby noted that 'individual' is first cited in *OED* from 1626. In the seventeenth century 'the word market was transformed, another of those sleights of tongue obscuring a change of meaning'.[82] 'The quality' comes to mean those of good social position, independent of birth: the meaning is connected with access to high-quality goods.[83]

There is room for serious linguistic study of the new words which appeared in the seventeenth century, and of old words whose meaning shifted. Such a study would tell us a great deal about the social changes which took place then, and might even help us in dating them. Meanwhile I think we can place the shift in the meaning of 'revolution' well before 1688.

---

[80] For 'credit' I am indebted to Susan Amussen's unpublished DPhil thesis (Brown University, 1982), esp. pp. 342–6. She kindly allowed me to read this thesis, and I benefited greatly from discussing the subject with her. See now her article in *Annales* (1985), p. 273. For 'value' and 'worth' see Louise Lecocq, 'Le Débat sur la valeur dans *Troilus et Cressida*', *Confluents*, vol. 2 (Lyon, 1976), p. 3 and *passim.*

[81] I owe this point to discussions with Peter Burke.

[82] Appleby, *Capitalism*, pp. 15, 30.

[83] Nicholas Jose, *Ideas of Restoration in English Literature, 1660–71* (1984), p. 19.

---

and C. Ricks (eds), *The State of the Language* (California U.P., 1980), pp. 570–2. I have also drawn on correspondence from Professor Skinner on this subject. For 'honesty' see also S. N. Zwicker, *Politics and Language in Dryden's Poetry: The Arts of Disguise* (Princeton, NJ, 1984), pp. 206–7. 'Imagination' had a perjorative sense in the seventeenth century.

NICHOLAS FERRAR
AND LITTLE GIDDING

A REAPPRAISAL

Robert Van der Weyer

Introduction

Nicholas Ferrar, the founder of the first Little Gidding Community, appears in the new service book of the Church of England under the list of 'Lesser Festivals and Commemorations',[1] along with such other great saints as Thomas More and Mother Julian of Norwich. His date is shown wrongly – it should be 4 December, the anniversary of his death – but his inclusion is just recognition that he and his community make a vital chapter in the history of English Christianity.

Sadly, however, those who have written about the Community during the past two centuries[2] have on the whole been hagiographical, often painting a dull and insipid picture. Its members appear as too good to be true, devout and quiet in the extreme, without any hint of common-or-garden human sin; one may admire such heroic religious perfection, but cannot feel inspired to emulate it. Worse still, they have been appropriated by one party within the Church, the Anglo-Catholics, as forerunners of their brand of Christian devotion, and as early pioneers in the revival of monasticism in the Church of England. But in fact a more relaxed interpretation of the primary sources at our dis-

---

[1] *The Alternative Service Book* (Oxford, 1980), p. 21.

[2] P. Peckard, *Memoirs of the Life of Mr Nicholas Ferrar* (1790); T. M. Macdonogh, *Brief Memoirs of Mr Nicholas Ferrar* (1837); T. T. Carter (ed.), *Nicholas Ferrar* (1892); H. P. K. Skipton, *The Life and Times of Nicholas Ferrar* (London, 1907); A. L. Maycock, *Nicholas Ferrar of Little Gidding* (London, 1938) and *Chronicles of Little Gidding* (London, 1954).

posal[3] reveals them as flesh-and-blood human beings with the same capacity for anger and jealousy, as well as tenderness and love, as any group of people; and the inner tensions and outward conflicts of the varied assortment of personalities who comprised the community make a fascinating story. The inspiration for us is that this mixed bag of people, led by an intense and ambitious young man, managed to live together in comparative harmony, establishing a simple and unpretentious pattern of community life, incorporating both families and single people, in an age which had rejected traditional forms of religious community. Moreover, far from being identified with any religious faction, their worship was both Puritan in its austerity and Catholic in its devotion to the sacraments. Thus, as even Charles I recognized when he visited them, they were truly a light of peace in a country darkened by religious division and political enmity.

Nicholas's Early Years

Nicholas Ferrar was born in 1592, the third son of a wealthy businessman who was one of the founders of the Virginia Company, set up to colonize the New World. Both father and mother were devoutly religious, and Nicholas himself was a serious-minded, rather priggish child, who preferred to stay indoors reading to playing outside with friends. His favourite book was Foxe's *Book of Martyrs*, which included an account of his ancestor, Bishop Ferrar of St David's, who was burnt at the stake in 1555 for his unbending Protestant opposition to Queen Mary. Nicholas from the age of six wanted to be a clergyman, and announced to his mother that, whatever his brothers wore, he would not wear lace, but only plain clothes as befitted a future priest. When he was confirmed by the Bishop of London in 1598 he managed to have hands laid on him twice, explaining proudly afterwards: 'I did it because it was a good thing to have the

---

[3] *Life of Nicholas Ferrar by His Brother John*, written c.1655; *Life of Nicholas Ferrar by Doctor Jebb*; Edward Lenton's letter to Sir Thomas Hetley, 1634. These three primary sources are printed in J. E. B. Mayor, *Cambridge in the Seventeenth Century*, pt 1, *Nicholas Ferrar* (1855). Hereafter they are referred to as JF, Dr J and EL respectively, citing the page numbers in Mayor.

Bishop's prayers and blessings twice, and I have got it.'[4]

Some time afterwards he had an experience which he came to regard as his true conversion to the Christian faith. It occurred one cold and frosty night, shortly before he was to be sent away to boarding school. He was unable to sleep, and as the night hours passed he was overcome by a sense of remorse. He got out of bed, went into the garden, and threw himself face downwards on the frozen grass, sobbing and crying. He begged God that 'a true fear and care of his divine majesty' would fill his heart, and 'that this fear and love of God might never depart' from him; and he prayed that God would reveal 'how he must serve him'. He gradually felt a great weight lifting from his heart, and at last he stood up and returned to bed, inwardly peaceful. The intensity of this childhood experience stayed with him for the rest of his life, and as an adult in his daily prayers he consciously renewed the commitment he made on that night.[5]

At the age of thirteen he was sent to Cambridge University, where he studied at Clare Hall under Austin Linsell, later Bishop of Peterborough. Nicholas was academically bright and his conversation stimulating and witty, so that after a year he was elected a Fellow Commoner, sitting at high table amongst the Fellows. Linsell encouraged Nicholas to read the works of the early Fathers of the Church, and Nicholas, an impressionable teenager, tried to model his life on theirs: he ate sparingly; he rose early to go to prayers at five o'clock in the college chapel, and he read till late at night; he dressed simply, and he scrupulously avoided the more bawdy student pastimes.[6]

But throughout his time at Cambridge Nicholas suffered from what his physician described as 'aguish dispositions' which were attacks of high fever, sometimes with a rash breaking out over his body.[7] The usual prescription was starvation, which Nicholas, inspired by the saints, seems to have relished. But the attacks seemed to grow more severe and frequent, and eventually the doctor declared that it was the cold damp climate of Cambridge

---

[4] JF, pp. 305. Dr J, pp. 165–9.

[5] JF, pp. 5–6; Dr J, pp. 169–71.

[6] JF, p. 6; Dr J, pp. 171–2.

[7] JF, pp. 12–13; Dr J, pp. 174–5.

that was at fault. So, in 1613, Nicholas was forced to abandon a promising academic career, and to travel abroad, in the hope that a warmer climate would restore his health. He expected to die during his journey, and wrote a long letter to his parents filled with self-pity, and resentment at life's unfair treatment of him.[8]

He spent three years touring Europe, and proved a most resourceful and adventurous traveller. And there is little doubt that what he saw abroad inspired his interest in community life. He began his journey accompanying Princess Elizabeth Stuart on her journey to Germany. And while they passed through Holland he visited the Anabaptist communities, whose austerity and simplicity of life deeply impressed him. He then broke free of the royal party, travelling on his own over the Alps into Italy, where he lived for two years in Padua, studying medicine at the university. He read avidly the spiritual literature of the Counter-Reformation, such as Francis de Sales' *Introduction to the Devout Life*. And he must have become familiar with the new religious communities that were springing up, including the Congregation of the Oratory in Padua, a new religious order whose members did not take vows, so as to remind them that their commitment was free and voluntary; much later at Little Gidding he prevented members of his community from taking vows for similar reasons. He then went on to Spain, where we know little of his movements, and returned to England in 1618. The accounts of his journey show that in the course of it the self-conscious and narrow-minded piety of his adolescent years gave way to an energetic curiosity into every aspect of human affairs. He was fascinated by all kinds of religious rituals and ceremonies, including those of the synagogues in Amsterdam; but also he was constantly inquiring into the commercial and political life of the countries he visited, and took copious notes about the banking system in Hamburg as well as the Holy Week celebrations in Rome.[9]

On his return Nicholas was offered an academic post in London, and could have resumed his career in Cambridge. But partly out of family duty, and also out of his new-found enjoyment of the affairs of the world, he decided to join the Virginia

[8] Dr J, pp. 176–80.

[9] JF, pp. 13–16; Dr J, pp. 180–201.

Company. His father was retiring and, although his elder brother John was already a member of the Company, his father saw Nicholas as his successor. Nicholas quickly became absorbed in the business, pressing the company to expand its activities in the New World by employing French silk farmers to establish silk production there, in order to export the yarn back to England for weaving. He also formed plans to start a university in Virginia, and sent out bibles and financial support for schools.[10] But Nicholas's entrepreneurial flair was partly responsible for King James's growing hostility to the company, because, in threatening the Spanish colonial plans in the New World, it seemed to jeopardize his hope for the Prince of Wales to marry the Spanish Infanta. Almost undoubtedly under Spanish pressure the King set in motion a series of official investigations and interventions in the company's activities which at one point involved Nicholas and his brother being put under house arrest, and which eventually led to the Privy Council closing the company. Nicholas led the company's defence, showing himself as a subtle and skilled debater, able to present complex arguments clearly and lucidly; and he seemed to relish the pressure under which he was forced to work. For a brief period he served in Parliament, not only defending the company from its benches, but also playing a leading role in the impeachment of the Earl of Middlesex, the Lord Treasurer, on charges of bribery and corruption. Middlesex had opposed Nicholas over the Virginia Company, and now Nicholas in an act of revenge made a powerful, vitriolic speech for the prosecution.[11]

Despite the collapse of the Virginia Company, Nicholas seemed to have a promising career ahead. His abilities had been noticed, even by his erstwhile opponents, and he was offered two important government posts, a clerkship to the Privy Council and the British ambassadorship in Savoy. And some time earlier a wealthy family friend had offered Nicholas his daughter in marriage, with a handsome dowry.[12] But Nicholas felt increasingly disgusted with himself and his way of life. Although he was not the eldest

[10] JF, p. 17; Dr J, pp. 202–6.

[11] JF, pp. 20–2; Dr J, pp. 207–10.

[12] Dr J, p. 211; JF, pp. 109–10.

son, from early childhood his parents' hopes and ambitions had rested on him; and for this reason he himself was ambitious and proud, always setting himself the highest standards of achievement. But it also gave him a dread of failure, and a sense of his own unworthiness and inability to live up to such expectations. The cold night spent sobbing in the garden was a childhood manifestation of his capacity for desperate remorse, and his part in Middlesex's condemnation filled him with guilt which haunted him until his death. In the political and commercial world he took easily to positions of authority, and enjoyed his own gifts as a speaker and a leader; but he was fearful of these gifts as the exercise of them in the world both fed his pride and heightened his fear of failure, and he was painfully embarrassed by the praise and honour heaped upon him. As a child his greatest satisfaction had been found in precise religious observance; now as an adult a life devoted to religion, in which he could deliberately channel his ambition and energy towards the service of God, increasingly appealed to him as the only means of resolving his inner conflict.

By now his father was dead, and in 1625 he began to speak to his mother and the rest of the family about the possibility of their purchasing an estate in the country, where as an extended family they could form a small religious community. His mother was not only herself devoutly religious, but also highly possessive of her beloved younger son; and as a widow the prospect of spending her remaining years with him in a life of quiet devotion readily appealed to her. John, too, agreed to join him, along with his wife and children. His faith was more simple, but no less strong, than that of Nicholas: but his decision may also have been influenced by his financial situation, for he had lost almost his entire inheritance in a dubious business venture which collapsed at the same time as the Virginia Company's demise. More surprisingly, his elder sister Susanna, a forthright and strong-willed woman, and her husband John Collett were also enthusiastic. And so in 1625 they purchased the manor at Little Gidding in Huntingdonshire, and a year later prepared to sell their house in London to move there.[13]

At Easter in 1626, Nicholas, now in the grip of intense religious

[13] JF, p. 23; Dr J, p. 220.

157

emotion, began to fast and to keep himself awake through the night in order to pray. Eight weeks later on Trinity Sunday, unbeknown to his family, he went to Westminster Abbey to be ordained deacon by Bishop Laud, attended only by his former Cambridge tutor, Linsell. When he returned home to announce his ordination to his family he took out from his breast pocket a sheet of vellum on which he had written a solemn promise to 'separate himself to serve God in this holy calling, to be the Levite himself in his own house, and to make his own relations, which were many, his cure of souls'. It is a measure of the personal respect in which Nicholas was held that his family reacted not with anger at his arrogance but with gratitude at his commitment to them.[14]

Community Life

When old Mrs Ferrar first visited Little Gidding in 1625 she went straight to the little church, refusing to set foot in the house until she had offered a prayer of thanksgiving. She was appalled to find it full of hay, and the vestry smelling foul, having until a few weeks previously been used as a pigsty. The original village of Little Gidding had died out at the Black Death, and so the church, long since redundant for worship, had been put to practical use by the local peasants. Nicholas had organized workmen to repair the old manor-house, standing to the west of the church, where they were to live; but his mother ordered them immediately to come and clear the church, and stood patiently watching them until she could enter and kneel down.[15] It was a telling incident, for throughout the early years of the community Nicholas's vision and leadership were constantly tempered by his mother's strict sense of good order.

The community immediately established a routine of daily prayer. The main services, for which everyone processed over to the church, were Morning Prayer at 6.30, followed by breakfast; the Litany at ten o'clock, followed by lunch; and Evening Prayer at four o'clock, followed by supper. In addition at each

[14] JF, p. 24; Dr J, pp. 226–7.

[15] Dr J, pp. 221–2.

hour through the day two or three people would hold a short service in the Great Chamber of the house, consisting of a Psalm and a Bible-reading. On Sundays the Litany was replaced by Ante-Communion, usually with a sermon from a visiting preacher; and on the first Sunday of the month there was also a full Holy Communion service early in the morning, celebrated by the Vicar of Great Gidding.[16] From the outset the community was accused of being 'papist', and rumours abounded about its 'ritualistic' practices. In fact the community followed the stipulations of the Book of Common Prayer fully and loyally, and their common life was a response to the vision enshrined in it. Morning and Evening Prayer in the Prayer Book are based on the old monastic Daily Offices, compressed into two acts of worship, with the intention that these should be the daily prayers of the whole church. Thus for Cranmer and the other compilers daily corporate prayer was no longer to be confined to monks and nuns – religious specialists – but was to be shared by ordinary families; it was this vision, at the heart of the English Reformation, that was the inspiration of Little Gidding. It was Cranmer's hope that Holy Communion, in which all partook, should be the main act of Sunday worship; and, although it was celebrated only monthly at Little Gidding, this was far more frequent than was commonly practised in the early seventeenth century. On the vexed question of the position of the communion table the community followed the practice laid down in the Prayer Book of bringing it down and placing it in the middle of the chancel, with the communicants standing round it – a practice which Bishop Laud sought to abolish in favour of the 'altar-wise' position.

Much of the first five years at Little Gidding was devoted to repairing and furnishing the church; in this desire to beautify their place of worship they were following the 'Catholic' inclinations of Laud and the High Churchmen. They installed wooden panelling, a brass font and lectern, and an organ; but most striking to the visitor were the rich tapestries made by the community, and the flowers and herbs which were regularly put into the church, picked from the garden near the churchyard. In the late 1620s the community converted the old dove-house into a

[16] JF, pp. 27–44; Dr J, pp. 233–45.

schoolroom, not only for the community's own children but also for others who wished to come. They also opened a surgery where they would bind wounds and give out simple medicines.[17] But their most famous work was making concordances in which parallel passages from the four gospels were shown side by side on the page, to enable the reader to compare the different accounts. They took basic lessons in bookbinding from a young woman from Cambridge, and then over the years developed the art, producing some of the most exquisitely bound volumes of their day. The initial stimulus to produce a concordance was for the Scripture readings at the hourly services during the day; but the King's interest encouraged them to produce more copies, as well as concordances of some Old Testament books.[18]

The permanent core of Little Gidding was Nicholas himself, his mother Mary, his brother John and sister Susanna and their respective families. It was thus a religious community based on an extended family. In addition there were three single men acting mainly as schoolmasters, and four elderly widows looked after by the community, who shared fully in its daily life. Also the community took in several teenage boys as part of their education, including one youth called John Gabbit whose wild behaviour defied even the community's stern discipline.[19]

Mary was without doubt a most formidable woman. She was over seventy when she arrived at Little Gidding, and in the initial years she organized the domestic arrangements of the house, and supervised the school, sitting in a special chair overlooking the children's work during the lessons. As her portrait shows, she had sharp, handsome features, and even when she was eighty, within a few months of her death, a visitor described her as 'a tall, straight, clear-complexioned, grave matron'.[20] She

---

[17] Dr J, pp. 229–32.

[18] JF, pp. 36, 38; Dr J, p. 243. The original concordance, which King Charles borrowed (see below), is now in the Harvard University Library. A concordance specially made for the King, bearing the date 1635, is now in the British Library. For a detailed study of the Little Gidding concordances, see C. Leslie Craig in the *Harvard Library Bulletin*, vol. 1, no. 3 (1947).

[19] Magdalene College, Ferrar MSS: Nicholas Ferrar to Arthur Woodnoth, 19 April 1631.

[20] EL, p. xxvii.

matched her son Nicholas both in intelligence and in a taste for rigorous self-discipline: she rose at five each morning, worked hard throughout the day, and ate so sparingly during Lent that at one point John Ferrar had to plead with her to be more lenient with herself; and one year she set herself the task of – and succeeded in – learning the entire psalter by heart.[21] She was largely responsible in the early 1630s for organizing a study circle in the community, which became known as the Little Academy, in which members told stories based on events in history.[22]

John Ferrar was a straightforward, guileless man, with a strong sense of duty and a capacity to feel contented with his lot. Although older than his brother Nicholas by two years, he admired and looked up to him, often embarrassing Nicholas with lavish praise: in relation to the community he described Nicholas as 'the eye to the body and the soul that giveth life unto it'.[23] His wife, Bathsheba, bitterly resented his subservience to Nicholas, and hated the quiet life of the countryside and the monotonous routine of the daily worship. Nicholas regarded her as 'troublesome', and John once wrote pathetically of 'how she goes about to make herself most unhappy, me most miserable and to ruin all her children both in souls and bodies'.[24] John lacked the force of character to restrain her fits of temper, patiently enduring her contempt for him, and devoting himself to the upbringing of their children.

Their eldest son Nicholas, born in 1620, was a brilliant scholar with an exceptional talent for languages. By the age of fourteen he had produced a translation of an Italian devotional work which his uncle had brought back from his travels. A few years later he presented to Charles I a gospel concordance in four languages, which so impressed the King that he offered to send young Nicholas to Oxford University, and then to employ him in the royal household. Nicholas was shy, and spoke with a stammer, a disability he shared with the King, who suggested he tried talking with a pebble in his mouth as a cure. Sadly, young

[21] JF, pp. 36, 38.

[22] E. C. Sharland (ed.), *The Story Books of Little Gidding* (1899).

[23] Magdalene College, Ferrar MSS: John Ferrar to Nicholas Ferrar, 23 July 1632.

[24] Magdalene College, Ferrar MSS: John Ferrar to Nicholas Ferrar, 20 February 1636.

Nicholas had always been frail, and died suddenly a few days after meeting the King.[25] Their other two children, Virginia and John, were both born at Little Gidding, and spent their whole lives there, John eventually inheriting the estate.

Susanna, Nicolas's elder sister, was more of a match to him than their brother John. She willingly argued with him on both community and family matters, curbing his authoritarian instincts; and on one issue Nicholas became so frustrated by her opposition that he accused her openly of making statements which were 'neither true in the matter, nor done on that ground which she pretends, that is out of love'.[26] She was both pious and strong-willed, constantly writing letters of stern advice to friends and relatives; but she was saved from unbearable self-righteousness by a sharp sense of irony, often at her own expense. She was an accomplished lute-player and a skilled nurse. Her husband, John Collett, was an easy-going, ineffectual man who willingly went along with his wife's wishes – including moving from the small estate he owned at Bourne near Cambridge to join the community at Little Gidding.

By the time they came to Little Gidding, Susanna was in her late forties, and had borne sixteen children. Two had died in infancy, and most of the rest had grown up and left home. However, the two eldest daughters, Mary and Anna, remained at Little Gidding, becoming completely absorbed in the religious life of the community. Mary was already in her mid-twenties when the family arrived at Little Gidding, and as old Mrs Ferrar declined so Mary came to be regarded as the 'mother' of the community. She ran the surgery and the bookbinding work, and she bound the first concordance presented to Charles I. Both Mary and Anna consciously committed themselves to a life of celibacy, with the support of Nicholas; but Nicholas decided that formal vows were wrong, and that continuous trust in the 'good guidance of their gracious Lord God and Master Jesus Christ' would give sufficient strength.[27]

---

[25] JF, pp. 126 ff.

[26] Magdalene College, Ferrar MSS: memorandum by Nicholas Ferrar dated 29 January 1631.

[27] JF, pp. 105–6.

Nicholas's position in the community evolved through the years. At the beginning he made the decisions and gave the orders, establishing its pattern of life. Although he had no manual skills, he was fascinated by the most mundane aspects of daily life, and could readily understand practical problems; so in the early years he frequently intervened in the organization of every aspect of the community's work, and he looked after its financial affairs. He was an authoritarian, even tyrannical leader, qualities necessary in the early stages of such a venture. But as things became more settled so he withdrew from practical responsibility, entrusting the care of the community not only to John but also to his nieces Mary and Anna; and he himself functioned as adviser and pastor – or 'visitor' as they sometimes described him. He worked eighteen hours a day, eating and sleeping little, maintaining his concentration by frequent changes in occupation: reading, writing, praying, meeting visitors, teaching the children, and giving counsel to members of the community. From the early 1630s he began a nightly vigil, rising at one o'clock to pray in the church or the great chamber until morning; usually one or two others, on a rota, would keep watch until Nicholas rose, so there was a continuous vigil of prayer.[28] Receiving Nicholas's spiritual direction could be a tough, uncomfortable business: he would ask penetrating and challenging questions, listening with intense concentration to the answers; then, once he felt he understood the situation, he would give clear, sharp advice.

In the summer of 1637, Nicholas became ill with the same 'ague' which had regularly afflicted him in his younger days. Although the immediate crisis passed quickly, it left him severely depressed, and his usual courage and enthusiasm deserted him. By the autumn his spirits had recovered, but he was now convinced that he was dying. In late October he shocked John when he told him that he was 'shortly to appear before my good Lord God', and entrusted the future of the community to John's hands. He urged John to maintain strictly the existing way of life, and he warned that 'there will be sad times to come' when the community 'will suffer much'.[29] A little while later, when John had

[28] JF, pp. 81–3; Dr J, pp. 271–3.

[29] JF, pp. 61–2.

digested what his brother had said, he came back to him in great distress, wondering how on earth they would cope if Nicholas should die – 'if the shepherd be thus now taken from us'. In a flash of anger Nicholas rebuked John for his feebleness, ordering him to 'go to church, and fast this day, and beg of God to forgive you'.[30] Nicholas died two months later, having lived at Little Gidding for just over eleven years. The community continued for a further twenty years; and it was the steady hand of John, loyal to the vision of his younger brother, and supported by Mary and Anna, which guided the community through the trauma of the Civil War.

Friends and Enemies

Over the chimneypiece in the parlour where visitors were received there was a brass tablet on which was engraved the community's attitude to visitors, in words composed by old Mrs Ferrar:[31]

IHS

He who (by reproof of our errors and remonstrance of that which is more perfect), and seeks to make us better, is welcome as an angel of God.

He who (by a cheerful participation and approbation of that which is good) confirms us in the same, is welcome as a Christian friend.

but

He who in any way goes about to disturb us in that which is and ought to be amongst Christians (Tho it and be not usual in the world) is a burden while he stays and shall bear his judgment, whosoever he be.

He who faults us in absence for that which in presence he makes show to approve of, doth by a double guilt of flattery and slander violate the bonds both of friendship and charity.

[30] JF, p. 101; Dr J, pp. 261–2.

[31] EL, p. xxx.

Little Gidding soon began to attract numerous visitors, and the community was in danger of having the quiet, industrious order of its life swamped by the demands of hospitality. So strangers who came simply out of curiosity were given a glass of wine or a tankard of ale, their questions were answered, and then they were sent on their way. They were not asked to stay for a meal, and this caused some offence to people of noble birth who expected a more lavish welcome. Only those in need were given food, and this prompted some visitors to pretend to be tramps in order to get a closer look at the community.[32]

This strict attitude meant that visitors had to stay locally, and two families living in the neighbourhood allowed their houses to be used for this purpose. One of the families was Roman Catholic, and on various occasions brought Catholic priests to the community. Despite the strong anti-Catholic feeling in the country, they were always welcomed, and Nicholas enjoyed long theological debates on the issues of doctrine which divided the Church. One Catholic priest was so impressed that he later remarked – a little ruefully – that Nicholas Ferrar's arguments against the primacy of the Pope would 'give their church her hands full to answer them, and trouble them in another manner than Luther had done'.[33]

Amongst the close friends of the community were two famous poets, Richard Crashaw and George Herbert. Crashaw was a man of frenzied emotion, who grieved at what he regarded as the spiritual and aesthetic impoverishment that the Reformation had brought on the Church of England. He was both saintly and sensuous, longing for the mystical spirituality and colourful ritual of the medieval church. He first came to Little Gidding when he was a student at Cambridge in the early 1630s, and he frequently used to share with Nicholas in his night watches. When he later became curate at Little St Mary's Church in Cambridge he instituted a similar pattern there of nightly prayers. As his poems reveal, Crashaw had a particular love of 'holy women', and Mary Collett, in her 'friar's grey gown', captured his heart; later he described her as 'the gentlest, kindest, most

---

[32] EL, p. xxxv; Dr J, pp. 247–8.

[33] Dr J, pp. 249–50.

tender-hearted and liberal-handed soul I think is today alive'. His poetry contains a number of references to the community, and one poem describing a 'religious house' clearly refers to Little Gidding:[34]

> Our lodgings hard and homely as our fare;
> That chaste and cheap, as the few clothes we wear.
> A hasty portion of prescribed sleep;
> Obedient slumbers that can wake and weep,
> And sing, and sigh, and work, and sleep again;
> Still rolling a round sphere of still-returning pain.
> Hands full of hearty labours; pains that pay
> And prize themselves; do much, that more they may,
> And work for work, not wages; let tomorrow's
> New drops wash off the sweat of this day's sorrows.
> A long and daily-dying life, which breathes
> A respiration of reviving deaths.
> No cruel guard of diligent cares, that keep
> Crown'd woes awake: as things too wise for sleep,
> But reverent discipline, and religious fear,
> And soft obedience, find sweet biding here;
> Silence, and sacred rest; peace, and pure joys;
> Kind loves keep house, lie close, and make no noise.

Nicholas Ferrar and George Herbert first became friends when they were both students at Cambridge; and in the early 1620s their lives crossed again when both served briefly in Parliament. There was a remarkable meeting of souls between these two men. In their early adulthood they both enjoyed academic and political success, and Herbert was undoubtedly ambitious. But like Nicholas from childhood he had been intensely religious, and even as a teenager had written two sonnets on the theme that the love of God is a fitter subject for verse than the love of a woman.[35] In the same year that Ferrar purchased Little Gidding, Herbert was ordained deacon to the parish of Leighton, about four miles south of Little Gidding. The church there was almost derelict, and at Herbert's request Nicholas and

---

[34] Richard Crashaw, 'Description of a Religious House and Condition of Life'.

[35] On his deathbed in 1633, George Herbert sent a manuscript of his poems to Nicholas for him to publish or destroy as he thought fit. Nicholas published them under the title *The Temple*, and over 20,000 copies were sold.

John supervised its restoration. In 1630, Herbert moved to Bemerton in Wiltshire, and the pattern of daily prayer he established there was inspired by the example of Little Gidding, carrying Nicholas Ferrar's vision of a household of faith into an ordinary country parish.

The most distinguished friend of the community was King Charles himself. His first contact came in the early 1630s when he was staying a few miles away at Apethorpe, the home of the Earl of Westmorland.[36] He was told of the gospel concordance that the community had made for their hourly prayers, and sent a messenger to Little Gidding to ask to borrow it. The King kept it for some months, using it in his own devotions. He wrote various notes in the margin, suggesting improvements to the text, one of which he carefully crossed out, writing below: 'I confess my error; it was well before, I was mistaken.'[37] His queen, Henrietta Maria, a Roman Catholic, also heard of the community, and was planning a visit, until she learnt that the road there was very bumpy. Instead she sent a courtier, who impressed her with his account of 'a Protestant family that outdid the severest monastics abroad'.[38]

When the King returned the concordance he asked that one like it be produced for him within twelve months. This was duly done, and when John Ferrar presented it to the King he described it as 'A rich and rare jewel', declaring: 'How happy a king were I, if I had many more such workmen and women in my kingdom. God's blessing on their hearts and painful hands.' He then went on to ask for a similar concordance of the books of Kings and Chronicles from the Old Testament: in his frequent readings of the books he said that he found 'some seeming contradiction', and hoped that by seeing parallel passages put together this might be resolved. He complained that 'I have often

---

[36] There has been confusion amongst biographers as to whether the King was at Apethorpe in 1631 or in 1634. John Ferrar, writing some twenty years later, seems to have been uncertain, as he altered the date on his original manuscript. However, since the date on the concordance made for the King is 1635, and since according to John this was presented to him only about eighteen months after he borrowed the original concordance, the probable date of this Apethorpe visit was 1634.

[37] JF, p. 117.

[38] Dr J, p. 253.

spoken to many of my chaplains about this thing; but they have excused themselves from it as a difficult work'. So the community set to work on this book, and presented it to the King a year later. Then the King asked for a gospel concordance for his son, Prince Charles, which John Ferrar's son Nicholas produced.[39]

The King visited Little Gidding in March 1642,[40] accompanied by Prince Charles Louis,[41] only five months prior to the outbreak of the Civil War. He was on his way northwards to secure a northern port, to ensure that if necessary he could receive military help from the Continent; and it is extraordinary that at such a fearful time the King could quietly spend a day with a religious community. After being shown the chapel the King spent some hours studying a copy of the Pentateuch which the community had produced and bound. He then went to see the widows whom the community cared for, and gave them five golden coins – it was, he declared, the only money he had with him, having won it at cards the previous evening! Meanwhile the Prince and the courtiers were being fed apple pie and cheese-

[39] JF, pp. 117–19.

[40] It has been widely accepted that King Charles made an earlier visit in 1633. The sources for this are Peckard, *Memoirs*, and J. Rushworth's *Historical Collections* (1680), vol. 2, pt 1, p. 178. However, closer investigation suggests that no such visit took place. Neither Peckard nor Rushworth is reliable on this point. Peckard appears to be quoting from memory from a letter written by Francis Peck, which was lost some twenty years before Peckard wrote. Rushworth's source appears to be a scurrilous pamphlet published in 1641 (see below, p. 169, n. 44) which was highly inaccurate, and moreover his account of the King's movements contradicts the *Calendar of State Papers, Venetian, 1632–1636*. More important, John Ferrar himself, who describes the King's contacts with Little Gidding in great detail, makes no reference to a 1633 visit. His description of the King's visit in 1642 makes it clear that this was the first occasion on which he came to Little Gidding.

[41] John Ferrar wrote of the King being attended by the Palsgrave or Count Palatine, who at that time was Prince Rupert of the Rhine. It is clear, however, from the *Calendar of State Papers, Domestic, 1641–1643*, that Rupert was in Holland at that time. He had paid a very brief visit to Dover in February 1642, and returned to Holland almost immediately with Queen Henrietta Maria and Princess Mary, arriving at The Hague on 11 March, which would have been 1 March in the English calendar. He stayed in Holland until August 1642 when he set out to join Charles I at Nottingham. It seems more likely that it was Rupert's brother, the Elector Palatine, Charles Louis, who was with the King at Little Gidding. He was amongst those who accompanied the King to York, and *CSP, Dom.* records letters which he wrote on his journey to York. Also C. V. Wedgwood in her brief description of the King's visit refers to the King's 'nephew, the Elector Palatine' (*The King's War* (London, 1959), p. 81), thus supporting the view that it was Charles Louis who attended the King, and not Prince Rupert.

cake by the community. At sunset the King mounted his horse to leave, and the whole community knelt down nearby, praying for God's blessing on him. The King took off his hat, and begged the community: 'Pray, pray for my speedy and safe return again.'[42]

As the community became well known and respected by many, so, too, it found itself increasingly a focus of suspicion and slander; and as the King's interest in the community grew his Puritan enemies became more hostile to it. Early in the 1630s a story gained wide circulation that there were twelve crosses in the east window of the church, and that the members of the community bowed to these crosses when they entered. The origin of the story was that the window had three upright iron bars and four horizontal ones, and that someone had mischievously suggested that the intersections of the bars were crosses. But such was the eagerness of people to believe such rumours that it was soon taken seriously, and visitors to the community began to inquire about it.[43]

Far more damaging was the publication in 1641 of a pamphlet about Little Gidding entitled *The Arminian Nunnery, or a Briefe Description Relation of the Late Erected Monasticall Place.* The term 'Arminian', though it had a theological meaning referring to the teaching of a Dutch theologian, was in this context a general term of abuse, being, as the pamphlet said, 'a bridge to Popery'. On the cover was a rough woodcut of a woman in nun's habit with a rosary in her hand. The pamphlet was based on a letter by Edward Lenton,[44] who had visited the community some years previously; but it grossly distorted Lenton's description. It referred to the members 'crouching, cringing and prostrating to the ground to the altar-like communion table, or the rich gilded candlesticks'; and to their 'promiscuous private prayers all the night long'. The pamphlet was widely circulated, and was submitted 'to the wise consideration of this present parliament', implying that Parliament should take steps to close

---

[42] JF, pp. 149–56. A similar but longer account of the King's 1642 visit is contained in a manuscript belonging to the Tangye Collection at the Museum of London. The author clearly had access to John's account of the visit, and probably also used John's biography of Nicholas to embellish his account with a general description of the community.

[43] JF, pp. 77–80.

[44] EL, pp. xxiii–xxxvi.

the community. Lenton himself was appalled by the misuse of his letter by 'such hucksters', and John Ferrar described it 'as stuffed with abominable falsehoods, and such stories as the devil himself would be ashamed to utter'.[45]

Parliament did not in fact act on the pamphlet; but the notoriety which it gave to Little Gidding meant that throughout the Civil War the community lived in fear of attack. They survived unmolested until the very end. On 2 May 1646, King Charles, defeated and alone, arrived at Little Gidding during the night seeking refuge. Fearing that the Parliament troops might come and search for him at Little Gidding, John Ferrar took him to a private house in Coppingford about four miles away.[46] The King left the following morning, and was arrested shortly afterwards. A few weeks later, in reprisal for harbouring the King, Parliament troops came and ransacked the church and house. The community had received warning of their approach, and were able to flee. The troops wrecked the interior of the church, ripping out the organ and gallery and burning them in the churchyard, and roasting six of the community's sheep on the fire. The brass font and the eagle lectern were thrown into a pond nearby.

A Haven of Peace

Nicholas Ferrar and his family came to Little Gidding to retreat from the conflicts and controversies of the world, and sought to have no influence on the religious and political issues of the day. Yet through the community life they established, and the impression they made on others, they became far more deeply involved in the world's problems, and their influence was far greater than if they had remained in London pursuing careers in commerce and government. One cannot point to any sequence of events whose cause was affected by the community, but their common life embodied the spirit of English Christianity at its finest, which in turn infused not only the religious but also the political life of the nation.

[45] JF, pp. 55–7.

[46] Peckard, *Memoirs*, p. 227. Peckard's source for this final visit by the King is the record of the examination of Dr Hudson, the King's chaplain, on 16 May 1646. This record can be found in Francis Peck's *Desiderata curiosa*, vol. 9, p. 9.

From the Reformation in the early sixteenth century there has been in the Church of England tension between 'high' and 'low' churchmanship, between the Catholic and the Protestant traditions. And there has been tension between Church and State, with the Church supporting and enjoying the protection of the political establishment, but at the same time retaining a degree of moral and spiritual independence. At times these tensions have led to bitter divisions and even bloodshed, never more so than in the early and mid-seventeenth century. In the Civil War religious and political tensions were intertwined, with questions of the theological legitimacy of political power being bound up with disputes about the nature and authority of the Church itself. But these same tensions could also be creative; and as the nation tore itself apart that quiet, remote group of Christians at Little Gidding bore witness to this possibility. They were indeed loyal to the political establishment in the person of King Charles I, even when he was, in Eliot's phrase, a 'broken king';[47] yet the simple pattern of life they established – a society in microcosm – indicated a very different notion of God's order from that which seemed to inspire their autocratic and petulant monarch. And despite the slander thrown at them they were passionately loyal to the established church, living up to its highest traditions; yet in doing so they transcended the party spirit which divided the Church, and represented a unity between her two traditions of spirituality – in the context of their time they were an 'ecumenical' community.

Strangely it is in the King's attitude that we can see most poignantly the significance of Little Gidding. As C. V. Wedgwood has said, it was for the King a 'haven of Anglican peace'[48] in a turbulent and troubled land. Its production of beautiful books appealed to the King's acquisitive instincts, and he was delighted with each new gift. But the holiness of its simple and unassuming way of life drew from him a much deeper spiritual response. Pauline Gregg has described how on his journey northwards in 1642 the King proceeded 'with little visible emotion';[49] yet his

---

[47] T. S. Eliot, 'Little Gidding', *Four Quartets* (London, 1943).

[48] Wedgwood, *The King's War, 1641–1647*, p. 555.

[49] P. Gregg, *King Charles I* (London, 1981), p. 350.

visit to Little Gidding 'broke through his defences' – one can sense the anxiety in the King's parting words to the community: 'Pray, pray for my speedy and safe return again.'[50] When he did return four years later it was, as Peckard concludes, 'the very last place where this most unfortunate Prince was in the hands of those whom he might safely trust'.[51] The community was not only a haven, but also a parable of peace, a place where king and commoner, Catholic and Protestant, could find welcome.

[50] JF, p. 154.

[51] Peckard, *Memoirs*, p. 232.

PLATE 6   Cabinet embroidered with representations of Charles I, Henrietta
Maria and their children, purchased in or before 1899 by Queen
Victoria from the descendants of the Ferrar-Mapletoft family,
who also preserved a Story-Book *Great Harmony and Great
Concordance* of Little Gidding. It is assumed that such cabinets
were not made so soon, but the iconography supports the family
tradition that it was the gift of Charles I to the Community.
(*Reproduced by gracious permission of Her Majesty the Queen.*)

CHARLES I
AND LITTLE GIDDING
Pamela Tudor-Craig

W E MUST reluctantly concede from Robert Van de Weyer's researches that a meeting at Little Gidding between Charles I and Nicholas Ferrar is unlikely to have taken place. However, it remains true that a lively connection was forged in the early 1630s between the community and the King,[1] a link apparently fostered by royal gifts of which the direct descent within the Ferrar family was recorded in 1899.[2] The purse there mentioned has not yet been traced,[3] but the casket

---

[1] It is a matter of only a few months, but I would suggest that the Apethorpe visit and the first request for a Little Gidding book were part of the journey to Scotland in May 1633. The deliberately circuitous nature of that journey and the leisure built into it provide a more likely context for the inquiry than 1634. J. Rushworth's circumstantial account (*Progresses*, vol. 2, p. 178) of a departure from London for Scotland on 13 May is supported by a letter from Archbishop Laud, which Rushworth also published (*Historical Collection 1618-29*, London 1659 14th May, pagination faulty), showing that Laud did indeed depart on that day. We know that the King stayed at Theobalds during that week and made a second departure from London a few days later. If the loan of the Harvard concordance took place on that journey, we have a foundation for Rushworth and Peckard's belief in a 1633 encounter; cf. also *Calendar of State Papers, Venetian, Correspondence, 1632-1636*, pp. 483 *et al.*

[2] E. C. Sharland (ed.), *The Story Books of Little Gidding* (1899), pp. v–vi.

[3] I am grateful to Lady Lyell for her help in tracing these objects; to the Librarians of Clare College, Cambridge, past (Sir Bryan Kippard) and present (Dr Nigel Weiss) for their endeavours to find the missing purse; and, above all, to Mrs Harland and Miss MacNeil of the Lord Chamberlain's Office for their collaboration in finding and photographing the cabinet in the Royal Collection. I understand from Miss Levy, Keeper of Textiles at the Victoria and Albert Museum, that no cabinets of this type have been identified with dates earlier than 1650. However, the Little Gidding Community had been dispersed at the outbreak of the Civil War, and would not have been in a position to make or to receive such an object after that date. It is possible, therefore, that the context of the community's association with Charles I may provide the evidence for an earlier start to the chronology of this type of casket than has been recognized hitherto.

was sold to Queen Victoria and is now in the library at Windsor Castle (Plate 6). It is a richly embroidered needlewoman's cabinet, a lavish example of the silk shading type, with, on the front, basically recognizable images of Charles I and Henrietta Maria (wearing her crown) and, on the top, images of the children with a dog. If these latter depend upon the Van Dyck group portrait of the children, then they cannot be dated before 1635–6, in every way the most probable circumstantial date for such a presentation. As some of the Little Gidding bindings were not of stamped leather, but of velvet or embroidery,[4] such a royal gift could well have been part of the King's response to the achievements of the needlewomen of Little Gidding. The cabinet could be a delayed addendum to the royal reaction at receiving the Great Concordance: 'God's blessing on their hearts and painful hands. . . . I know they will receive no reward for it. . . .' On 16 March 1642, when, as Robert Van de Weyer has explained, the King paid his first visit to Little Gidding, Charles had left London for the last time as a free man. He was no longer in a position to send appropriate gifts for 'painful hands'.

There is further evidence of the community's exchange with the King among the Story Books of the Little Academy, founded by Nicholas Ferrar on the Neoplatonic model.[5] The discourse

[4] The Kings–Chronicles concordance made for Charles I in 1637 has a binding of purple velvet. The concordance of the gospels in English, Latin, French and Italian made for the Prince of Wales (the book seen by Charles I and his company in 1642) is bound in green velvet. Little Gidding still possesses an example of the embroidered covers made by the ladies of the household. Their needles were plied with equal industry in the furnishing of the chapel. For John Ferrar's description of the blue Sunday and holy-day furnishings with their gold and silver lace and fringing, and the working-day tapestry carpets and green cloth, see *The Ferrar Papers* ed. B. Blackstone (Cambridge, 1938), pp. 27–8. Again there remains at Little Gidding a small portion of the 'tapestry' work. It is of the finest petit point.

[5] The Story Books of the Little Academy have been published in three instalments: (*a*) Sharland (*Story Books*) published the group of stories which purports to have been delivered in the Christmas season of 1631–2. The evidence that there followed a pause of over two years until spring 1634 is given on p. xliii. (*b*) The debate, and group of narratives illustrating it, which he termed 'The Winding Sheet', together with the Short Moral Histories, were published by Blackstone, *Ferrar Papers*. These were certainly initiated in 1634, but could contain later material. (*c*) 'On the Austere Life' and 'The Retirement of Charles V' were published in A. M. Williams, *Conversations at Little Gidding* (Cambridge, 1970). His introduction gives the most useful, if not definitive, account of the chronology of the Story Books, and attempts to identify the members

on 'Patience' which took place during Christmastide 1631 had included a sharp reprimand of the English aristocracy, which aristocracy took its tone, after all, from the King himself:

> ... the Impatiency of enduring that Paines and Care which belongs to Government makes our Gentry and Nobility cast up their owne and their Countries busines, and betake themselves to hunting, hawking and the like Riots. And these they magnify as noble Imployment, not because themselves are so perswaded (for their owne Consciences tell them they bee but unworthy Vanitys), but because by the appearance of bodily Labour they have a fair colour for the Idleness of their Minds, and in the Independency that these kind of Actions have to any others, a freedome for their inconstant Affections and humours to revell as they please. . . .[6]

No more assiduous huntsman than Charles I, whose perambulations in search of sport on the way to Scotland probably occasioned his first contact with Little Gidding. Yet by the time of the discourse of 'the Winding Sheet', which must be later than March 1634[7] and which may have been unfolded in 1635 or even later, a new note is struck in an elaborate comparison between one of the Holy Roman Emperors[8] and 'our Deare Soueraigne, who hath so embellished his Crown wth Deuotion, as he seemes no lesse a Prince in the Church then in the Realme, A supreme Example in the performance of sacred Duties, as well as the supreme head in Administration both of Ciuill & Ecclesiastical Iurisdiction . . .'. So much, apparently, from John Ferrar, in the character of the Repeater, to which the more moderate voice, thought to be that of Nicholas in the guise of the Register, replies: 'Wee may verely . . . affirme that of him. . . . That he is ye Ornament of Christian Religion. . . .'

[6] Sharland, *Story Books*, p. 135.

[7] *Ferrar Papers*, pp. 101–201.

[8] ibid., pp. 184–5. The Emperor in question is presumably Henry II (973–1024), 'the Saint'. The source for this Imperial story is the Italian cardinal and Oratorian, Baronius (1534–1607).

under their assumed titles. The conversations were in fact the earliest delivered at Little Gidding, dating from the summer of 1631, during Nicholas's absence in London. There is much more work to be done on the Little Academy and its sources, and my remarks are only provisional.

LEARNER: And long may he bee so, & perfect both this and those other glorious titles, wch the general consent of Historians hath bestowed on this selfsame Henry.
APPRENTICE: What were they I pray?
LEARNER: Semper Augustus and Father of his Countrey.
APPRENTICE: They are iustly due to our Charles & could not bee more deserued by Henry then by him. so doth the good Estate both of Church & Common wealth, as farre as reason can conceiue wholly depend on his safetie & welfare & is maintained in the Flourishing Condition, wch wee enioy, chiefly by his Pietie and iustice. . . .

And more to the same effect.

This conversation is the only direct reference in the Story Books to the well-known loyalty of the community.

The Little Academy is a mine of information about the stance of Christianity to which Charles I gave his special imprimatur and which has been little explored by twentieth-century historians. It is almost impossible to believe that all the sessions of the Little Academy took place within two non-consecutive years. The originals have come down to us in the form of fair copies, and it is reasonable to suspect that the sisters rearranged their notes with an eye to cogency. A sudden change in character towards the end of the collection published by Blackstone under the name of 'the Winding Sheet' could reflect a conscious attempt within the community to meet the external criticisms which were to come to a head in 1641 with the publication of the *Arminian Nunnery* pamphlet.[9] The charges of bowing and scraping in that pamphlet are so closely related to those brought against Archbishop Laud in the same year[10] that they may have been directly derived from the attack on Laud. Disregarding these, and *pace* the outraged protestations of John Ferrar – 'stuffed with abominable falsehoods and such stories as the devil himself would be ashamed to utter'[11] – the Story Books disclose that Little Gidding

---

[9] For which we have Peck's transcript among the Middle Hill manuscripts at Clare College, Cambridge. The engraving of a 'Nun' from this pamphlet is pasted on to the flyleaf of an early eighteenth-century Bible, which belonged to a Mapletoft of Cambridge, in the collection of Hampstead Parish Church.

[10] At his dedication of the Church of St Katherine Creed: cf. Rushworth, *Historical Collection*, vol. 2 (*1629–40*) (London, 1680), pp. 76–9.

[11] Quoted by A. L. Maycock, *Nicholas Ferrar of Little Gidding* (London, 1963), p. 136.

was indeed thoroughly Arminian, in the best sense of its major terms:

1. A return to the earliest, pre-Schismatic Christian Sources common to all Churches.
2. A belief in the free operation of divine grace beyond the confines of orthodoxy.
3. A care for the upkeep of churches, their embellishment and the celebration of an ordered liturgy therein.[12]

The first and second of these tenets can be illustrated from the choice of material within the Little Gidding Story Books, and the third is illustrated by the practice derived from this place. If we analyse the stories into categories we find that tenet 2 is illustrated by eight edifying stories drawn from non-Christian classical sources. Tenet 1 is illustrated by far the largest block – thirty-four tales drawn from the Doctors of the Church, the Desert Fathers, from early martyrologies, from Greek Christianity of the pre-Schismatic period, and from related material. An interest in early British history is supported by stories of Oswin, Edward the Elder, and Emma, mother of Edward the Confessor. The Oswin story is recounted 'as neer as possibly I can without variation from the original relation of venerable Bede himself'.[13] There are three exempla from the lives of early Popes.[14]

Moreover, eighteen stories relating to relatively recent European history are drawn exclusively from the non-Reformed countries of France, Italy and Spain. The setpiece, the longest story of all, is that of the retirement of the Catholic Emperor Charles V,[15] who vacated his throne to Phillip II, husband of the Mary under whose orders the bulk of the English Protestant

---

[12] For the latest account of Arminianism and the threat that it was believed to offer to the Reformed Church, cf. Nicholas Tyacke, 'Puritanism, Arminianism and Counter-Revolution', in C. Russell (ed.), *The Origins of the English Civil War* (London, 1973), pp. 119–43. Hostility to Arminianism was not new in 1641. In the debate in Parliament of February 1629 the 4th Earl of Bedford saw it as 'the little thief put into the window of the church to unlock the door' (to Rome): ibid., p. 136.

[13] Sharland, *Story Books*, p. 243. A collected edition of Bede appeared in Cologne in 1612.

[14] Gregory the Great, Adrian VI and Marcellus II.

[15] The prime (but not the only) source for the abdication of Charles V has been identified as Jacques-Auguste de Thou, *Historia sui temporis*, published in a complete edition of his works in 1620 (Williams, *Conversations*, p. xlv).

martyrs suffered. The example of Charles V was further under-lined by Nicholas Ferrar's choice, supported by George Her-bert,[16] for translation of the *Divine Considerations* of Charles V's spiritual adviser, John Valdesso. A copy of François de Sales' *Introduction to the Devout Life*[17] was bound by the sisters of the community. The fervour with which Nicholas Ferrar inspired those around him was of the mountain air of Counter-Reformation mysticism. We know from George Herbert's correspondence with the community that he borrowed from Nicholas Ferrar his Italian edition of Savonarola's *Of the Simplicity of Christ*.[18] There is evidence of familiarity with the work of Thomas More,[19] illustrated by More's anecdote of the southern juryman who could not give a verdict that went against his conscience and, also probably, by a story favourable to Catherine of Aragon.[20]

If we look, on the other hand, for the study at Little Gidding of the standard writings of the Protestant Reformers, the evidence is relatively scanty, and bunched together towards the end of the dialogue termed 'the Winding Sheet'. Here we find a glancing

[16] Maycock, *Nicholas Ferrar*, pp. 270–2.

[17] Published in 1609. In the dialogue 'On the Austere Life', the Guardian bursts out in praise of this work: 'what I lately read in most Diuine & Learned Sallis . . .' (Williams, *Conversations*, p. 297). A proclamation calling in all copies of a book called *An Introduction to a Devout Life* in order that they might be publicly burnt was issued on 14 May 1637, printed by Nicholas Oakes of London. It contained, according to the proclamation, 'diverse passages . . . tending to popery', and a copy had been examined by the Chaplain to the Archbishop of Canterbury. See proclamation in the possession of the Society of Antiquaries, no. 223. Nicholas Ferrar also translated Ludovico Carbone's treatise on *The Christian Education of Children* (Venice, 1596; England, 1636), and Leonardo Lessiùs' *Treatise on Temperance*. Lessius was a Belgian Jesuit: cf. Maycock, *Nicholas Ferrar*, p. 272.

[18] cf. *Ferrar Papers*, p. 268.

[19] Sharland, *Story Books*, pp. 220–2. The most likely source would have been Thomas Stapleton's *Vita Thomae Mori*, published in Latin in 1588 in Douai, Paris, Cologne, Frankfurt, Leipzig and Graz – but not, of course, in England. Nicholas Ferrar had been in Leipzig, for example, for five months of the latter part of 1613.

[20] Sharland, *Story Books*, pp. 36, 37. (The Submisse) comments: 'The Cause was undoubtedly just, but the affections and courage of the King full of unkindnes and harshnes. . . .'

[21] *Ferrar Papers*, p. 134.

reference to Zwingli[21] and an even less prominent one to Martin Luther.[22] The only anti-Papal story in the whole collection concerns Pope Paul II, and it draws down upon the teller something approaching criticism.[23] On the other hand, we are regaled with a story of Marsilio Ficino.[24] There are references to Cosimo de'Medici,[25] quotations suggesting knowledge of Robert Burton's *Anatomy of Melancholy*[26] Boethius' *De Consolatione Philosophae*[27] and Sir Philip Sidney.[28] John Ferrar frequently uses proverbs, which he could have derived through a familiarity with Erasmus' collection,[29] and the use of Aesop's Fables may reflect the edition of 1610. We are beginning to have an idea of the character of Nicholas Ferrar's bookshelves.

The burning of the three great hampers of Nicholas Ferrar's secular books on the eve of his death is frequently described.[30] The only works specifically condemned to that bonfire are Spenser's *Faerie Queene* and Ariosto's *Orlando Furioso*.[31] The reason for the special damnation of *Orlando Furioso* is of great interest: 'the world and the Devill owe to these histories of Chivalry the making of that Match between Christianity and revenge, which could never, though diligently laboured from the first, bee brought to pass until these last and perillous times of

---

[22] ibid., p. 149. Luther is only mentioned because of his relationship with the Electors of Saxony.

[23] ibid., pp. 153–6: 'I perciue y^u have been busied in others wardrobes as well as y own & that y^u haue reaped the teares wth ye wheat. . . .'

[24] Sharland, *Story Books*, p. 87.

[25] ibid., pp. 54, 167.

[26] First published in 1621, though three further editions of 1624, 1628 and 1632 came out in Nicholas Ferrar's lifetime: cf. Williams, *Conversations*, pp. lxxxiv and 254, nn. 1 and 2.

[27] ibid., p. lvii.

[28] ibid., pp. 206–7. John Ferrar quotes Sir Philip Sidney's sonnet, 'Leave me, O Love which reaches but to dust . . .': cf. folio edition of 1598.

[29] Erasmus' more melancholy work, *De praeparatione ad mortem*, was familiar to the community. *Ferrar Papers*, p. 126. For John Ferrar's use of Proverbs, see Sharland, *Story Books*, pp. 104, 124, 126, 131; *Ferrar Papers*, p. 121.

[30] For example, by Maycock, *Nicholas Ferrar*, p. 298.

[31] Sharland, *Story Books*, p. 119.

ours . . .', an attack made at Christmas 1631.[32] Charles I had copies of the offending Spenser and Ariosto beside him in his last days; but, then, he also had Herbert's *The Temple*.[33]

But what of Foxe's *Book of Martyrs*, the diet of Low Churchmen? The *Arminian Nunnery* pamphlet accused the community of having 'the Book of Martyrs in the Chappell, but few or none be suffered to read therein, but only it is there (I say) kept for show'. Bishop Lindsell, however, described old Mrs Ferrar as often reading in the *Book of Martyrs*, and this image is borne out by her quotation from Foxe – but a quotation referring to Pico della Mirandola.[34] The martyrdoms quoted from Foxe's book are only six[35] and they are grouped in association with relatively current stories of witchcraft. This economy in martyrdoms is not due to any distaste at ghoulish details (especially martyrdoms of children in which their mothers appeared to exalt): a gaunt area of early Christian heroism to which the ladies of Little Gidding appear to have been peculiarly drawn.

Against the picture so generally favourable to the mainstream of Catholicism, and so moderate in its criticism thereof, Nicholas Ferrar's protestation that he would burn down a room of his house in which a popish mass had taken place reads as if it were occasioned by the need to protect his family.[36] We may interpret the statement put in his lips by the *Arminian Nunnery* pamphlet, 'That he did as verily believe the Pope to be anti-Christ, as any article of his faith', as similarly prompted. The overall impression to be gained from the Story Books is that Nicholas's inter-

---

[32] John Ferrar's account of Nicholas's deathbed speech (quoted by Blackstone, *Ferrar Papers*, p. 63) includes the passage: '. . . the having an Orlando in the house is sufficient ground to have it burnt down over y^c heads, that truly feare God'. It was clearly worse than a Mass.

[33] C. V. Wedgwood, *The Trial of Charles I* (London, 1964), p. 15.

[34] Peckard's *Memoirs of the Life of Mr Nicholas Ferrar*, quoted by Blackstone (*Ferrar Papers*, p. 9), shows that Nicholas Ferrar and his brothers and sisters were brought up in the usual way, on a daily portion of the Scriptures and the *Book of Martyrs*.

[35] James Bainham, Peter Marchesy, Hugh Laverock, John Apries, Peter Clark and William Hunter. They are all grouped together, among more ancient martyrs, under the stories told through the Feast of Christmastide 1632: Sharland, *Story Books*, chs 13–15.

[36] Quoted from John Ferrar's Life by Blackstone, *Ferrar Papers*, p. 75.

pretation of what he called 'the good old way'[37] would have veered more towards Catholicism than towards Puritanism. But there is no doubt he determined always to keep the middle path as quaintly defined by George Herbert[38]

> A fine aspect in fit array
> Neither too mean, nor yet too gay
> > Shows who is best.
> Outlandish looks may not compare:
> For all they either painted are,
> > Or else undrest.
>
> She on the hills, which wantonly
> Allureth all in hope to be
> > By her preferr'd,
> Hath kiss'd so long her painted shrines,
> That ev'n her face by kissing shines,
> > For her reward.
>
> She in the valley is so shie
> Of dressing, that her hair doth lie
> > About her eares:
> While she avoids her neighbours pride
> She wholly goes on th' other side,
> > And nothing wears.
>
> But, dearest Mother what those misse,
> The mean, thy praise and glory is,
> > And long may be.
> Blessed be God, whose love it was
> To double-moat thee with his grace,
> > And none but thee.

A poem which makes up in self-satisfaction for what it may lack in felicity of imagery. The Ferrar Anglicanism is of special importance since, after the disgrace of Laud, and while under overt attack from the Puritans, Charles I so deliberately aligned himself with churchmanship as practised at Little Gidding.

---

[37] ibid., p. 85.

[38] In the poem 'The British Church' published in *The Temple*, edited by Nicholas Ferrar (1633). For the Ferrars, and for Herbert, the quarry of their spiritual quest was not High or Low Churchmanship, but the encounter with God. Herbert's 'mean', Ferrar's 'good old way' recognized the ring of true spirituality wherever they found it.

The third prominent characteristic of Arminianism was a care for the upkeep and embellishment of church buildings and the ceremonial therein.[39] Here the leadership of the Ferrars may have been more influential than is generally realized. The story of old Mrs Ferrar's setting about the reinstatement of Little Gidding Church, which had declined to a farm building, before she was prepared to lay her head to rest is well known.[40] In so reacting, she was following the pattern of her married life. Her husband had repaired and reseated the church of St Bennet Shirehog in London. It is also established that Nicholas Ferrar was behind George Herbert's restoration and partial rebuilding and refurnishing of Leighton Bromswold in 1632.[41] In this transaction Arthur Woodnoth, goldsmith and banker in Foster Lane, cousin of the Ferrars, took an active part. Woodnoth regarded Nicholas Ferrar as his spiritual director.[42] The friendship between Nicholas Ferrar and George Herbert was more equal.[43] Another close relative and friend of Little Gidding is our link with the other notable example of parish church rebuilding of

[39] Herbert's laborious analogy between the types of Christianity and dress was also taken up in the *Declaration or Resolution of the County of Hereford*, which was printed in London in 1642 (Proclamations in the Society of Antiquaries, no. 255):

Wherefore we as faithful subjects to his Majesty, as free-born Englishmen, do joyn in an unanimous resolution to maintain:
a) the Protestant Religion
b) the King's just Power
c) the Laws of the Land
d) the Liberty of the Subject.
For the first, the Protestant Religion, we cannot but with grief of heart remember how it hath been assaulted in the Inworks and skirts of it the Liturgy, and decent Ceremonies established by Law. . . .

From internal evidence, the Declaration post-dates the King's arrival in York. Mrs Jill Croft-Murrary has suggested that this pamphlet may have been drafted by Sir Herbert Croft (1603–91), at this time Chaplain to Charles I, to be Dean of Hereford in 1644 and Bishop from 1661 to his death.

[40] Maycock, *Nicholas Ferrar*, pp. 129–33.

[41] *Ferrar Papers*, pp. 58, 77, 275, 276.

[42] For the Nicholas Ferrar–Arthur Woodnoth relationship of Spiritual Director and neophyte, see ibid., pp. 257 and 276–7.

[43] Maycock, *Nicholas Ferrar*, p. 233, quoting Barnabas Oley (1652): 'Their very souls cleaved together most intimately, and drove a large stock of Christian intelligence together. . . .'

the period: Staunton Harold in Leicestershire built by Sir Robert Shirley in 1653. Robert Mapletoft, who preached the address at Nicholas Ferrar's funeral, found shelter during the Civil War with Sir Robert Shirley. So that fair church and the fairer inscription – 'When all things sacred throughout the nation were either demolished or profaned, Sir Robert Shirley, Bart, founded this church, whose singular praise it is to have done the best things in the worst of times, and to have hoped them in the most calamitous' – go back, at only one remove, to Nicholas Ferrar.

The King's visit to Little Gidding in March 1642 can be seen in the light of a counter-declaration of his religious position, aligning it with that of this community. But the visit of May 1646 could only have been in search of counsel from John Ferrar, the faithful mirror of his more outstanding brother. We have relatively few direct statements from Nicholas Ferrar of his religious position, other than those already quoted. It was reflected, of course, in his personal austerity and in the rule of life and activity here pursued. But the stories are totally consistent in the approach to Christianity which they reveal. They indicate a coherent and closely reasoned stand against violence. It is evident in the bias of exempla chosen for admiration, which celebrate in multiplied instances the turning of the other cheek. It is the basis of the long discussion on 'Patience':[44] 'the proper Armes of Christian Religion. . . . Hee that refuseth to beare Patience for his Coat must pass over into some other Family. Hee may be a Gallant, a martiall Man, a great Man of this world; a Saynt of Heaven, a good Christian hee cannot bee. . . . Hee must bee a Christian in earnest and not in appearance that weares this peice of Armour. . . .' The speaker goes on to accuse Chivalric Romance of presenting a violent image as acceptable in Christian terms: 'through faire appearances and encouragements . . . the Impatiency of Offences, the requitall of Injuries, the shedding of Bloud, as if it were but shedding of water, have been bred and nourished. . . .'

The first anecdote chosen for Ash Wednesday 1631[45] ex-

---

[44] Sharland, *Story Books*, pp. 103–53, esp. pp. 118–21.

[45] ibid., p. 4.

pounds the Little Gidding view of conquest. Cineas questions Pirrhus as to his purpose in planning to conquer first the Greeks, then the Romans, then the Carthaginians. 'What shall wee then doe? Pirrhus: Oh Cineas, sayeth hee, then will wee give our selves to rest and quiet, to Banquets and Games, and enjoy all the happiness which wee shall have purchased. If that, sayd hee, dread Soveraigne, bee the upshott of your intents and aimes, who forbid you now to accomplish the same with saving of all that Labour and hazard which wee shall undergoe, and perhaps be overwhelmed with?' Pirrhus, needless to say, ignores Cineas, and goes on to be 'miserably slaine by a peice of Timber cast downe from the top of a house by a woman's hand'. So much for the war of aggression.

To the issue of the 'Just War' the community gave more serious attention. Their position was most clearly set out in the context of a story of John Frederick, Elector of Saxony,[46] who refused the offer of a mighty army to recover for him his lost possessions. The Apprentice, one of the ladies, exclaims: 'Here's a Testimone, y^t cannot be inhanced. It is so full, so plain, so pregnant. of a witnes, y^t is beyond all touch of Exception, of incomparable iudgement, of matchless Experience. He will rather sitt on ye ground, then be raysed aloft by Armes. & continue a looser in Peace, then recouer one of the fairest dignities on Earth by warre. And this he deliuers as his final determination out of aboundance of Conscience, out of strength of grace, out of height of courage, out of depth of wisedome ... and how should we dare to question any thing in opposition or presume to add in confirmation.'

So much for the 'Just War'. The same conversation at Little Gidding furnishes their prophetic comment on treachery and civil war. It was the custom of the Little Academy to rival one another in the tales of heroic virtue they recounted. In response to the claim made here by the Apprentice that the decision of the Elector of Saxony represented the summit of grace, courage and wisdom, Nicholas Ferrar himself made one of his rare contributions to the debate in the person of the 'Register': 'y^t so illustrious a passage may not goe alone, Giue me leave to accompanie

---

[46] *Ferrar Papers*, esp. p. 152.

it wth Gaspar Collignies resolution[47] . . . when he was impor-
tunately disswaded from going to Paris vpon iust suspicion of
that stupendious Treacherie, wch afterwards proued too true, he
made Answere, y^t Peace being now concluded & ye obliuion of
all former matters agreed on, he was determined to committ
himself to ye Kings faith & he for his part would rather make
choice to be drawn by a hook vp & down ye streets of Paris then
to haue recourse againe to civill warres'. To which John Ferrar
adds: 'Ciuill warres are indeed the worst of all others howsoeuer
they oftimes seeme to haue the fayrest colo^r. . . .'

Had Charles I consulted the community on his first visit here
as to his most Christian course of action at that fateful point, we
know what they must needs have said to him. But in 1642, alas
for Charles and for his kingdom, he may have sought ratification
of his churchmanship, but not advice. Did John Ferrar's remark
on the Cross within the Crown (see above) carry a second meaning? If so, it was too soon for the King to observe it.

But when, desperate, Charles I returned in 1646 advice is the
only gift he could have sought or received. Any serious words that
may have passed between John Ferrar and his sovereign on that
fleeting occasion must have tended towards the quality most
admired throughout the time of the first community in this
place: the giving up of this world, either by adopting a hidden
life or by martyrdom, for a spiritual kingdom.[48] We may believe
that John Ferrar will have pointed beyond the giddy years of the
Crown by Divine Right towards the Source and Pattern of that
Crown.[49] The spirituality fostered by the Ferrars and the remarkable group around them may have helped the King to make
sense of the sorrows of his last days, and to find in his recognition
of the steps to martyrdom a rarer exaltation.[50]

---

[47] Comte Gaspard de Chatillon Coligny (1519–72), Protestant Admiral of France. The
story, Nicholas Ferrar acknowledges, is derived from Thou.

[48] In 1646 the future Charles II was only sixteen years old. It was perhaps too soon to
suggest the model of abdication set by the Emperor Charles V.

[49] Within months of Charles's second visit to Little Gidding, George Fox preached his
first sermon.

[50] Luminously described in Wedgwood, *Trial of Charles I*.

THE DEBATE
ON 'THE OTHER HOUSE'
IN RICHARD CROMWELL'S
PARLIAMENT
Ivan Roots

WINNOWED to six members by expulsions and defections, the House of Lords was abolished in 1649 as 'useless and dangerous', condemned by failure to join in the trial of Charles I and by a suspected propensity to negotiate still with a king over the water. The Rump Commons, the 'representative' body, claimed and exercised sovereignty. Yet in April 1660 the Upper Chamber was back in the Convention Parliament, useful now and, so far from dangerous, a guarantor of order and stability. It still survives, though now and then, particularly in times of crisis, as in 1831–2 and 1909–11, impugned. Still essentially male and hereditary, though slightly modified by bringing in life peers and some women, to many it seems an anachronism.

The Parliament Act of 1911, reducing its delaying powers, promised drastic reform of its composition. But diversity of attitudes between and among the parties has inhibited that. Some see 'improvement' of any sort as likely to make it a stronger and more effective clog upon the initiative of the elective chamber, where parliamentary power ought exclusively to reside. Others value it as a check upon rash or unduly partisan action by a Commons majority, providing thereby time for fresh thoughts and advice by detached men and women experienced both in and out of politics. It has also taken on some of the burden of parliamentary work, not solely of a routine nature. It has been commonly assumed that 'Mr Balfour's poodle' would be more useful and less dangerous to right-wing than to left-of-centre governments, but recent experience has shown an inclination to transcend the limitation of a built-in conservative (or even Conservative) majority by criticism to the point of frustration of controversial measures from the Tories. A Labour Party committed to root-and-branch abolition may yet glimpse advantages in the retention of a second chamber, one no doubt shorn of hereditary lordship and free of the connotations of 'the Upper House' – something, indeed, devised as 'the other House' or 'another House'.

Such terms and attitudes are reminiscent of the Parliament of 1659 called by Protector Richard Cromwell, where the Commons poured out intelligence, learning, eloquence and, above all, time on debating its own relationship to 'the other House' set up by the revised constitution of June 1656 which in its original form had offered Oliver Cromwell a crown. Constitutional development in the 1650s was a mishmash of opinions about a past culminating in 'the late troubles' and of diverse formulation of what was just and apt for the present and future. Men saw themselves as trustees to posterity of something called 'the ancient constitution' but they disagreed on what it was. Some found its essence in traditional kingship. Others would purge it of monarchical 'exorbitances' and improve it by positive reforms. Some – 'loyalists', they might be called – would serve any *de facto* regime providing security. The history of the Protectorate can be taken as an attempt, not entirely unsuccessful, to reconcile contrary views by intertwining change and continuity, the new and re-formed merging with the old and tried. An example is a state church loose in structure. Another is Parliament itself, initially in the Instrument of Government a single chamber and then, more traditionally, in the Humble Petition and Advice bicameral, but with novel features such as 'representation' from Scotland and Ireland. Responses were mixed to such expedients or experiments. The second session (January–February 1657/8) of the second Protectorate Parliament found the Commons dominated by the returning MPs kept out from the first session, indignant, many looking back to 'the golden years' of the sovereign Rump. They would have nothing to do with the nominated Other House which met at the same time and was itself, in fact, doing nothing in particular. The upshot was a sharp dissolution. Soon Oliver was dead, succeeded quietly by his eldest son, Richard, to the chagrin of Royalists who had expected at least 'perturbations', if not 'interreigns'. Richard soon called a Parliament, broadly under the terms of the Humble Petition, this time without exclusions and with the Other House named by his predecessor. Almost at once the debates set off a year before were renewed and extended.

The first open argument for a return to a bicameral Parliament had come in December 1656 when the Commons took up 'the case of James Nayler', the Quaker. The problem of how to deal with this 'horrid blasphemer' was met by the claim that the powers of the defunct House of Lords had automatically devolved upon the Commons, which now possessed judicial power to examine, prosecute, manage, try, decide upon and penalize offences of the sort hitherto dealt with by prescribed procedures, as in impeachment, of two Houses. The assertion of authority delighted opponents of wide religious toleration but disturbed others to whom Nayler, whatever else he was, was an Englishman entitled to an Englishman's protective liberties. A large precedent was being set for future Commons inclined to pursue 'strange courses'. Unease deepened during debates following the Protector's polite inquiry about the grounds upon which they had proceeded ('wholly without Us'). What answer could they give that did not underline dangers already sensed? Worse, what if the Protector rejected their arguments and pressed his point home? Who or what could arbitrate between them? All that was being gained in this Parliament – and a lot was, both by government and governed – would be squandered if the House and the Single Person glared eyeball to eyeball.

Out of such fears and prognostications emerged, early in 1657, Sir Christopher Pack's 'paper', which became the Humble Petition and Advice. The offer of a new monarchy lodged in the House of Cromwell was the most conspicuous feature of the next few months, but there was more to the proposed constitution than that. Oliver Cromwell himself pointed out to critical army officers the need for 'a screen or balance', lacking in the Instrument, between himself and the Commons. That could be provided by a second Chamber, akin to but not the old House of Peers. Eventually Cromwell rejected kingship but accepted the Other House. He was given *carte blanche* to fill it – unfortunately, as it turned out. While welcoming a check upon the Commons, he understandably did not set out to bring together a body of notables who could act independently as a check upon the Privy Council and himself. Though he summoned a few known or suspected opponents, like the commonwealthsman Sir Arthur Hesilrige, who promptly turned him down, the bulk of his nominees were men he could trust – 'swordsmen and decimators', office-holders, relations, government spokesmen from the Commons. This engendered a sort of political vacuum there, filled (as indicated above) by the previously excluded Members, many experienced and skilful exponents of the parliamentary game. Hence their abrupt dissolution.

Most of these men were returned to the 1658–9 Parliament, alongside many new and young Members, whom they patronized as political innocents. The objective of 'the old guard' was to criticize, embarrass, frustrate, even to destroy the Protectorate. I have surveyed elsewhere the tactics of the commonwealthsmen (republicans) in the early debates on the Bill of Recognition of the Protector. A minority, they were unable in the event to prevent acceptance of government by a Single Person and a Parliament of two Houses because on that the 'court party' was augmented by some loyalists, genuine independents and presbyterians and by crypto-Royalists, who took recognition of a Chief Magistrate to be the insertion of the thin end of a wedge labelled 'King Charles II' into the prevailing constitution. Not at all put out by this failure, the commonwealthsmen were prominent in ensuing debates on the nature, functions, powers, composition and title of the Other House assembled by writ of the Lord Protector and regarded from the start by the government and by itself as guaranteed by the Humble Petition and Advice. As it was, for two or three weeks the matter of the Other House jostled out almost all other matters of moment – foreign policy, public accounts, disputed elections and breach of privilege – which otherwise would have proved absorbing.

The debates can be followed to some extent in newsletters and correspondence such as Secretary John Thurloe's with Henry Cromwell, in memoirs such as Edmund Ludlow's, propaganda pamphlets such as *A Brief Narrative of the Parliament Called by Richard Cromwell* (1659) by Slingsby Bethel (MP, Knaresborough, who in 1668 would publish a devastating attack on protectoral foreign and commercial policy in *The World's Mistake in Oliver Cromwell*). Much more detailed are three parliamentary diaries. Those of Guibon Goddard (MP, Castle Rising) and Sir John Gell (MP, Derbyshire) are unpublished. T. J. Rutt's edition of Thomas Burton's devotes two volumes each of some 500 pages to this Parliament. Unlike many diarist MPs Burton was neither selective nor obviously partisan. The entry on him in the *Dictionary of National Biography*, intending to be derogatory, remarks 'the diarist was a mere reporter'. That is, in fact, a virtue. Burton (MP, Westmorland) was not driven to inflate the speeches of those he approved of, nor to abridge or omit the rest. He puts down, often verbatim and with only brief rare comments, what was said, formulated, pushed, pulled, turned inside out and upside down in the Commons before MPs came (if they did) to resolutions. Obviously he listened hard and recorded furiously. The result is insights, sometimes vivid, always with an authentic ring, into the work and words of a Commons which had its unique features but also fulfilled at least a few of the expectations made of early and mid-century Stuart Parliaments. It shows clearly the tactics of the republicans but those, too, of a range of other 'parties' and individuals, including backbenchers. The Other House got them all going.

Consideration of the Other House began seemingly *en passant* during the debate of 18 February 1658–9 on the 'bounding' of the Chief Magistrate with particular reference to 'the negative voice' (veto). Someone suggested the Other House, too, might be a restraint upon him. John Lambert (MP, Pontefract), smarting still from the obliteration of his Instrument of Government and his own dismissal, doubted if it could: 'This is rather a further strengthening and enlarging than a bounding . . . as [they have] a dependence upon him and nothing to oppose to the least public interest but their own goodness.' Clearly he did not rate that highly. Once awakened the matter was not let sleep by proponents of a legislative power lodged solely in the Commons. Henry Neville (MP, Reading), tireless – and repetitive – in his exposition of Harringtonianism, prophesied that when it came to be debated 'it will not be found that a House of Peers shall be of that use as formerly. We are upon alterations and no thought is now to be taken of John of Gaunt and such fellows. The Lords much outweighed before, [but] now the Commons and the people outweigh . . . so you build upon an ill foundation if you aim at the old way. You cannot build up that which God and nature have destroyed.' This reminder that the constitution had once included King and lords was not universally unwelcome. To secret advocates of legitimate monarchy – and there were certainly some there – a second chamber akin to the House of Peers might be the first step up a ladder to the return of the House of Stuart.

It was apparent that a protectoral veto and the function and authority of another House were ravelled together. To tackle the one before determining the others was to put superstructure before foundation. Decide now where the legislature lay and see where a second Chamber stood in it. Where did the present Other House come from? It was surely not 'of itself nor came out of the clouds'. Some would say it was created by the Humble Petition and as a balance 'to tell the minutes between the two estates'. Within minutes, indeed, the issue of the Other House or *any* other House was exciting interest and controversy.

At this point Hesilrige (MP, Leicester) wondered (as was his wont out loud) how did 'this Other House [come in] when you are bounding the Chief Magistrate', and so, says Burton in a rare side-comment, Hesilrige 'beat the old point that the negative voice be gone into according to the order' [of business]. On cue Edmund Ludlow (MP, Hindon, Wiltshire) rose to suggest instead discussion of the anomalous position 'in the parliament of England' (and Wales) of persons from Scotland and Ireland. His object and Hesilrige's was to put in and keep going as many distractions as possible and, though the commonwealthsmen supported a motion to give priority to the veto, they cannot have been distressed by a resolution to take the Other House the following day (19 February) 'and nothing to intervene'.

Once started the debates stretched out till 9 March with a binding postscript on the twenty-eighth. The delaying manoeuvres of the republicans were assisted by Sir Anthony Ashley Cooper (MP, Shaftesbury, the future Earl of Shaftesbury), something of a lone wolf, and by the fussy procedural points of 'the father of the House', Sir Walter Erle (MP, Dorset). Feeble

193

direction by the Speaker, Challenor Chute, already knocking on death's door, was a boon, too. Moreover, fervent urging by 'the court party' to get quickly on to a decision favourable to itself – the recognition as a co-ordinate chamber of the Other House as at present constituted – stirred what could be called 'the cavalier-ish party' of MPs young and old. There seemed at times a politicking alliance between republicans and reactionaries, while outside the walls of the House informal discussions were obviously being pursued on objectives, strategy and tactics, reinforced by press and pulpit propaganda, all for 'the good of the nation', something distinguishable from the interests of the regime.

Debate proper began on 19 February with an immediate bone of contention thrown in – the right of the old Lords *en bloc* or restricted to 'the faithful lords' of the 1640s. 'That right doth but sleep and . . . will at one time or another awake upon us. . . . We may [indeed] have a barons' war again.' Away with 'those insignificant mincing terms: Other House'. Let there be a – if not the – House of Lords. No, said others. There was neither need nor constitutional basis for another House. That provided in the Humble Petition had been personal to Oliver Cromwell and was dead and buried with him. This claim shook the courtiers, putting as it did the Humble Petition and all that hung upon it up for sale by retail, if not in gross. The riposte by the Chancellor of the Duchy of Lancaster (Nicholas Lechmere, MP, Worcester-shire) to the argument that the Triennial and the Own Dissolution Acts of 1641 were still of force was that 'by the same rule Magna Charta may be called for' and the restoration of the Lords spiritual as well as temporal. 'I know not where you will end till you recognize Charles Stuart for king.' (A silent hear! hear! from some quarters.) The Attorney-General's hope that the House would not look back but go forward went unheeded.

The history of England and its ancient constitution were rehearsed again and again from Ethelbert to the 1650s. Magna Carta was reverently mentioned as 'the fruit of the barons' who had 'always fought battles for our liberties'. The peers' antiquity was stressed: 'ever since the fourth of William the Conqueror you will find the nobles in the House of Peers'. More recently a petition of twelve peers had secured a Parliament in 1640 and many – Essex and Warwick were named – had done 'great things in the quarrel'. To restore them was surely 'a point of policy and prudence' or 'for reasons of utility'.

Some approached Clio from a different direction. 'What was this right of the old Lords?' One 'by usage' alone – 'and a greater power than that that made that hath taken it away . . . God himself by a long series of providences'. (Providence had not died with Oliver Cromwell.) The inexorability of Providence was met with sarcasm. 'Let no man attempt to set up a Commonwealth!' 'Because Constantinople was taken from the Christians, *ergo*, they must not end endeavour to recover it!' No. 'No good Christian can argue from events.' 'What God does providentially he does not always approve of.' The Lords had had a right for 700 years and England had in fact been 'tumbling ever since' they – and, a thought unspoken, the old monarchy – had been taken away.

Sir Henry Vane (MP, Whitchurch), ever ready for historical or politico-philosophical exposition, confessed himself 'exceeding perplexed'. Where were they going? So far no question (motion) had been formulated about the Other House. To get one proved – as he knew it would – difficult. Too many MPs still had too much to say to come yet to anything specific. 'Let us not be too hasty, but hear one another.' And so it went on until later that day they resolved that it should be part of the Bill of Recognition to declare Parliament to consist of two Houses – not, in fact, much of an advance since it settled nothing about a putative second chamber – its composition, functions, relationship to the Commons, and the Single Person, and its name. What's in a name? Evidently a great deal. The presbyterian Griffin Bordwda (MP, Beaumaris) would have it a House of Lords since – his eye was no doubt upon Henry Neville – 'none here would surely mean it to be a House of Ladies'. Members seemed to be inclining towards a high priority for 'bounding'. To call the other House peers to start with would, Neville suggested, be 'like that which was said of the king – it is like hedging the cuckoo'. So it was resolved to consider 'next Tuesday 22 February . . . the bounding of the powers of *another* House' (my italics).

The resumed debate was not so narrowly confined. The rights of the old lords would not lie down, nor could the composition of the current other House. 'Some [there] have the long sword by their side and may perhaps help to hew you down and pull your house over your head.' Name the persons first and then bound *them*. No. Decide the bounds and then come to persons and the name. 'Begin first with this, that they should not be hereditary.' 'Whatever resolution you take for bounding them', Major-General Kelsey (MP, Dover) could 'hardly believe, they will consent to it. . . . It is hard to limit men's power, they will strive to enlarge it [as] I have found by woeful experience.' 'Let us declare what this other House is that we intend.' If it were to be a house of peers, with old lords in it, 'you will lay a foundation for Charles Stuart's coming over'. Some contributions to the debates were so imprecise that Richard Knightley (MP, Northamptonshire) was driven to beg that 'when a point is before us, we may discourse upon some [particular] thing. So long as we are in a wide field, and never a gap open, we shall ride round and round and never get out.' (Silent cheers by the common-wealthsmen.) Points continued to be offered, ignored, refuted, reiterated, restated, reviled. Were they on 'a restitution' or on 'a foundation'? The 1649 abolition was said to be illegal. If so, then everything done by the Rump and since might have no foundation and that would 'draw all the soldiers upon us and the purchasers of public lands and a great deal of confusion'. Later someone observed drily that he would not suppose 'whether Charles Stuart should be at the bottom of this debate . . . [but] peerage will bring in regality, high and great enough that all done . . . from 42 to 48, hence to 52, thence to 53 and hence from there hither all are void'.

Even without misdirections by astute and loquacious republicans the House would have stumbled into 'a wilderness', 'a wood'. No wonder 'the nation is puzzled when the wisdom of the nation is puzzled in this place'. If now and then over the next couple of weeks the debate looked like running out of steam to the point of silence, it could be set simmering again by motions for adjournment or by having the Humble Petition read out. Custom, prescription, common law, statute law, the law of nature, reason – all were appealed to. MPs who were cautious about derogating members of the other House, particularly the hard-faced swordsmen, were told by Hesilrige to 'fear nothing here but God and the neglect of our duty. If at last we be sent down as wise as we came up, there is no harm in it.' This was the attitude which had led to the dissolution of February 1657/8. To whose advantage? Hesilrige still could not grasp that on occasion it might be politically intelligent to keep a Parliament going by appropriate gestures. He, and many others, would pay a heavy price for their lack of imagination. That great survivor, Colonel John Birch (MP, Leominster), *per contra* was unhappy about 'going down to the country again . . . to tell them this was the cause why I came down so soon. They will hardly be satisfied. . . .'

So debate went on, now tepid, now intense, but still havering about a conclusive question. Aristotle and Harrington were cited. Much time was spent – 'misspent' said someone – on superficialities. 'All your proceedings are at a stand till this be clear' – fine for the Scots, Hesilriges and Vanes, anathema to 'the Court'. At length the presbyterian John Swinfen (MP, Tamworth), who had been secluded at Pride's Purge, proposed that 'the best and nearest issue will be to put whether this House now sitting will transact with the other House now sitting as a House of Parliament'. This, he thought, 'will take in all men's senses'. He would also have some provision, too, for calling the old faithful lords. Guibon Goddard comments: 'This Q thus proposed was immediately 2ded and 3ded by some little ones of the same [court] party and was soone apprehended as a thing that had bin studiously contrived and forgd at Court or by common consent of that party, insomuch as before the end of this dayes debate their party began to be called by the name of Transactors.'

Commonwealthsmen moved in quickly to offset a snap vote which would mean swallowing the Humble Petition 'at once'. Vane asked fellow-Members were they 'so sinew-shrunk and manacled' that they could effect nothing unless they transacted with 'these men'. 'You have [in fact] as much power to make a House of Lords with the concurrence of the Lord Protector as the last parliament had.' 'It has pleased God' – and he might have added himself and 'the great Sir Arthur' – 'to confound us in our debates that we cannot come to a question. Leave the Other House until the next parliament.' When Swinfen's proposal was commended Hesilrige came briskly in with yet another history of the 1640s and 1650s, through 'a little thing called a parliament' (the Nominated Assembly), the Instrument ('a law made without doors'), the Major-Generals to the Humble Petition, which in his view was not 'the laws of the Medes and Persians'. 'If it were as ancient as the Conquest, if we find any inconveniency in it we may repeal, alter and amend it.' The Presbyterian Serjeant John Maynard (MP, Newtown, Isle of Wight), who, like Hesilrige, had been excluded from the 1656 Parliament, but had since made his peace with the Protectorate, running through 'the revolutions we have run through' came to a different conclusion, foreseeing 'a fearful precipice' opening if the Humble Petition was not taken for a law under which both the Commons and the present Other House had been called to transact with each other. But a brother of the Long Robe, Serjeant John Wyld (MP, Droitwich), would have the Petition probed 'to the bottom' before any approaches were made. To a suggestion to adjourn till tomorrow and then not to rise until they actually had a question, Vane asked why the rush? 'Do not tempt Providence by turning night into day.' Finally at 3 p.m. – late for the period – they rose on a motion that next day's proceedings should focus on transacting (passed by 177 to 113 with Hesilrige and Neville tellers for the *noes*).

Next day began with a harangue by Thomas St Nicholas (MP, Canterbury) against transacting. Since Richard was not Protector until this House of Commons had voted him so, he had no right to issue writs for assembling another House. Government supporters piled in to correct this misconception, pressing both legality and *de facto* arguments. The rights of the faithful peers could be recognized alongside those of current members, men who deserved 'as well as any persons that sat there, though short in birth and pedigree'. So transact. No – 'they are all officers, councillors, judges and chancellors. If you should complain against them you must complain to themselves.' (What would have been the situation if Parliament were a single sovereign Commons of the sort admired by Rumpers? Ask James Nayler.) To the charge that there were military men in the Other House who had 'forced' Parliaments before, someone pointed out appositely that the old Lords had included lord marshals, lord admirals and lord-lieutenants.

Arthur Annesley (MP, Dublin), already in touch with

Royalists and on his way to the earldom of Anglesey, attacked at tedious length – Burnet says he had 'a faculty of speaking indefatigably upon every subject' – Harringtonianism. He knew five or six peers who even now could buy out all of those presently in the Other House. A motion was formulated that they should transact 'not intending thereby to exclude such of the ancient peers who have been faithful from their privilege of being summoned and sitting [as] members'. After tossing that and a few other items about, they adjourned, till Friday, 4 March. Secretary John Thurloe reported to Henry Cromwell that 'the Commonwealth party sat still, resolving to give their vote to the greatest disadvantage to his Highness'.

On Friday routine business gave way to a deep silence, broken by Sir Walter Erle, who remarked as if it were a revelation that to have the old faithful lords back at Westminster would be 'useful'. But Members, to the disgust of Arthur Annesley, continued to churn out delaying 'additions' – 'some to the beginning, some to the middle, some to the conclusion'. 'What one moves another crosses presently.' One of the new young Members, who had resolved to say nothing, felt compelled to object to transacting as 'giving too much away too soon . . . all in a lump'. Someone then told 'a long story of Adam' that even Burton found too boring to record. Hesilrige, to momentary astonishment, said he was all for another House, but – he went on – only so long as 'the Commons of England may bind and approve them and we know upon what foot they are presently called'. He was accused with perfect justice of taking great pains to prevent them coming to a question but he was not the only one to enjoy procedural pyrotechnics. Should the question be put in the affirmative or in the negative? Should they adjourn? Yes. They did.

Next day (5 March) began with commonwealthsmen denying that lords ancient or modern should or could re-create a balance in the State. The present Other House – which in their view was not another House – was as useless and dangerous as the old. The Speaker was begged, in vain, to 'keep us to something'. The Attorney-General (Sir Edmund Prideaux, MP, Lyme Regis) rose to speak 'because you, Mr Speaker, do not'. 'I cannot,' wheezed the Chair. At this rate, the Attorney-General prophesied, they would still be at it next month. Hesilrige objected to the bright notion that they should sit on Sunday. Certainly they had done that in the past – when occasion warranted it. This did not. His point was taken.

Monday (7 March) found them as wordy as ever. Someone commented on the failure of the Other House to 'show themselves' all this while. 'I fear they are troubled with King's evil.' (Certainly they were doing – perhaps tactfully – very little.) Ashley Cooper would not transact because it was 'against the rights of others, the rights of this House, and the rights of the nation' – the lot! The Solicitor-General took the view that either they transacted with the Other House 'or with the Protector [whom they *had* recognized] or without him, or alone, or not at all. If you say you will transact with him alone, *he* may refuse to transact with *you* alone.'

Few new points of substance emerged in a debate which went on well into the afternoon. There were further 'stories of the late troubles' and the Good Old Cause. Prynne and Selden were quoted, Ranters and Quakers for some reason deplored. There was talk of men 'trepanned' (brainwashed). Hesilrige urged priority for religion and the public accounts. Lambert would not have the Instrument of Government raked out of its grave. Transactors got a vote to have doors shut 'from any of the members going out'. (Sir Walter Erle was allowed to retire, sick.) Pushing adjournment to the following week Hesilrige claimed not to have 'spoken to the matter yet'. To laughter he added, somewhat truthfully, 'for I never speak to the matter'. Burton concludes that the crowding in of several 'perplexed additions' made the House weary. They adjourned.

On Tuesday (8 March) the House seemed at last generally inclined to come to a vote. It was that the Other House be recognized as a House of Parliament, with an addition that 'it is not hereby intended to exclude such Peers as have been faithful to the parliament from the privilege of being duly summoned to be members of the Other House'. 'A great debate' flared up over whether the *yeas* or the *noes* should go out. At length the *noes* did, on the main question. They lost 184 to 203. On the addition the *yeas* trooped out and won 195 to 188. But, note, so far the Other House had only been recognized; nothing about transacting. The republicans, however, aware that that would be pressed hard by 'the Court', threw in again 'the bone' of the right of the Scots and Irish Members to sit and take part in voting. With them out of the way they might (they felt) have done better in the divisions. The issue was good for a couple of weeks' sharp debating, with Members snarling at one another. 'A member of no great quality' ruffled Hesilrige by sneering at the Rump and accusing him and Vane of wanting to be 'the great Hogen Mogens to rule the Commonwealth'. The Scots were approved on 20 March and the Irish on the twenty-third.

Debate on transacting was resumed on 28 March. Most MPs by now had had enough. Henry Neville might tell them that they were 'in a sea and saw not land'. They preferred to glimpse the shore and threw out (by 183 to 148) a proposal to have transacting delayed until all the Members were approved by the Commons. (Tellers for the motion were Hesilrige and that Sir George Booth who would lead a crypto-royalist rising later on that year. Necessity and political manoeuvring make strange bedfellows.)

Soon afterwards Richard, pushed to it by the army officers, dissolved the Parliament, and then sensibly resigned. During the next twelve months the Rump came back and went and came back again – without a second chamber. When, in February 1660, General George Monck 'persuaded' them to readmit the Members 'secluded' at Pride's Purge, the latter undertook to make 'no alterations of government other than in preparation for a parliament to succeed them'. Monck, sensitive to the temper of the still not completely down-and-out English armed forces and to the need for a quick self-dissolution of the Long Parliament, held off pressure from some peers to be allowed to assemble in the Lords' Chamber. Scot, Hesilrige and some others, whose names the continuator of Baker's *Chronicle* in the reign of Charles II forbore to mention 'because they are yet living and have repented the rashness of their former proceeding', resisted even then an abrogation of the Engagement to the Commonwealth 'as the same is now established without king or House of Lords'.

On 17 March 1660 the Long Parliament at last dissolved itself, after arranging for a new Parliament (the Convention) to meet on 26 March, significantly with a resolution 'to keep the royal party out of *both Houses of Parliament*' (my italics). In fact open

Royalists were returned and, though initially disputed, allowed to sit. The House of Peers automatically assembled and chose the Earl of Manchester (son of Cromwell's Manchester) as their Speaker. On 27 April the Declaration of Breda was brought first to the Lords' chamber, without the Commons being informed. The Lords quickly voted that they 'do own and declare that according to the ancient fundamental laws of the Kingdom, the government is and ought to be by King, Lords and Commons'. Only then was the Declaration taken down to the Commons, which agreed at once with the Lords' vote and resolved to raze from the records everything inconsistent with government by King, Lords and Commons. The Restoration was all but a fact – a restoration not only of monarchy in the old line but of Parliament in its historical form of two Houses, the upper one of peers and a *sine qua non*. There was now no question about transacting with the Other House. It was already happening.

In their determined campaign to frustrate the Protectorate the commonwealthsmen had, in fact, helped to bring the Stuarts back with parliamentary Lordship triumphant. Before long the bishops, who had been excluded in 1642 by a genuine Act of Parliament, were back among the lords temporal. By then the republicans had consigned themselves to political limbo, exile or death. Yet *a* Restoration, let alone *the* Restoration, had not been inevitable, nor yet a demonstration that for Englishmen (and presumably for Welsh, Scots and Irish) monarchy and aristocracy were naturally the best policy. Rather, it was the effect of the unreadiness of advocates of the Good Old Cause to come together, rising above their principles, to define and defeat it, leaving the way clear for George Monck 'and his boyes' to effect what was really a sudden revolution, one which caught both the astrologers and Charles II by surprise.

Bibliographical Note

This article is based emphatically upon volumes 3 and 4 of *The Diary of Thomas Burton, Esq., MP*, ed. J. T. Rutt, 4 vols (1828), reprinted with additional material, ed. I. Roots (New York, 1974), with some recourse to the Commons Journals, vol. 7, Guibon Goddard's unpublished diary (British Library Add.

MS 5138) and W. A. H. Schilling's transcript of 'The Parliamentary Diary of Sir John Gell' (unpublished MA thesis, Vanderbilt University, Nashville, Tennessee, 1961). Among other sources are *Thurloe State Papers*, ed. T. Birch, 7 vols (1742); *The Clarke Papers*, ed. C. H. Firth, 4 vols, Camden Society (1891–1901); *The Memoirs of Edmund Ludlow*, ed. C. H. Firth, 2 vols (Oxford, 1894); Sir Richard Baker, *A Chronicle of the Kings of England*, 9th edn, with continuation (1969); and the partisan pamphlet by Slingsby Bethel mentioned on p. 191. Secondary works providing a context include G. Davies, *The Restoration of Charles II, 1658–1660* (San Marino, Calif., 1955); A. H. Woolrych, 'Historical Introduction' to vol. 7 of *Complete Prose Works of John Milton*, ed. D. M. Wolfe, 8 vols (New Haven, Conn., 1953–82); and I. Roots, *The Great Rebellion, 1642–60*, 5th edn (London, 1983). E. R. Foster, *The House of Lords, 1603–1649* (Chapel Hill, NC, 1983), is an admirable survey of the structure, procedure and business of the chamber which the Other House was intended to replace. The later careers of some of the speakers in the debates can be followed in *The History of Parliament: The House of Commons, 1660–1690*, ed. B. D. Henning, 3 vols (London, 1983). A biography of Hesilrige by B. Denton, under the title *Parliament's Forgotten General*, is forthcoming. Two relevant articles of my own are referred to above: 'Lawmaking in the Second Protectorate Parliament', in H. Hearder and H. R. Loyn (eds), *British Government and Administration: Studies Presented to S. B. Chrimes* (Cardiff, 1974); and 'The Tactics of the Commonwealthsmen in Richard Cromwell's Parliament', in D. Pennington and K. Thomas (eds), *Puritans and Revolutionaries: Essays in Seventeenth-Century History Presented to Christopher Hill* (Oxford, 1978). The phrase about Monck 'and his boyes' on p. 202 comes from Robert Wild's poem *Iter Boreale: Attempting Something upon the Successful March of General Monck* (1660).

JOHN WILDMAN
AND THE POST OFFICE

Maurice Ashley

THE POSTAL SERVICE under the Tudors was concerned almost entirely with the dispatch of official letters from London to places in England, Scotland, Ireland and overseas.[1] The first Master of the Posts received the modest fee of £66 13s 4d a year plus the expense of carrying the letters.[2] He set up a number of postal stations along the main roads at which a messenger, who was carrying the royal mail all the way, could pick up a fresh horse; he would be accompanied to the next station by a post boy, also on horseback, who could show him the way and lead the other horse back after they reached their destination. The sum of 12d a day was paid to the stage posts for keeping one horse always available (or two shillings for three horses), a penny a mile for the use of the horse, and a tip of fourpence (one groat) for the post boy. The stages were usually about fifteen miles long, and the rate at which the messenger travelled was seven miles an hour in the summer and five miles an hour in the winter. It took nine days to send a letter from London to Carlisle, a distance of over 300 miles.

It was not until towards the beginning of the seventeenth century that ordinary people were allowed to send letters by the royal mail. Apart from the Merchant Adventurers, who had their own postmaster, the government did not approve of the carriage

---

[1] The best book on the subject is *The British Post Office* by Howard Robinson, an American historian (London, 1948). Curiously, it is not included in the standard *Bibliography of British History, 1603–1714*, revised in 1970. J. C. Hemmeon, *The History of the British Post Office* (Cambridge, Mass., 1912), does not mention Wildman, and H. Joyce, *The History of the Post Office* (1893), gets the length of his tenure wrong.

[2] *Report of the Secret Committee on the Post Office*, a parliamentary paper reporting to the House of Commons in 1844, p. 4.

of letters except by those employed by the Master of the Posts because it feared that such correspondence could be employed to concoct plots or organize other treasonable activities. During the reign of Elizabeth I, for example, her prisoner, Mary Queen of Scots, was able for a long time to correspond in cipher with her adherents, even plotting the assassination of Elizabeth, until, kept in close captivity, she was denied the use of paper.[3] After James I came to the throne the unauthorized conveyance of letters was strictly forbidden. From towards the end of Elizabeth I's reign private people were allowed to take advantage of the royal service by paying $2\frac{1}{2}d$ or $3d$ a mile for the horses riding post or by getting a post boy to carry their letters. But at the outset of the reign of Charles I the inland postal service was costing the government £3400 a year.[4]

In 1635 the service received a thorough overhaul. Thomas Witherings, a London merchant who also held a position at the court of the Queen, Henrietta Maria, managed to obtain control both of the inland post and of the overseas post. In 1619, Mathew de Quester, a native of Bruges but naturalized, had been granted a patent for sending packets to foreign parts. In 1632, Witherings took over from him and in 1635 he also acquired control of the inland post. Although he only held the office of Postmaster-General for a few years, he carried out important reforms. He fixed standard rates for postage – $2d$ for a single letter going 80 miles, $4d$ for up to 140 miles, and $8d$ if it was sent to Scotland. At the same time 'byposts' were instituted. For example, if letters were sent along a main postal road to Exeter, a foot post would pick them up once a week to carry them on to Barnstaple or bring letters from Barnstaple to catch the return post to London. Regular services by packet boat were also arranged between Dover and Calais, letters from London being timed to arrive at Dover in daylight. Through these reforms the postal service was put on a paying basis. It has been claimed that Witherings was 'the most distinguished name in the annals of the British Post Office'.[5]

---

[3] Antonia Fraser, *Mary Queen of Scots* (London, 1969), p. 495.

[4] *Report of the Secret Committee*, p. 5.

[5] Hemmeon, *History*, p. 14.

With the coming of the Civil War the Post Office went through a confusing period. In 1640, Charles I replaced Witherings with another London merchant, Philip Burlamachi, to whom he was in debt. In September 1644 the House of Commons appointed Edmund Prideaux, a Member of Parliament for Lyme Regis and a lawyer who was to become Attorney-General, as Master of the Posts (although the Earl of Warwick claimed that he had been appointed to the office by the House of Lords). In 1653 – the Post Office now being a profitable business and the government being hard up – the office of Postmaster was sold to John Manley for £10,000 a year. Monopolies were not thought highly of during the Interregnum, and Manley (and previously Prideaux) met with competition from interlopers who undercut the official rates. But what was of more concern to the Protectorate was that correspondence was a means employed to plan risings by Royalists and others against the government. To prevent this John Thurloe, Oliver Cromwell's able Secretary of State and head of his intelligence service, was appointed Postmaster-General in July 1655: he also paid £10,000 for the farm. An Act of Parliament, the first to deal with the Post Office,[6] was passed in 1657, which empowered the Protector to grant the office of Postmaster for life or any term not exceeding eleven years; it also prescribed the rates to be charged for the postage of letters and laid it down that by the erection of the General Post Office 'the people of these nations . . . will discover and prevent many dangerous and wicked designs, which have been, and are daily contrived against the peace and welfare of the Commonwealth, the intelligence whereof cannot well be communicated but by letter'. Such was the justification for maintaining the monopoly.

John Thurloe employed two men to examine letters which were suspected to be treasonable. One was Isaac Dorislaus, who worked every post night from eleven o'clock onwards, which left him, as he admitted, very sleepy.[7] The other examiner was Samuel Morland, who copied out the contents of letters by an

[6] The Act of 1657 is printed in the *Report of the Secret Committee* and in C. H. Firth and R. S. Rait (eds), *Acts and Ordinances of the Interregnum, 1640–1660*, 3 vols (London, 1911), vol. 2, pp. 1110–13.

[7] C. H. Firth, 'Thurloe and the Post Office', *English Historical Review*, vol. 13 (1898), pp. 527–33.

offset process of pressing damp tissue against the ink. Morland boasted that he could then seal up the letters again in such a way that the recipient would not know they had been opened.[8]

It was in the late 1650s, when Thurloe was Postmaster-General, that Major John Wildman was first associated with the postal service. Up till then he had enjoyed a varied career.[9] He was educated at Cambridge and the Inns of Court and acquired the rank of major very briefly in 1649. As a young man he acted as second-in-command to John Lilburne, 'Freeborn John', in the Leveller movement which stood, roughly speaking, for a more democratic electorate, regular meetings of Parliament, greater freedom of trade and complete liberty of conscience. Wildman had advocated a constitution known as the Agreement of the People, which he himself drew up, and debated forcibly with Oliver Cromwell and Cromwell's son-in-law, Henry Ireton, asserting that 'every person in England hath as clear a right to elect his representative as the greatest person in England' and 'that all government is in the free consent of the people'.[10] When the Cromwellian Protectorate was established he plotted against it and entered into communication with exiled Royalists, hoping for a genuinely constitutional monarchy. He even offered to arrange for the seizure of a port, where Spanish auxiliaries of Charles II could land, provided he was well paid for the effort. But a Leveller plot against Cromwell was discovered and, in March 1655, Wildman was imprisoned without trial in the Tower of London. He actually got in touch with Royalist leaders when he was in the Tower.

In July 1656, Wildman obtained his release from the Tower on a bail of £10,000 and evidently on the understanding that he would act as a spy on the Royalists for Thurloe. In a remarkable document, written for the benefit of the Restoration government, endorsed 'about intelligence', Wildman observed: 'There is now no Cromwell or Thurloe to manage the intelligence and therefore we may not act securely.'[11] The Secretaries of State, he pointed

---

[8] H. W. Dickinson, *Sir Samuel Morland* (1870), p. 96.

[9] Details of his career are given in Maurice Ashley, *John Wildman: Plotter and Post-master* (London, 1947).

[10] A. S. P. Woodhouse, *Puritanism and Liberty* (London, 1938), p. 66.

[11] Firth, 'Thurloe and the Post Office', p. 527.

out, had insufficient means to pay for information about plots against the State, and he therefore proposed that 'a fit person be chosen to take knowledge of ordinary carriers and foot posts in or about the City, administer an oath of fidelity to them, and give them licences'. That procedure, he insisted, would be much better than Cromwell's and Thurloe's of simply opening suspicious letters, which was 'but to shoot at rovers'.

In fact at about this time – the summer of 1660 – Wildman was already directly involved with the Post Office. Thurloe had continued in office after the end of the Protectorate until 25 December 1659, avowing that he personally had made no money out of it, but 'had improved that office £4000 per annum to the State voluntarily, which I might have put in my own purse'.[12] The Convention Parliament, which invited Charles II to return to London, had on 14 August 1660 appointed Henry Bishop, who lived in Parham in Sussex, to the office of Postmaster-General. It subsequently passed legislation similar to that in the Act of 1657 prescribing the rates of postage and empowering the King to appoint any Postmaster he chose for life. Bishop had to find £21,500 a year for the monopoly in quarterly instalments. There is little doubt that Wildman, who had amassed a personal fortune during the Interregnum by buying and selling estates, financed Bishop. Nevertheless, their friendship or association is somewhat curious. Everyone agreed that Bishop was a trustworthy Royalist, which was certainly not true of Wildman, and in fact it seems that he hoped to use the control of the Post Office for conspiring against the returned monarch. Bishop was known to have stayed at Nonsuch House in Bow Street, a tavern owned by Wildman and kept by his servant, William Parker, and Parker's wife, whenever he came up to London from Sussex before his appointment as Postmaster-General. Clearly he must have been under financial obligations to Wildman.[13] One of the Post Office clerks avowed to the Secretary of State, Sir Edward Nicholas, that the Post Office was in 1661 being managed by those who were active for Cromwell and the Protectorate government, notably Wild-

---

[12] Cited in D. L. Hobman, *Cromwell's Master Spy* (London, 1961), pp. 163–4, from the Thurloe State Papers.

[13] Statement by Joseph Bilcliffe, 9 September 1661: *Calendar of State Papers, Domestic, 1661–1662*, p. 86.

man, whom he described as 'a subtle Leveller and anti-monarchy man'.[14] The postmaster at Newbury earlier offered the information that many members of the Post Office staff were 'ill-affected' and that Major Wildman and two Anabaptists (who had tried to set up their own personal service during the Interregnum) 'put in and out whom they please'.[15] In December 1661, Nicholas was informed that a Post Office clerk, appointed by Bishop and Wildman, had intercepted the western mails in Hounslow, which the Act of 1660 had forbidden without authority from the Secretaries of State, who were also comptrollers of the Post Office. Wildman was arrested and again imprisoned in the Tower of London without trial. When he took out a writ of habeas corpus he was packed off to the Scilly Isles where the writ did not run and it was not until 1667 that he was released.

Meanwhile Bishop's contract was revoked and he sold the remainder of his lease to Daniel O'Neill, a friend and servant of Charles II, who had been one of his intimates when in exile. O'Neill paid the government the same price for the farm as Bishop – £21,500 a year – and by another Act in 1663 the profits of the Post Office were assigned to James Duke of York and his male heirs. When O'Neill died his widow carried on but, in 1667, Lord Arlington, the senior Secretary of State, was appointed Postmaster-General, thus reverting to the situation ten years earlier, which enabled the government to examine suspicious letters for evidence of treasonable activities. But the effective head of the Post Office was Arlington's brother, Sir John Bennet, who was known as the Deputy Postmaster-General or Governor of the Post Office. The General Letter Office was burnt down in the Great Fire of London. In 1678 the offices of the inland and foreign mails were separated. But the most important event during Charles II's reign was the introduction of a penny post in the capital during 1680.

Hitherto the inhabitants of the City who wanted to post letters at home or overseas had either to take them to the General Letter Office or hire a messenger to do so, for no postal service existed within London itself. A merchant named William Dockwra

[14] Account of the Post Office, 2 August 1661: ibid., pp. 55–6.

[15] Information of Humphrey Cantell, postmaster at Newbury, 10 December 1660: *Calendar of State Papers, Domestic, 1660–1661*, p. 409.

instituted such a service conveying letters or parcels under a pound in weight within all parts of London, Westminster and the suburbs for one penny each. But the Duke of York, to whom the profits of the Post Office had been assigned, brought an action against Dockwra and the penny London post was absorbed into the general postal service with offices scattered throughout the London area and a staff of sorters and messengers. Both Bishop and Dockwra used postmarks to show when a letter was posted.[16] Those who posted letters within the London area had to pay their pennies in advance, while outside the posts were paid for on receipt.

Such was the position when the Duke of York came to the throne in 1685 as King James II. The profits of the Post Office, which had been a perquisite of James, conferred on him by Act of Parliament, now reverted to the Crown. Consequently the Lord Treasurer, who at the outset of the new reign was James's brother-in-law (by his first wife), the Earl of Rochester, was also technically Postmaster-General. But William III, after he had ousted his uncle and father-in-law in the revolution of 1688, put the Treasury into the hands of a commission, to which the Postmaster-General was responsible; this may have given him more independence. The new head of the Post Office appointed on 12 April 1689 was none other than Major John Wildman.

After his release in 1667, probably through the good offices of the second Duke of Buckingham, of whom, according to Samuel Pepys, Wildman was 'a great creature' (Pepys also wrote that, in 1668, Buckingham met Wildman and other commonwealthsmen daily and 'that when he is with them he makes the King believe he is with his wenches'),[17] Wildman was mixed up in every plot against the monarchy. He was closely associated with the Earl of Shaftesbury, the leader of the Whig party, and Algernon Sidney, an avowed republican. He was concerned in conspiracies for an insurrection and even talked airily about murdering the King. Not surprisingly, he found himself again in the Tower of London towards the end of Charles II's reign, and after James II came

---

[16] This and the previous paragraph are based on Robinson, *British Post Office*, ch. 5. Examples of the postmarks are given on pp. 58 and 73.

[17] Samuel Pepys, *Diary*, ed. Robert Latham and William Matthews (London, 1974–6), vol. 8, p. 570, and vol. 9, pp. 347–8.

to the throne he played a prominent but ineffective part in the Duke of Monmouth's rebellion against his uncle. After Monmouth's defeat at the battle of Sedgemoor on 5 July 1685, Wildman fled abroad and was proclaimed an outlaw. He returned to England in November 1688 in the entourage of Prince William of Orange.[18]

Once William became King of England he clearly felt he was under an obligation to Wildman, because he had a hand in drawing up the declaration which William published on 30 September castigating James's 'evil counsellors' and claiming that the birth of a son by James's second wife was a fraud, the child 'not being born of the Queen'.[19] The misrepresentations in this declaration were not untypical of Wildman's polemical writings. Wildman's reward was that he was made Governor of the Post Office with a salary of £1500 a year.[20] His main office, where he lived, was in St Martin's Lane. He also had a house in the country.

New material enables us to gain a pretty clear picture of Wildman's handling of his appointment.[21] Although he was certainly called Postmaster-General by his subordinates, he was, like his two predecessors, Colonel Roger Whitley and Sir Philip Frowde, really the Governor of the Post Office or Deputy Postmaster-General. In 1685 the Earl of Rochester as Lord Treasurer had certainly been the nominal Postmaster-General and was given a grant of £4000 a year out of the Post Office receipts. The evidence that Wildman was not entitled to call himself Postmaster-General is clear: for in May 1690 when he discovered in the post two written papers of verses together with a newsletter, all of which he judged 'to be mischievous and dangerous to their Majesties and the present Government', he

---

[18] Gilbert Burnet, *History of His Own Time* (1823), pp. 294–6.

[19] William III's declaration is printed in Maurice Ashley, *The Glorious Revolution of 1688* (London, 1966), pp. 203–4.

[20] In my *John Wildman* I wrongly stated that Wildman must have paid a large sum for the farm of the Post Office. No doubt there were perquisites as well as his salary.

[21] This material, now in the manuscripts department of the British Library, came from the Blenheim archives. I printed some of it in my *John Wildman* by permission of the then Duke of Marlborough, but not the extracts given here. The material is catalogued Add. MSS 61689 and 61690. It is not clear how it came to Blenheim, possibly through Sidney Godolphin, who was Chancellor of the Exchequer when Wildman was Governor of the Post Office.

(as he noted) 'showed them to the Postmaster-General with whom he left them and received his orders to find him notice thereof'. Who this Postmaster-General was is not clear, but obviously he was one of William III's ministers, presumably either the Earl of Monmouth, who was First Lord of the Treasury, or the Earl of Shrewsbury, who was senior Secretary of State.

Decisive evidence that Wildman's office was that of Governor is provided by an instruction given by William III on 13 May 1690 when he ordered 'Major Wildman, Governor of the General Post Office to take care to cause a post to be settled and go between London and Milford [Haven] three times a week'.[22] It was from Milford Haven that ships sailed to southern Ireland. William was to set out for Ireland three weeks later to fight his father-in-law at the battle of the Boyne.

During Wildman's first year in office he paid the Exchequer a total of £58,561 16s 3d; in addition the London penny post yielded £3273 10s 6d.[23] From this had to be deducted a year's pension of £4700 due to the Duchess of Cleveland, Charles II's first *maîtresse en titre*, and the Earl of Rochester's pension of £4000. Another £500 was due to a certain Richard Graham and Dame Barbara Allibon. This sum of £500 has an amusing history. Samuel Morland, who, like Wildman, had worked for Thurloe but at the same time entered into correspondence with Charles II and his exiled court, had managed to get over to Holland and returned with the royal fleet in 1660. The King received him graciously and rewarded him with a knighthood and a pension of £500 secured on the Post Office. However, when Morland later learnt (in advance) that the Duke of York was going to have the revenues of the Post Office settled on him he sold his pension for a lump sum to a 'chapman' who bought it for a certain Lady Green.[24] Some historians have wrongly assumed that this Lady Green was, like the Duchess of Cleveland, one of Charles II's many mistresses. Presumably Lady Green or her heir sold the pension in turn for a lump sum.

[22] Add. MS 61689, fo. 128.

[23] ibid., fo. 120. The yield from the penny post is given in *Calendar of Treasury Books, 1689–1692*, vol. 9, pt 2, pp. 432–4.

[24] Dickinson, *Morland*, p. 117: the reference is taken from Morland's autobiography, which is in Lambeth Palace. The 'chapman' was Sir Arthur Slingsby.

Sir Samuel Morland, who was an inventor of considerable ingenuity and was married altogether five times, was still going strong when Wildman administered the Post Office. Just after Wildman's appointment Morland wrote him a letter offering to show him how easily he could imitate the King's handwriting and also that of the Earl of Shrewsbury. If they wrote twelve lines with their own hands in ordinary ink on the finest paper, he undertook to counterfeit them in such a way as to be indistinguishable from the originals, provided the originals were not marked with the prick of a pin 'as that would not be a fair trial of the skill I pretend to'.[25] But the King would have nothing to do with the tampering with Post Office letters. This was hard luck on Morland, who had an extravagant taste in wine, as he confessed 'that [wine] was the only content I had in the world, all other things' (including his five wives) 'proving cross and full of trouble and bitterness'.[26] Another figure from the past was more generously treated: William Dockwra, the inventor of the London penny post, was belatedly given a £500 a year pension on the Post Office for seven years.

Wildman certainly had to work hard to earn his salary. After the reign of James II it was naturally feared that 'papists' would plot against the new government so as to restore the Jacobites. So local postmasters and other staff needed to be vetted. It was reported, for instance, to Wildman that 'William Howell', a sorter of the Westminster penny post, was 'a disaffected person who drinks the health of the late King and neglects his duties'.[27] Other 'debauched persons' were said also to be employed in the offices of the penny post. The postmaster at Petworth in Sussex was reported to be a papist, who had replaced a zealous Protestant.[28] The postmaster of Bridgwater in Somerset was described as being 'a person of haughty proud temper and very disobliging to all persons of quality and others and was not well affected to their Majesties or present Government'.[29] Others,

[25] Morland to Wildman, 18 June 1689: Add. MS 61689, fo. 51.

[26] Dickinson, *Morland*, p. 118.

[27] Add. MS 61689, fo. 106.

[28] Add. MS 61690, fo. 39.

[29] ibid., fo. 56.

however, were sponsored strongly on religious grounds. The influential Lord Macclesfield, for example, recommended to Wildman accountants and letter-carriers who were Protestants. Thomas Butler, a postman who carried letters from the London General Post Office to Wapping and Stepney, was enthusiastically supported in a document with many signatures as 'an honest sober and diligent man steady to the Reformed Protestant religion'.[30] Wildman himself boasted of his Protestantism (although he was probably an agnostic). When he went to Pontefract soon after his appointment to see if all was well with the postal arrangements there, he wrote a letter referring to

> the wonderful revolution for rescuing this undeserving land from that ruin both of religion and civil liberties which was designed against us by the enemies of both and by various methods and artifices endeavouring to be brought upon us which the Omnipotent and Wise God hath in part frustrated . . . [it was] his earnest desire of the happiness and welfare of my native country which every sincere Christian and true Englishman ought to be solicitous about. . . .[31]

Another problem that confronted Wildman was the competence of local postmasters and postmen. For there was no scarcity of applicants for such positions. The provision of post horses was a particularly profitable business. When the postmaster-general in Scotland died £5000 was offered for the right to succeed him.[32] Should women be acceptable as local postmasters? The inhabitants of Totnes in Devon testified that the post office there had been excellently run for twenty-four years by Mrs Elizabeth Gaylor (who was now a widow) and her husband: they were very diligent, never losing letters.[33] Apparently she was allowed to carry on. Then there was Mrs Margaret Bowles, another widow, at Deal in Kent.[34] Her house, it was

---

[30] Add. MS 61689, fo. 68.

[31] Wildman's letter, presumably addressed to the Postmaster-General, dated 15 June 1689 from Pontefract is in Add. MS 61689, fo. 47.

[32] ibid., fo. 127.

[33] ibid., fo. 96.

[34] Add. MS 61690, fo. 1.

said, was 'very fitting to be a post house'. Many noblemen who went to Deal, including the Duke of Grafton and Admiral Herbert, stayed with her there. And of course pathetic cases existed. One was the carrier, Rowland Beile, who collected letters in the evening by ringing a bell. He had a wife and small children to maintain; his continuance in employment would be an act of charity. The Duke of Norfolk put in a plea for John Holmes, another carrier, who had been expelled from his job upon the complaint of the chief of the Penny Post Office for 'neglecting one letter for one hour'.[35]

The inland post, when Wildman was in charge, was carried on the northern road via Berwick to Edinburgh, the Kentish eastern road to Dover, the south-east road to Chichester, the western road to Bristol, the north-west road to Chester and to Holyhead.[36] From each road were byposts. These routes do not seem to have been altered much since Elizabethan times. Besides the inland post and London penny post Wildman was responsible for the overseas post. When William III went to war with France packet boats still sailed between Dover and Calais often carrying letters destined for Spain and elsewhere. Wildman instituted a direct service between Falmouth and Corunna. He also had to arrange for a more frequent service from Chester to Ireland when William was campaigning there in 1690. In view of his earlier career as a plotter it was natural that Wildman should be accused, notably by the Marquis of Carmarthen (the former Tory politician, Danby), who was Lord President of the Council, of abusing his position for private purposes: Carmarthen told King William that Wildman was 'a very dangerous man to the Government' and accused him of 'foul play'.[37] But when the King ordered Wildman's dismissal in February 1691 it was undoubtedly because he was believed to be inefficient. Queen Mary II was

---

[35] Add. MS 61689, fo. 128.

[36] ibid., fo. 45.

[37] Carmarthen's letters to William III about Wildman are printed in full in Andrew Browning, *Earl of Danby* (Glasgow, 1944), vol. 2, pp. 164, 165, 166, 192. Professor Browning wrote in vol. 1 (Glasgow, 1951) that Wildman was bent upon tapping the King's correspondence in the interest of the Whigs. I have discovered no evidence for this and, as Professor Browning pointed out, Carmarthen was prejudiced against Wildman because he believed his son had been promised the office of Postmaster-General.

particularly indignant that letters from her husband, when he was in Ireland, Flanders or Holland did not reach her more quickly. Wildman's dismissal was said to be 'the talk of the Town'.[38] He was replaced by two Postmasters-General, and two Postmasters-General continued to be appointed until 1823.[39] This suggests that Wildman was in effect overworked in the office, especially as, at the outset of his career as Postmaster, he was also a prominent and active Member of Parliament. The King bore him no grudge. In 1692 he became Deputy-Lieutenant of Middlesex and was knighted. He died a wealthy man on 4 June 1693 aged about seventy.

[38] Ashley, *John Wildman*, ch. 21.
[39] Robinson, *British Post Office*, p. 78.

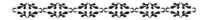

THE DATE OF THE DIGRESSION IN MILTON'S
History of Britain
Austin Woolrych

PART OF THE strength and charm of Veronica Wedgwood's historical writing has lain in her sensitivity to the interaction between literature and history.[1] This has been manifest not only in her major works on the Great Rebellion but also in her *Poetry and Politics under the Stuarts* and *Milton and His World*, books whose grace and insight must have persuaded many a reader that the two disciplines ought not to be kept in watertight compartments. This essay is about a brief and minor piece of Milton's, but since its few pages contain the frankest reflections of the greatest poet of his age on the greatest upheaval of seventeenth-century England, and on the cause to which he devoted much of his life, a reappraisal of it may, it is hoped, be not inappropriate to this happy occasion.

These reflections of Milton's take the form of a Digression, designed to be inserted in his *History of Britain* just before the Saxon invasions, a point which he had reached in 1648. The *History*, however, never advanced beyond the Norman Conquest, and when Milton eventually published it in 1670 he suppressed the Digression. The latter has ever since been a problem to Miltonists, who have all assumed that it was written in 1648, or possibly just before or after.[2] The difficulty is to recon-

---

[1] I am most grateful to Dr Gordon Campbell of the University of Leicester for reading this essay and offering valuable comments and suggestions.

[2] e.g., David Masson, *Life of John Milton*, 7 vols (1859–94), vol. 7, pp. 810–11, though only as a hypothesis, and with the possibility that Milton wrote it a year or two later; C. H. Firth, 'Milton as an Historian', reprinted in his *Essays, Historical and Literary*

cile its profound pessimism over England's prospects with the vigorous optimism of Milton's previous prose tracts and of the political writings that were so shortly to follow, from *The Tenure of Kings and Magistrates* onwards. How could Milton have pronounced so final a judgement on the failure of the victors in the Civil War when victory was so recent and the possibilities for the future still so open as they were in 1648, and for years afterwards? What purpose could Milton possibly have had in committing such a premature judgement to posterity, and how can it be squared with his own account of the chronology of his writings?

The reason why the date went unquestioned for so long is that, until the Harvard University Library acquired a manuscript of the Digression in 1926,[3] the only version of it known was a heavily edited one, published by Henry Brome in 1681 as *Mr John Miltons Character of the Long Parliament and Assembly of Divines in MDCXLI*. The hack who prepared it for the press suppressed the whole of the first two pages as they stand in the Harvard manuscript and he prefaced it with a note to the reader which linked the piece with Milton's own failure to recover money that he had lent on the public faith, plainly implying that Milton wrote it before he entered the Commonwealth's service in 1649. This editor may genuinely have thought so, on the basis of what he could gather of the Digression's references, but his knowledge of those times was clearly sketchy, since the title-page of the *Character* gets the date of the Westminster Assembly wrong by two years. He also tells the reader '*That this Character of Mr Miltons was a part of his History of Britain, and by him designed to be Printed: But out of tenderness to a Party . . . it was struck out for some harshness, being only such a Digression, as the History it self would not be discomposed by its omission*'.[4]

[3] Printed in *CP*, vol. 5, pp. 441–51, opposite the parallel text of *Mr. Miltons Character of the Long Parliament*. Hereafter the printed pamphlet is cited as the *Character* and the Harvard manuscript as the Digression, and in quotations obvious misprints in the one and mere slips in the other have been silently corrected. For the provenance and authenticity of the manuscript, see *CP*, vol. 5, pp. 406–8.

[4] *CP*, vol. 5, p. 440.

(Oxford, 1938), pp. 95–100; *Complete Prose Works of John Milton* (hereafter cited as *CP*), ed. D. M. Wolfe, 8 vols (New Haven, Conn., 1953–82), vol. 5, p. 433; W. R. Parker, *Milton: A Biography*, 2 vols (Oxford, 1968), vol. 1, p. 337; Christopher Hill, *Milton and the English Revolution* (London, 1977), p. 102 ('probably written in 1647–8').

Subsequent editors have taken him to mean that the Digression was an integral and continuous part of Milton's original work, written when he reached that point in book III of the *History* at which we now know it was to have been inserted. Considering his gaffe on the title-page and his butchery of Milton's text, this editor's statements, including those about Milton's financial troubles, should be treated with scepticism. But, to do him justice, he did not expressly say what later editors have taken as his sense. He states only that the Character was a part of the *History* and originally intended by Milton to be printed. So much can be accepted. Nothing in his preface is inconsistent, however, with the possibility that the Digression was an afterthought, composed later than books III and IV with the object of pointing the moral of certain parallels between the Britons' calamities and some particularly black phase through which Milton was living, but suppressed when its aptness as a tract for the times diminished.

That is the hypothesis advanced here. No reader of book III who was unaware of the Digression would suspect the excision of about six large pages (twelve in the Harvard manuscript); the continuity is seamless. There are clear signs of neat literary patchwork, however, at the beginning and end of the Digression. The whole piece is a large and awkward interruption of Milton's narrative, unparalleled elsewhere in the *History*. But the main evidence for assigning a later date to it is internal, and to that this essay is addressed.

That fine scholar David Masson had shrewd doubts about the integrity of the 1681 *Character*'s text,[5] and it is doubtful whether he or Sir Charles Firth would so readily have accepted it as contemporary with book III of the *History* if the Harvard manuscript had been known to them. Modern scholars have agreed, surely rightly, that the manuscript with its characteristic Miltonic spellings bears all the signs of authenticity. If its heading, which states where it was to have come in the *History*, is contemporary with the rest of it, it cannot be earlier than 1670, for it gives a page reference to the printed edition of that year, but it has been generally accepted as an early and exact copy of what Milton wrote or dictated, and so it is here.

[5] Masson, *Milton*, vol. 6, pp. 810–12.

If a historian could come fresh to the Digression, without any but internal evidence to help him date it, he would conclude from its content as a whole, but particularly from the two opening pages which the *Character* excised, that it was pronouncing a despondent retrospective judgement on the failure of all that had been attempted between 1640 and 1660. Despite its emphasis on the Long Parliament and the Assembly of Divines, he would not suppose it written in 1648. In a tone of painful acceptance of final defeat, it pronounces a harsh verdict on the political, military and religious leaders who have wasted the nation's great opportunity. The Parliament and the Assembly come in for particular criticism as the institutions in which the crucial wrong decisions were taken, or the right ones missed, but one senses a much longer perspective than the year 1648 afforded. *All* the efforts of the victors in the Civil Wars have foundered; the people themselves have become incapable of liberty. There is a strong affinity between the Digression and *The Readie and Easie Way to Establish a Free Commonwealth*, and the date here proposed for it is not long after the second version of that work, and quite soon after the Restoration; in other words, probably the second half of 1660.

Its very opening proclaims the magnitude and the tragic burden of Milton's theme. 'Because the gaining or loosing of libertie is the greatest change to better or to worse that may befall a nation under civil goverment', and is the touchstone of its potential for 'justice and civilitie', he proposes to recapitulate the reasons why the Britons, having been offered by the Romans' departure the fairest opportunity to secure their liberty, 'should let it pass through them as a cordial medcin through a dying man without the least effect of sence or natural vigor'.[6] He also proposes to inquire,

> since god after 12 ages and more had drawne so neare a parallel betweene their state and ours in the late commotions, why they who had the chiefe management therin having attain'd, though not so easilie, to a condition which had set before them civil government in all her formes, and giv'n them to bee masters of thir own choise, were not found able after so many years doeing

[6] *CP*, vol. 5, p. 441.

and undoeing to hitt so much as into any good and laudable way that might shew us hopes of a just and well amended commonwealth to come.[7]

It is obvious why the editor of the *Character* suppressed these opening pages. Any reader in 1681, or at any time after 1660, would have understood Milton to mean that England had had her golden chance of establishing her liberty when it was open to the victors in the Civil Wars to frame any government of their choice, especially after they had abolished the monarchy in 1649, but that they had missed it time and again. The implication was that the Restoration had been a huge calamity, and the admission of irreversible defeat and profound national failure grows more explicit as the Digression proceeds. The historical parallel was never as close as Milton pretended, but it was between the Britons' self-imposed subjection to the Saxons and England's willing resubmission to the yoke of monarchy. It would have been preposterous in 1648 to write of a final loss of liberty or to compare England to a dying man whose body could respond to no 'cordial medcin', but it would have been natural enough after the total collapse of the Commonwealth in the winter of 1659–60. 'The late commotions', and 'the late troubles' a few sentences later, were expressions commonly used after the Restoration to refer to the whole period of the Civil Wars and the Commonwealth,[8] and one need not suppose that Milton intended them otherwise. His allegation that the country's leaders had failed to lay the foundations of 'a just and well-amended commonwealth to come', 'after so many years doeing and undoeing', would have been incomprehensible in 1648, but all too telling after the many and drastic changes of government between 1649 and 1660.

If it was absurdly premature to pronounce final judgement on 'the gaining or loosing of libertie' in 1648, that is just how Milton did see the issue when he dictated the *Readie and Easie Way* in 1660, especially when he hazarded his life and his yet unwritten epics to bring out an enlarged edition within weeks of the Restora-

---

[7] ibid.

[8] For example, Sir William Dugdale's *A Short View of the Late Troubles* was published in 1681, and a translation of George Bate's *Elenchi motuum* was published in 1685 as *A Short Historical Account . . . of the Late Troubles in England.*

tion. The choice as he saw it was between 'the establishment of a free Commonwealth' and 'this noxious humor of returning to bondage'.[9] Faced with the massive tide of popular enthusiasm for recalling the King, he asked that 'If thir absolute determination be to enthrall us, before so long a Lent of Servitude, they may permitt us a little Shroving-time first, wherin to speak freely, and take our leaves of Libertie'.[10] He lamented

> That a nation should be so valorous and courageous to winn thir libertie in the field, and when they have wonn it, should be so heartless and unwise in thir counsels, as not to know how to use it, value it, what to do with it or with themselves; but after ten or twelve years prosperous warr and contestation with tyrannie,[11] basely and besottedly to run their necks again into the yoke which they have broken, and prostrate all the fruits of thir victorie for naught at the feet of the vanquishd . . . will be an ignomine if it befall us, that never yet befell any nation possessd of thir libertie.[12]

To such passages, and to the marvellous peroration to liberty with which the *Readie and Easie Way* closes,[13] the Digression sounds like a muted coda, but its theme is plainly related. It could not openly asperse the Restoration if the *History* was to get past the censor, but alert readers would not miss its import.

The superficial plausibility of the traditional date has rested mainly upon a supposed triple connection between Milton's personal financial hardship as a creditor of the State and the condemnation in both the Digression and the sonnet to Fairfax of 1648 of the Long Parliament's failure to honour debts upon the public faith. There is certainly some common ground between the sonnet's complaint that 'avarice and rapine share the land' and the Digression's excoriation of 'innumerable theeves in office'.[14] The Digression's accusations, however, are wider-

---

[9] *CP*, vol. 7, p. 407.

[10] ibid., pp. 408–9.

[11] Implying that the cause had prospered until about 1652–4: confirmation that in retrospect he regarded the Protectorate as a wrong turning.

[12] *CP*, vol. 7, p. 428.

[13] ibid., pp. 461–3.

[14] *CP*, vol. 5, p. 445.

ranging and more specific, and it will be shown later that, while some of them could credibly be assigned to 1648, others strongly suggest an experience that extended to at least the earlier 1650s. As for Milton's personal finances, there does not seem to be any real evidence apart from that of the egregious 1681 editor that he himself had lent heavily upon the public faith. Such difficulties as he experienced in drawing an income from the estate of his deceased Royalist father-in-law were resolved in March 1648, and according to Parker his only major financial worry came in 1650.[15] There probably is an autobiographical element in the complaints of financial oppression and fraud in both sonnet XV and the Digression, but it is natural that grievances of which he was keenly aware in 1648 should be voiced again in the more comprehensive indictment that he wrote later. There was certainly a widespread feeling by 1648 that too many agencies of the Long Parliament were oppressive, extortionate and corrupt.[16] But the Digression offers no hope of a remedy; 'Of those who swayd most in the late troubles', it says that 'they had armies, leaders and successes to thir wish, but to make use of so great advantages was not thir skill'.[17] Sonnet XV, by contrast, is a celebration of victory, and urges Fairfax to further action: 'O yet a nobler task awaits thy hand.' There is much still to put right, but Milton obviously has not yet despaired of the victors in the Civil Wars, any more than in the sonnet to Cromwell of 1652, with its similar call to action: 'yet much remaines/To conquer still; peace hath her victories/No less renownd then warr'. It is scarcely credible that he should have indulged in the defeatism

---

[15] Parker, *Milton*, vol. 1, pp. 397 ff. Milton's reference in *Defensio secunda* to his loss of income and to unjust financial exactions is vague and undated: *CP*, vol. 4, p. 627. Dr Gordon Campbell has pointed out to me that Milton suffered his most serious financial loss in 1660, when he failed to recover £2000 which he had saved from his Secretary's salary and invested in excise bonds: see Helen Darbishire (ed.), *Early Lives of Milton* (London, 1932), pp. 48, 78.

[16] See, for example, D. E. Underdown, *Pride's Purge* (Oxford, 1971), pp. 90–5, 97–9; J. S. Morrill, *The Revolt of the Provinces* (London, 1976), ch. 3, and his 'Mutiny and Discontent in English Provincial Armies', *Past and Present*, no. 56 (1972), pp. 48–74; Robert Ashton, 'From Cavalier to Roundhead Tyranny, 1642–9', in J. S. Morrill (ed.), *Reactions to the English Civil War, 1642–1649* (London, 1982), a book whose excellent bibliography contains reference to numerous relevant local studies (see esp. pp. 214, 218).

[17] *CP*, vol. 5, p. 443.

of the Digression either shortly before he wrote sonnet XV, which he probably did soon after Fairfax received the surrender of Colchester on 27 August 1648, or in the brief period between then and his embarkation on *The Tenure of Kings and Magistrates*. Commentators have naturally been troubled to explain how he could sink to the despair of the English people's capacity for liberty which the Digression expresses at any time between his vision in *Areopagitica* of 'a noble and puissant Nation rousing herself like a strong man after sleep, and shaking her invincible locks',[18] and his trumpet-call to it in the *Tenure* to shake off tyranny and advance to a heroic future. They should give up the attempt. It will be argued, first, that there was never a point in 1647–8 when Milton could have pronounced so final a verdict on the good old cause as the Digression does and, second, that the piece contains other indications of a much later date, besides those already cited.

A rapid sketch of the political prospects in 1647–8 can well begin with the New Model Army's defiance of the Parliament's attempt to disband it in June 1647.[19] That averted a threat, which had been growing since early in the year, that the Presbyterian politicians who had lately dominated Parliament would join with the strongly Presbyterian corporation of the City of London, and possibly with the Scots, too, to reinstate Charles I on terms that would have seemed to Milton a betrayal of the cause for which the Civil War had been fought. An attempt at counter-revolution by London's citizens and militia forces was scotched when the Army marched into the capital in August. But the Army was not anti-monarchical – very few people were, as yet – and just before it marched on London it offered its own terms to the King. These terms were not what Milton would ideally have wished, but he must have greatly preferred them to those previously held forth by the Parliament, because they proposed a wide liberty of

---

[18] *CP*, vol. 2, p. 558.

[19] For fuller accounts of what follows, see S. R. Gardiner, *History of the Great Civil War*, 3 vols (1886–91), chs 50–2; Underdown, *Pride's Purge*, chs 4–6; Valerie Pearl, 'London's Counter-Revolution', in G. E. Aylmer (ed.), *The Interregnum* (London, 1972); Mark A. Kishlansky, *The Rise of the New Model Army* (Cambridge, 1979), chs 7–8; Mark A. Kishlansky, 'Ideology and Politics in the Parliamentary Armies, 1645–9', in Morrill (ed.), *Reactions*.

conscience in place of rigid Presbyterian uniformity, and some quite radical constitutional reforms. Charles, however, created a stalemate in the autumn by trying to play off the Army's terms against the Parliament's. Thereby he sowed a new but rapidly growing distrust of himself in the Army, especially among some radical junior officers and the 'agitators' elected by the soldiery. The Levellers, hitherto a civilian movement, tried hard to infiltrate and indoctrinate the Army during the summer and autumn, but though they found much support for manhood suffrage they failed to persuade the General Council of the Army to give up its quest for a peace settlement through Parliament and to impose one based instead on an Agreement of the People signed by all free subjects. The Levellers made much less impact on the Army than they had hoped, but they were dividing it at a dangerous time.[20] In mid-November, Fairfax and Cromwell and their fellow-commanders managed to close its ranks and restore its discipline just in time; for Charles had just fled from its custody to the Isle of Wight, where he soon signed the secret Engagement with commissioners from Scotland which was to launch the second Civil War in 1648.

Christopher Hill has suggested a close affinity with Leveller sentiments in the Digression,[21] but there are no specifically Leveller ideas in it, nor did Milton ever share with the Levellers much more than the common coin of contemporary republican thought. Milton's natural sympathies in 1648 must have been with the Army and its commanders, as the sonnet to Fairfax confirms, for the Army, with its morale and solidarity seasonably restored, was the necessary bulwark against a Royalist–Scottish victory and the loss of all that had been fought for. But the signs were hopeful to such as Milton early in 1648. As soon as it became evident that Charles was bent on renewing war rather than treating for peace, Parliament broke off negotiations with

[20] Army politics and Levellers' influences thereon are examined in detail by the present writer in his forthcoming *Soldiers and Statesmen: The General Council of the Army and Its Debates.*

[21] 'The Yale editors show how close Milton was to Leveller sentiments in the *Digression*,' writes Hill in *Milton and the English Revolution*, p. 102. But none of his six citations from *CP*, vol. 2, suggests any connection between the Levellers and the Digression; and French Fogle, whom he cites from *CP*, vol. 5, links them only with heavy qualifications (and in my view mistakenly).

him on 17 January, through the Vote of No Addresses. The Army's reactions held out still more exciting hopes. A great body of officers met at Windsor at about the end of April to seek the Lord in prayer before they took the field against the first Royalist insurrections, and they concluded that it was their duty, if they came home alive, 'to call Charles Stuart, that man of blood, to an account' for warring against the Lord's cause and people.[22] It is not credible that Milton should, as French Fogle suggests, have written the Digression and its avowal of total defeat in the late spring of 1648,[23] when Parliament had temporarily renounced the temptation to seek a reactionary peace with the King, and the Army was preparing to engage the common enemy with every prospect of success.

Through the summer the news was all of victory. Cromwell crushed the insurgents in south Wales during May and June; Fairfax dealt with the only other dangerous risings, in Kent and Essex, and put the remaining southern Royalists under siege in Colchester, which surrendered late in August upon the news that Cromwell had annihilated the invading Scottish army at Preston and points south. These triumphs did not entirely clear the sky for radicals like Milton, for even before they were won Parliament was under heavy pressure from the City and from the gentry in many counties to reopen negotiations with Charles, and the majority of its Members would still have come to terms with him if they could – terms that must have struck Milton as squandering the fruits of victory. Commissioners of the two Houses did renew negotiations with him in the so-called Treaty of Newport, which proceeded on the Isle of Wight from just after mid-September until the Army interrupted it on 6 December. With Fairfax plainly unhappy about violating either the King's or Parliament's authority, with Cromwell lingering over the siege of Pontefract in November and still wrestling with his own conscience as to whether providence required the Army's assistance, and with public feeling running powerfully in favour of an agreement with

---

[22] William Allen, *A Faithful Memorial* (1659), reprinted in *Somers Tracts*, *VI*, pp. 500–1; Gardiner, *Great Civil War*, vol. 3, pp. 363–7. My *Soldiers and Statesmen* will present evidence that (*pace* Gardiner and others) agitators were probably not present at Windsor, and a caveat against accepting Allen's account too uncritically.

[23] *CP*, vol. 5, p. 433.

the King, so that his would-be prosecutors walked in danger of their lives,[24] it is likely enough that Milton went through a period of despondency while the Treaty was in progress.

If one were forced to consider a date in 1648 for the Digression, it would have to fall within that eleven-week period. But besides the internal pointers to a later date, and besides the difficulty of reconciling its tone of utter defeat with that of sonnet XV so shortly before and that of the *Tenure* so soon after, one would have to accept Milton as a political weathercock who could not even tell which way the wind was blowing. It was no time for a final verdict of failure upon those who had been hailed as the country's deliverers.[25] Fairfax was out of his depth, admittedly, and Cromwell was agonizing as to whether military intervention was justified yet,[26] but the Army was never likely to stand by while an unsafe peace was concluded and, from early November, Ireton was mustering it for decisive action. On 18 November the General Council of Officers approved a crucial Remonstrance, demanding that Parliament should bring the King to trial for his life and set an early date for its own dissolution. When Parliament pressed on with the Treaty, the Army acted – not to dissolve it, as it first intended, but upon the insistence of the Members who opposed the Treaty to purge it instead of all who were seeking to close the deal with Charles. Pride's Purge, inaugurated on 6 December, removed all fears of a sell-out peace, and despite Cromwell's initial hesitations the hard core of the Rump and the Army moved forward inexorably from then on to the trial and execution of the King.[27]

Before further considering the internal clues in the Digression, there is Milton's own testimony about his writing of the *History* to reckon with. The apparent sense of the relevant passage in *Defensio secunda* is that he turned to it only after he had written the *Tenure*, and that he had completed four books when the kingdom was turned into a republic and he was taken into the

[24] Underdown, *Pride's Purge*, p. 115.

[25] *CP*, vol. 5, p. 449: 'Thus they who but of late were extolld as great deliverers. . . .'

[26] *Writings and Speeches of Oliver Cromwell*, ed. W. C. Abbott, 4 vols (Cambridge, Mass., 1937–47), vol. 1, pp. 676–8, 696–9.

[27] Underdown, *Pride's Purge*, pp. 117–200.

employment of the Council of State.[28] His chronology is vague; strictly, he placed these events in the wrong order, for his appointment was voted on 13 March 1649, whereas it was not until 19 May that the Rump passed the Act which formally constituted England 'a commonwealth and free state', and even the Act abolishing the office of king became law just *after* his entry into the public service.[29] Biographers have naturally been chary of believing that Milton wrote four books of the *History* in less than two months, but there is no reason to doubt his word that he had finished the four by mid-March. The interesting question is when he began book III, partly because of the allusion to contemporary events in its introduction, and partly because he intended the Digression to be inserted early in that book. It would have begun on the twelfth page of book III in the first edition, if Milton had not decided to omit it.[30] Assuming, as one surely must, that he did not write it earlier than the preceding pages in book III, an approximate date for the latter would determine the earliest possible date for the Digression. This particular line of inquiry points to probabilities rather than certainties, but they strengthen the case for redating.

There is no certainty as to when Milton began writing the *History*, but Parker makes a plausible case for 'some time in 1648'.[31] The combined length of books III and IV exceeds that of the *Tenure* by just over half; uniformly printed in the Columbia edition, they fill ninety-four pages, compared with the *Tenure*'s fifty-nine. Milton is commonly reckoned to have written the *Tenure* from start to finish in two or three weeks, and he later wrote *Eikonoklastes*, which fills 247 pages in the same edition, between March and October 1649, though the task went against

---

[28] *CP*, vol. 4, pp. 627–8.

[29] C. H. Firth and R. S. Rait (eds), *Acts and Ordinances of the Interregnum, 1642–1660* (hereafter cited as *A & O*), 3 vols (London, 1911), vol. 2, pp. 18–19, 122.

[30] 'To com in Lib. 3 page 110. after these words. [from one misery to another]'. There is no need to doubt the authenticity of this direction, for the Digression fits more appropriately at this point than at any other, and much better than where Thomas Birch placed it in the 1738 edition. The Columbia editor altered '110' to '114' to tally with his own edition: *Works of John Milton*, ed. F. A. Patterson and others, 20 vols (New York, 1931–40), vol. 18, p. 317.

[31] Parker, *Milton*, vol. 2, p. 939.

the grain and he had all his routine duties as Secretary for Foreign Tongues to perform.[32] Considering that he had no other commitments besides the *Tenure* when he wrote books I–IV of the *History*, that he was drawing heavily on the reading that he had done in 1639–41, and that he himself gives the impression in *Defensio secunda* that he was forging ahead rapidly until the time when he was called away to his public duties, it is perfectly possible that he began book III after Pride's Purge, or at least when the Army's intervention was plainly imminent. He opened it with a strong implication that great changes were afoot:

> This third Book having to tell of accidents as various and exemplary, as the intermission or change of Government hath any where brought forth, may deserve attention more than common, and repay it with like benefit to them who can judiciously read: considering especially that the late civil broils had cast us into a condition not much unlike to what the *Britans* then were in, when the imperial jurisdiction departing hence left them to sway of thir own Councils; which times by comparing seriously with these later, and that confused Anarchy with this intereign, we may be able from two such remarkable turns of State, producing like events among us, to raise a knowledg of our selves both great and weighty. . . .[33]

Firth surmised that Milton wrote this 'about the close of 1647 or the beginning of 1648',[34] but even without the persuasive evidence, marshalled by Parker, that he probably began the whole work in 1648 the allusions in the passage quoted are much more apt to December 1648 or January 1649. The Vote of No Addresses opened up some prospect of a real 'change of government' in January 1648, but only a faint and fleeting one, because the overwhelming weight of parliamentary and public opinion was still in favour of an ultimate monarchical settlement. On 28 April the Commons voted that they would not alter 'the fundamental Government of the Kingdom, by King, Lords and Commons', and under strong public pressure, especially from London, both Houses committed themselves to resuming nego-

---

[32] ibid., vol. 1, p. 361; vol. 2, p. 939.

[33] *CP*, vol. 5, pp. 129–30.

[34] Firth, 'Milton as an Historian', p. 64.

tiations with Charles, long before the Scots and the Royalists were defeated in the field.[35] In the view of most of the political nation England was still a monarchy, Charles was still King, and the only problem was to make him accept such modifications of the ancient constitution as would minimize his power to do further mischief. There was no real casting-off of the monarchy (the parallel to 'imperial jurisdiction'), no 'interreign' or interregnum, until the Army's intervention, signalled by the Remonstrance of 18 November and executed in Pride's Purge, enabled a radical minority to bring Charles's reign to a violent end. By December, Milton really could write of 'intermission or change of government', and his reference to 'the late civil broils' may well have embraced Pride's Purge as well as the two Civil Wars. His account of how the fifth-century Britons had failed through pusillanimity, corruption and lack of vision to rise to their great opportunity was probably meant as a cautionary tale to those of his contemporaries who through false fears and effete traditionalism were failing to grasp theirs. His heavy emphasis on incursions by the Scots suggests that Hamilton's invasion which had ended at Preston was fresh in his mind. So probably were the Presbyterian politicians who had pursued the Treaty of Newport and the Presbyterian preachers who were opposing the trial of the King, when he cited Gildas on the Britons' 'hatred of truth':

> Lies and falsities, and such as could best invent them, were only in request. Evil was embrac'd for good, wickedness honour'd and esteem'd as virtue. And this quality thir valour had, against a foren Enemy to be ever backward and heartless; to civil broils eager and prompt. In matters of Government, and the search of truth, weak and shallow, in falshood and wicked deeds pregnant and industrious.[36]

It is instructive to compare this with what Cromwell wrote of the Newport treaty in a letter to Colonel Robert Hammond on 25 November:

> Dost thou not think this fear of the Levellers . . . had caused some to rake up corruption; to find it lawful to make this ruining

---

[35] Underdown, *Pride's Purge*, pp. 93–104; Ian Gentles, 'The Struggle for London in the Second Civil War', *Historical Journal*, vol. 26 (1983), pp. 277–305.

[36] *CP*, vol. 5, pp. 139–40.

hypocritical agreement, on one part? Hath not this biased even some good men? I will not say, their fear will come upon them; but if it do, they will themselves bring it upon themselves. Have not some of our friends, by their passive principle . . . been occasioned to overlook what is just and honest, and [to] think the people of God may have as much or more good the one way [i.e. the Treaty] than the other? Good by this Man, against whom the Lord hath witnessed?[37]

Milton's strictures on the Britons, in a narrative whose contemporary relevance he himself underlined, is also in tune with the opening of the *Tenure* and its emphasis on the *moral* nature of the choice between tyranny and liberty.

But being slaves within doors, no wonder that they strive so much to have the public State conformably govern'd to the inward vitious rule, by which they govern themselves. For indeed none can love freedom heartilie, but good men; the rest love not freedom, but licence; which never hath more scope or more indulgence then under Tyrants. Hence it is that Tyrants are not oft offended, nor stand much in doubt of bad men, as being all naturally servile. . . . Consequentlie neither doe bad men hate Tyrants. . . .[38]

If the opening pages of book III and their allusions are correctly read here – and it is a case of probability rather than of certainty – they must have been written only weeks before the *Tenure*. That surely would put a date in 1648 for the Digression out of the question. The hopeful course of events that was soon to inspire the *Tenure* was, if this dating is correct, already in train when Milton wrote the passage into which the subsequent Digression was to be inserted. The Digression pronounced judgement on those who had formerly been extolled as the country's deliverers, lamenting that 'the heroic wisdom which is requir'd surmounted far the principles of narrow politicians: what wonder then if they sunke as those unfortunate Britans before them, entangl'd and oppress'd with things too hard and generous above thir straine and temper'.[39] In the Digression, they had not only proved

---

[37] *Writings and Speeches of Cromwell*, vol. 1, pp. 698–9.

[38] *CP*, vol. 3, pp. 190–1.

[39] *CP*, vol. 5, p. 451.

unfit to dispense liberty but had also unfitted the people to receive it. The *Tenure*, in total contrast, expressed a firm confidence that God would incline the people

> to heark'n rather with erected minds to the voice of our Supreme Magistracy, calling us to liberty and the flourishing deeds of a reformed Common-wealth; with this hope that as God was heretofore angry with the Jews who rejected him and his forme of Government to choose a King, so that he will bless us . . . who reject a King to make him onely our leader and supreme governour in the conformity as neer as may be of his own ancient goverment; if we have at least but so much worth in us to entertaine the sense of our future happiness, and the courage to receave what God voutsafes us: wherein we have the honour to precede other Nations who are now labouring to be our followers.[40]

Milton looked forward to unborn generations, 'Who perhaps in future ages, if they prove not too degenerat, will look up with honour, and aspire toward these exemplary, and matchless deeds of thir Ancestors, as to the highest top of thir civil glory and emulation'.[41]

It is not only the opening pages of the Digression, suppressed in the *Character*, which convey an impression of greater finality and a longer perspective than a standpoint in 1648 would afford. It was not lack of strength or courage in war that had wasted the fair opportunities for liberty, wrote Milton, but 'other causes equally belonging both to ruler, priest, and people':

> which as they brought those antient natives to miserie and ruin by libertie which rightly us'd might have made them happie, so brought they these of late after many labours, much blood-shed, & vast expence, to ridiculous frustration, in whom the like defects, the like miscarriages notariouslie appear'd, with vices not less hatefull or inexcusable; nor less inforcing, whosoever shall write thir storie, to revive those antient complaints of Gildas as deservedly on these lately as on those his times.[42]

Later in the piece he castigates those false deliverers who 'had a people wholy at thir devotion', but 'by so discharging thir trust

[40] ibid., vol. 3, p. 236.

[41] ibid., vol. 3, pp. 237–8.

[42] ibid., vol. 5, p. 443.

as wee see, did not onely weak'n and unfitt themselves to be dispencers of what libertie they pretended, but unfitted also the people, now growne worse & more disordinate, to receave or to digest anie libertie at all'.[43] The wholesale ascription of vice and corruption to the victors in the Civil Wars, found in both these passages, would have been offensively inappropriate in 1648, when Fairfax was Lord General and Cromwell, the younger Vane, Bradshaw and other heroes of Milton were still rising to the peaks of their careers, but understandable enough in 1660, after the Commonwealth had foundered amid the quarrels between the remnants of both Parliament and Army, and Fairfax had helped to bring back the King.

That bitter sentence about the faults of ruler, priest and people which had brought the nation 'after many labours, much bloodshed, & vast expence, to ridiculous frustration' would have been utterly extravagant and unjust if written in 1648, but it takes on a full load of meaning when it is assigned to the same context as parallel passages in the *Readie and Easie Way*. There Milton exclaims that

> for this extoll'd and magnifi'd nation, regardless both of honour wonn or deliverances voutsaf't from heaven, to fall back or rather to creep back so poorly as it seems the multitude would to thir once abjur'd and detested thraldom of Kingship, to be our selves the slanderers of our own just and religious deeds, though don by some to covetous and ambitious ends . . . to betray a just and noble cause for the mixture of bad men who have ill manag'd and abus'd it . . . not only argues a strange degenerate contagion suddenly spread among us fitted and prepar'd for new slaverie, but will render us a scorn and derision to all our neighbours.[44]

He wrings his hands over the shame of

> making vain and viler then dirt the blood of so many thousand faithfull and valiant *English* men, who left us in this libertie, bought with thir lives; losing by a strange after game of folly, all the battels we have wonn . . . all the treasure we have spent . . . treading back again with lost labour all our happie steps in the progress of reformation; and most pittifully depriving our selves

---

[43] ibid., vol. 5, p. 449.

[44] ibid., vol. 7, p. 422.

the instant fruition of that free government which we have so dearly purchasd, a free Commonwealth.[45]

There is a particular reason, among these several parallels in tone and content, for ascribing the Digression to the same period as the *Readie and Easie Way*. It admits that the people themselves have become incapable of liberty, so disordered have they grown under their unworthy new governors. That process surely required a longer time-span than the couple of years between the first Civil War and the second. Milton's verdict is all but incomprehensible if ascribed to 1648, but fully understandable in the context of 1660. One constant factor in his earlier tracts from *Of Reformation* through *Areopagitica* and the *Tenure* to the whole series of vindications which he wrote as the Commonwealth's servant from 1649 to 1654 is his faith in the English people's readiness to rise to the call of right leadership. It is only in his last political writings of 1659–60 that he accepts that 'the multitude' prefer slavery to liberty.[46] In the *Readie and Easie Way* he strains to suspend disbelief in their unworthiness, but in the Digression it is too late. Thraldom cannot be explicitly identified with monarchy if the *History* is to be published, but the message is plain enough.

Defenders of the traditional date may object that the Digression specifically mentions only the Long Parliament among the five that sat during the Interregnum, says nothing about the abolition of the monarchy, and expresses grievances about sequestrators, committee-men and the dishonouring of the public faith that chime closely with the last three lines of the sonnet to Fairfax. But if Milton had alluded directly to the regicide in the only way that he honestly could he would probably have caused the whole *History* to be refused a licence. Writing in 1660, his very good reason for mentioning only one Parliament was that since the summer of 1659 he himself had repudiated the legitimacy of every government, and hence of every Parliament, between the expulsion of the Rump in 1653 and its reinstatement six years later.[47] The *Readie and Easie Way* also gave an account

---

[45] ibid., vol. 7, pp. 423–4.

[46] e.g., ibid., vol. 7, pp. 422, 442, 455, 481–2.

[47] ibid., vol. 7, pp. 274, 324–5, 364–6; A. Woolrych, 'Milton and Cromwell: "A Short

of the Long Parliament, but of no other; indeed, it brushed aside the intervening regimes between April 1653 and May 1659 as 'those unhappie interruptions, which God hath remov'd'.[48] It was the Commons of the Long Parliament, with the secluded Members restored, who between 22 February and 16 March 1660 set in train the measures that led inexorably to the Restoration. A further possible motive for not raking into what had gone wrong since 1649, any more specifically than in the general reflections that he borrowed from Gildas, is that Milton had taken the wages and sung the praises of both the Rump and the Protectorate, and was now concerned with diagnosing the failure of a whole nation rather than looking for particular scapegoats.

As for the charges of extortion, oppression and nest-feathering by the agents of the Long Parliament, and their accord with the closing lines of sonnet XV, it has been conceded that Milton's personal experiences doubtless helped to fuel them. But all the Digression's accusations have more cogency and a wider reference if they can be read as applying to the whole period of the Rump's rule, and in some cases beyond it, rather than merely to that of the unpurged Long Parliament. The Members of the latter had certainly been accused of abusing their power for the sake of profit, but the proportion of placemen to the total of active MPs was considerably higher in the Rump. The pickings were richer after 1648 and, though the charges of self-enrichment were generally exaggerated and too indiscriminate, suspicion and resentment seem to have intensified during the Rump's rule.[49]

---

[48] *CP*, vol. 7, p. 421: the account, fuller in the second edition, begins on p. 409. It is far more favourable than that in the Digression and uninhibited in vindicating the Rump's rejection of monarchy, but Milton was still trying at great personal risk to rally the remaining supporters of the good old cause, whereas by the time he dictated the Digression the cause was lost.

[49] See the magisterial discussion of corruption in the whole period 1649–60 in G. E. Aylmer, *The State's Servants: the Civil Service of the English Republic, 1649–1660* (London, 1973), pp. 139–67.

---

but Scandalous Night of Interruption"?', in M. Lieb and J. T. Shawcross (eds), *Achievements of the Left Hand: Essays on the Prose of John Milton* (Amherst, Mass., 1974), pp. 185–218. My conviction that Milton intended to repudiate the Protectorate, and understood 'a single person' to apply to a Protector as well as to a king, is unshaken by Robert T. Fallon, 'Milton in the Anarchy, 1659–1660: A Question of Consistency', *Studies in English Literature, 1500–1900*, vol. 21 (1981), pp. 123–46.

More specifically, the Digression speaks of 'all the wealth of the church, not better imploy'd, but swallow'd up into a private gulfe'.[50] That had not yet happened in 1648. The sale of the bishops' lands had been launched by a series of ordinances beginning in October 1646 but, though more than two-thirds of those lands had been sold or contracted for by April 1648, measures to remove obstructions to their sale were still being passed in November of that year and in June 1649.[51] The bishops' lands, however, were the lesser part of the Church's wealth. The sale of the lands of deans and chapters, which exceeded them in value by more than half, was not even begun until well into 1649, and enough remained unsold five years later to be used as security for further government borrowing.[52]

Mention of borrowing and of the sale of confiscated lands takes us to what Milton may have meant when he wrote that 'that faith which ought to bee kept as sacred and inviolable as any thing holy, the public faith, after infinite summs receiv'd . . . was not ere long asham'd to confess bankrupt'.[53] It is certain that in 1648 he already resented the Long Parliament's treatment of its creditors, since sonnet XV demands that 'Public Faith' be 'cleard from the shamefull brand/Of Public Fraud'. But the more sweeping allegations in the Digression suggest a longer experience, especially the charge that 'Some who had bin calld from shops & warehouses without other merit, to sit in supreme councel[54] & committies, as thir breeding was, fell to hucster the common-wealth'.[55] Those last three words surely refer to the

[50] *CP*, vol. 5, p. 445.

[51] For a useful index to and summary of these enactments, see *A & O*, vol. 3, pp. 18–19; and, for the best modern study, Ian Gentles, 'The Sales of Bishops' Lands in the English Revolution, 1646–1660', *English Historical Review*, vol. 95 (1980), pp. 573–96.

[52] *A & O*, vol. 3, pp. xcvi, 45–6; H. J. Habakkuk, 'Public Finance and the Sale of Confiscated Property during the Interregnum', *Economic History Review*, 2nd ser., vol. 15 (1962–3), pp. 70–88, esp. p. 87.

[53] *CP*, vol. 5, p. 445.

[54] Singular in the manuscript; amended to 'councels' in the *Character*. But Milton may well have been referring to the Council of State, which only came into existence in 1649. On the other hand, he may have meant Parliament, which he addressed as 'Supream Councel' in *A Treatise of Civil Power*: *CP*, vol. 7, p. 242. Either way (*pace* the Yale edition) the singular is probably what he intended.

[55] *CP*, vol. 5, p. 445. For the proliferation of revenue committees and agencies, both before and after 1648, see Aylmer, *State's Servants*, pp. 24–9.

selling-off of the State's public assets, particularly the vast quantities of land that it confiscated. By the end of the first Civil War the Long Parliament had borrowed far more 'on the public faith' than it could hope to repay out of current taxation, which was chronically overstretched by the needs of the armed forces and remained so throughout the Interregnum. After the abolition of the monarchy, the crown lands were put up for sale and the proceeds earmarked for the Army's arrears of pay. Most other lands that were put on the market, however, especially those sold from 1649 onwards, which included all the deans' and chapters' lands and those confiscated from hundreds of individual Royalists, were made primarily available to creditors of the State who were prepared to 'double', which meant that if they lent as much again as they were owed, they acquired bills which gave them security for the doubled sum on the properties offered in the various acts of sale. Thus a creditor who had lent £100, and now advanced a further £100, would receive a bill securing his loans on £200 worth of such property. Moreover, such bills could be used at face value for the purchase of the lands so offered, and the better-off creditors naturally took the chance to take repayment in the form of real estate, since even doubled bills could only be cashed at a heavy discount. They circulated at fourteen or fifteen shillings in the pound in 1649–50, but then and later *un*doubled bills commonly commanded less than ten shillings, and often very much less.[56]

The sale of confiscated lands and the associated procedure of doubling were in their infancy in 1648. As has been said, the bishops' lands had been on sale since late in 1646, but their total estimated value was reckoned at £676,387, less than half of one year's annual revenue from customs, excise, direct taxation and compositions for 'delinquency' in the late 1640s. By comparison, the Rump from 1649 onwards proceeded to dispose of £1,170,000 worth of deans' and chapters' lands, £1,434,000 worth of crown lands, fee-farm rents to the tune of £816,834, and estates confiscated by successive Acts from individual Royalists to a total value of £1,224,916.[57] In other words, nearly seven times as

[56] Habakkuk, 'Public Finance', pp. 81–2 and passim. To Habakkuk's magisterial article these paragraphs are deeply indebted.

[57] ibid., p. 87.

much public or confiscated land was put on the market *after* 1648 as had been offered by that year. To talk of 'huckstering the Commonwealth' in 1648 would have been extravagant hyperbole, but any time after the early 1650s the shaft would have struck home. By then, of course, the word 'commonwealth' itself had acquired an added resonance.

As for Milton's charge of bankruptcy, the State never confessed itself bankrupt or repudiated its debts in the way that the Spanish monarchy had done several times since the late sixteenth century, but there was never a chance in the 1650s that it would be able to honour its debts at par. Professor Habakkuk, rebutting later claims by republican politicians that the Commonwealth had been fully solvent when Cromwell expelled the Rump in 1653, writes that

> taking government debt as a whole, it is doubtful whether there has ever been in English history a regime whose obligations circulated at so heavy a discount. To say that the Long Parliament was solvent when it was dismissed is, therefore, highly misleading. It would be nearer the truth to say that it was an undischarged bankrupt.[58]

In the later 1650s the government's credit grew worse rather than better, so once more an accusation that would have been premature in 1648 has much greater force from the standpoint of 1660.

So it is with the reproach that the Members 'would continually finde such worke, as should keepe them from ever being brought to the terrible stand of laying downe thir authoritie for lack of new buisness, or not drawing it out to any length of time though upon the necessarie ruin of a whole nation'.[59] Admittedly there were many in 1648 who thought that the Long Parliament had sat too long, even though a large minority of Members, the 'Recruiters', had only been elected since 1645-7. But discontent with its longevity became very much stronger in the early 1650s, when the Rump showed little inclination to keep its initial promise to make way for a new Parliament as soon as possible. Milton naturally had nothing to say against its long sitting in the *Tenure* or *Eikonoklastes* or any other work that he wrote as the

[58] ibid., p. 82.

[59] *CP*, vol. 5, pp. 445, 447.

servant of its Council of State, but he did condemn it in his apostrophe to Cromwell in *Defensio secunda*:

> When you saw delays being contrived and every man more attentive to his private interest than to that of the state, when you saw the people complaining that they had been deluded of their hopes and circumvented by the power of the few, you put an end to the domination of these few men, since they, although so often warned, had refused to do so.[60]

Five years after writing that, Milton greeted the restored Rump as 'the authors and best patrons of religious and civil libertie, that ever these Ilands brought forth';[61] and, after Monck had in February 1660 restored the Members 'secluded' by Pride's Purge, Milton had hailed the reconstituted Commons of the Long Parliament as 'our old Patriots, the first Assertours of our religious and civil rights'.[62] He went on to propose, rather desperately, that they should be erected into a perpetual Grand Council of the Commonwealth.[63] But he was grasping at straws by then, and the subsequent conduct of the House in paving the way for the Restoration and attempting to restore the Presbyterian church settlement must have completed Milton's disillusion with it.

That last attempt may explain why the Digression, in dealing with the wasted opportunities for a reformation of religion, placed so much emphasis on the Westminster Assembly of Divines. The authority accorded to that body, and the partnership in which the Long Parliament joined with it, impressed Milton in retrospect as the cardinal errors from which the whole subsequent failure to secure religious liberty, as he understood it, derived. But there were special reasons why the Assembly and all its works should be fresh in his mind in 1660. Between Monck's readmission of the secluded Members on 22 February and the Long Parliament's self-dissolution on 16 March, the Commons tried to reinstate the Presbyterian ecclesiastical settlement of 1645–6. It re-established the Westminster Con-

---

[60] ibid., vol. 4, p. 671.

[61] ibid., vol. 7, p. 274.

[62] ibid., vol. 7, p. 356.

[63] ibid., vol. 7, pp. 368 ff.

fession as the public profession of the Church of England, it ordered that the Solemn League and Covenant be read out in every church in the land, and it resumed from the 1640s the task of dividing the counties into classical presbyteries. It passed a new Act for Approbation and Admission of Ministers, naming strongly Presbyterian clergy to approve candidates for livings, and it reinforced the payment of tithes.[64] It was not clear until after the election of the Cavalier Parliament in 1661 and the failure of the Savoy Conference that the resurgent Presbyterians would be disappointed in their hopes of a religious settlement that would accommodate themselves but exclude all Puritan radicals.

There are other indications that Milton was contemplating the lost cause of religious liberty from a longer perspective than that of 1648. Much of this part of the Digression carries the same message, in close summary, as the twin tracts of 1659, *A Treatise of Civil Power* and *The Likeliest Means to Remove Hirelings*. He had of course arrived earlier at his conviction that the State should renounce all authority over matters ecclesiastical, but was it so clear-cut in 1648? The Digression is particularly critical of divines who combined comfortable headships of Oxford and Cambridge colleges with parish livings in which they did not reside.[65] There were several examples of such by 1648, but considerably more in the 1650s.

Perhaps the crux of this section, however, is what Milton referred to when he wrote:

> And well did thir disciples manifest themselves to be no better principl'd then their teachers, trusted with committiships and other gainfull offices, upon their commendations for zealous, &, as they stick'd not to term them, godlie men, but executing thir places more like childern of the devil. . . . So that between them the teachers and these the disciples, there hath not bin a more ignominious and mortal wound to faith, to pietie, nor more cause of blaspheming giv'n to the enemies of god and truth since the first preaching of reformation.[66]

---

[64] Godfrey Davies, *The Restoration of Charles II* (Oxford/San Marino, Calif., 1954), pp. 297–8; *CP*, vol. 7, p. 194; *A & O*, vol. 3, pp. cviii–cix.

[65] *CP*, vol. 5, p. 447; cf. p. 455, n. 22.

[66] ibid., vol. 5, pp. 447, 449.

The teachers were evidently the Assembly divines, but who were their disciples? Milton probably meant to include the various committees and commissions which in the wake of the Assembly had acted as agencies in filling the livings and supporting the clergy in the state church, both in its nominally Presbyterian form in the later 1640s and in the broader, looser establishment of the 1650s. Among these were the Committee for Plundered Ministers, which from modest beginnings at the end of 1642 grew into 'a board of ecclesiastical commissioners for a completely disestablished and a partially disendowed English Church',[67] and which functioned until the Rump fell in 1653; the Trustees for Maintenance of Ministers, set up in June 1649 and active all through the next decade; and the two Commissions for the Propagation of the Gospel, one for the four northern English counties and the other for Wales, which the Rump set up for three years in March 1650. But Milton may have had particularly in mind the Commissioners for Approbation of Public Preachers, better known as the Triers, which Cromwell and his council established by ordinance in March 1654, and the much more narrowly Presbyterian commissioners set up by the restored Long Parliament's Act for Approbation and Admission of Ministers in March 1660, though the latter had very little time in which to act. It was a proposal by some Independent ministers to the Rump's Committee for the Propagation of the Gospel early in 1652, a proposal which in principle foreshadowed the Cromwellian system of Triers and Ejectors, that prompted Milton's sonnets to Cromwell and Vane, with their common plea to save religion from the 'secular chaines' of the civil magistrate's authority. In *Defensio secunda*, Milton strenuously urged Cromwell as Protector to renounce all such authority, and Cromwell's very different view of the responsibilities of a Christian ruler probably did more than anything else to alienate him from the Protectorate.[68]

Relating to such matters the printed *Character* has two short

---

[67] W. A. Shaw, *A History of the English Church during the Civil Wars and under the Commonwealth*, 2 vols (1900), vol. 2, p. 195. Shaw's ch. 14 is still the best authority on the organizations mentioned in this paragraph.

[68] *CP*, vol. 4, p. 678, and vol. 7, pp. 30–45; Woolrych, 'Milton and Cromwell', pp. 191–7.

passages that are not in the manuscript Digression. Both are probably inauthentic. The first, after a sentence common to both versions which condemns the Assembly divines for persuading the civil magistrate to support clerical authority with physical compulsion, adds: 'Distrusting the Virtue of their own Spiritual weapons, which were given them, if they be rightly called, with full warrant of sufficiency to pull down all thoughts and imaginations that exalt themselves against God'.[69] This is probably an editorial interpolation of 1681, for it is difficult to imagine Milton allowing the clergy even spiritual weapons of such potency over the individual conscience. The other addition is found six lines later. To the charge of 'setting up a Spiritual Tyranny by a Secular power, to the advancing of their own Authority above the Magistrate,' it adds: 'whom they would have made their Executioner, to punish Church-Delinquencies, whereof Civil Laws have no cognizance'.[70] Such had been the high Presbyterians' intentions, but the civil government's practice never matched them. After Pride's Purge there was never any serious thought of enforcing ecclesiastical censures with secular sanctions, and the Rump's Act of 27 September 1650, which repealed all penalties for not attending parochial worship, ended the possibility of any coercive ecclesiastical jurisdiction. Under the Protectorate the written constitution confirmed the subject's immunity from any church discipline that he did not voluntarily accept. Milton *could* have written the words last quoted, but they read more like an editorial gloss.[71]

No single one of the particular allusions considered so far is conclusive, though cumulatively they go far to indicate a considerably later date than 1648. But the strongest reason for proposing 1660, not long after Charles II had been welcomed home with overwhelming public enthusiasm, lies in the sheer finality of the Digression's verdict upon 'the late commotions'. The

---

[69] *CP*, vol. 5, p. 446.

[70] ibid.

[71] Blair Worden's brilliant exposure of the extent to which a late seventeenth-century editor, probably Toland, mangled Edmund Ludlow's memoirs should put scholars on their guard against any text of the period for which there is not a manuscript original or the author's known approval: see Edmund Ludlow, *A Voyce from the Watch Tower*, ed. A. B. Worden, Camden 4th Series, XXI (1978), introduction.

opportunity to win liberty has been lost decisively, despite pro-
longed efforts and not a few changes of regime ('so many years
doeing and undoeing'). What Milton has strained agonizingly in
the *Readie and Easie Way* to avert has come to pass; the little
shroving-time is over, and he is indeed taking his leave of liberty,
since the people have been rendered incapable of receiving it.

> For stories teach us that libertie sought out of season in a corrupt
> and degenerate age brought Rome it self into further slaverie.
> For libertie hath a sharp and double edge fitt onelie to be handl'd
> by just and vertuous men, to bad and dissolute it becomes a
> mischief unwieldie in thir own hands.[72]

The valedictory tone, so clear in that passage and in the opening
pages, can be heard just as plainly towards the close, where
Milton can see a ray of hope only in a distant future:

> For the sunn, which wee want ripens witts as well as fruits; and
> as wine and oyle are imported to us from abroad, so must ripe
> understanding and many civil vertues bee imported into our
> minds from forren writings & examples of best ages: wee shall
> else miscarry still and com short in the attempt of any great
> enterprise. Hence did thir victories prove as fruitless as thir
> losses dangerous, and left them still conquering under the same
> grievances that men suffer conquerd, which was indeed unlikely
> to goe otherwise unless, men more then vulgar, bred up, as few
> of them were, in the knowledge of Ancient and illustrious deeds,
> invincible against money, and vaine titles, impartial to friend-
> ships and relations had conducted thir affaires.[73]

What, Milton finally asks, could 'the confluence of all these errors,
mischiefs & misdemeanours' be expected to bring forth but what
befell the Britons, 'confusion in the end'?[74]

He plainly *meant* the end, at least for his time. The very
finality of his judgement on all the heirs of Parliament's initial
victory makes it virtually impossible to entertain any intermediate
date between 1648 and 1660. One can rule out the years from the
Tenure to the first *Defensio* in which he vaunted the young

[72] *CP*, vol. 7, p. 449.

[73] ibid., vol. 7, p. 451.

[74] ibid., vol. 7, p. 451.

Commonwealth against its enemies on all sides. He was probably less happy with it by 1652, the year of his sonnets to Cromwell and Vane, but he could not have written wholesale condemnations of its leaders while Cromwell, Vane, Bradshaw and others whom he admired were still at the height of their careers. We know little of what he thought of Barebone's Parliament, but its five-month session can hardly have plunged him into such despair as the Digression breathes. Not long after Cromwell became Protector Milton was rejoicing 'that I was born at a time in the history of my country when her citizens, with pre-eminent virtue and nobility and steadfastness surpassing all the glory of their ancestors, invoked the Lord, followed his manifest guidance, and after accomplishing the most heroic and exemplary achievements since the foundation of the world, freed the state from grievous tyranny and the church from unworthy servitude'.[75] Thereafter he gradually became somewhat disillusioned with the Protectorate, especially after Richard Cromwell succeeded Oliver. He wrote to Moses Wall in the spring of 1659, complaining (according to Wall's reply, which alone survives) 'of the Non-progressency of the nation, and of its retrograde Motion of late in Liberty and Spiritual Truths'.[76] But that sounds a long way from the Digression's admission of total defeat, and he addressed *A Treatise of Civil Power* to Richard's Parliament with a hopeful preface.[77] When the republic was restored shortly afterwards, he saluted the reinstated Rump with enthusiasm in the preface to the *Likeliest Means*.[78] He did not concern himself much with public affairs until the Army's second interruption of the Rump in October awoke him to the fact that the Commonwealth's very survival was in jeopardy. *A Letter to a Friend* expresses his shock.[79] But the tenor of that piece and of all his political tracts during the next few months, including both versions of the *Readie and Easie Way*, was not resignation to

[75] ibid., vol. 4, pp. 548–9.

[76] J. Milton French (ed.), *The Life Records of John Milton*, 5 vols (New Brunswick, NJ, 1949–58), vol. 2, pp. 267–9; *CP*, vol. 7, pp. 83–4.

[77] ibid., vol. 7, pp. 242–4.

[78] ibid., vol. 7, pp. 274–5.

[79] ibid., vol. 7, pp. 324–9.

defeat, as in the Digression, but an urgent quest for expedients that might yet stave off the return to monarchical servitude for which the misguided multitude was clamouring.

French Fogle perceived how contrary the tone of the Digression was to that of the other prose works from *Of Reformation* to *Defensio secunda*, but how closely it accorded with that of the *Readie and Easie Way*.[80] Is not the likeliest explanation that the two works stand very close in time, the revised *Readie and Easie Way* dictated shortly before the Restoration and the Digression shortly after? The suggested dating raises no problems as to why he suppressed the Digression when the *History* was first published in 1670, for there is no reason to doubt that the decision was his own. By the middle of 1662 fourteen regicides and other pillars of the Commonwealth had suffered the fearful death accorded to traitors. Most of them had been known to him in the years when he had attended the Council of State; the latest victim was Vane, who had not even been one of Charles I's judges. Of the company whom he had celebrated by name in *Defensio secunda*, Cromwell's and Bradshaw's rotting corpses had been disinterred and hung up at Tyburn, Whalley was a refugee in New England, and Lambert had had his death sentence commuted to life imprisonment, which lasted twenty-three years. Overton, Milton's special friend, was imprisoned almost continuously from 1660 to 1668, and Desborough alternated between prison and exile for almost as long. Fleetwood, Pickering and Sydenham were debarred from public employment for life. These and so many other upholders of the Commonwealth and Protectorate had paid or were paying the price that Milton must soon have become disinclined to publish the harsh censures that he set down in the first bitterness of defeat. It is difficult to believe that he composed the Digression after their sufferings had begun in earnest, still less after he himself had come uncomfortably close to sharing their fate.[81] Even the Presbyterian clergy had a claim on his charity, not only because they came under the proscription of the totally intolerant Act of Uniformity

[80] ibid., vol. 5, pp. 424–5.

[81] Parker, *Milton*, pp. 567–76; Godfrey Davies, 'Milton in 1660', *Huntington Library Quarterly*, vol. 18 (1955), pp. 351–63.

but also because many braved persecution to continue their ministry in despite of the Clarendon Code. If he could have foreseen that a hack would publish a doctored version of his Digression a few years after his death, when what was left of the good old cause was at its lowest ebb, would he have wished to destroy it? It represented only a passing phase in his thought. One would not want a word of his to be lost, but one can take pleasure that his last specific contribution to the cause of liberty, in the tract *Of True Religion* of 1673, was for all its limitations so much more positive. For the infinitely richer and more deeply pondered reflections of his experience of defeat, one reads between the lines of his great epics.

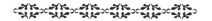

THE PRINCIPAL
PUBLISHED WRITINGS OF
C. V. WEDGWOOD

compiled by

Jaqueline Hope-Wallace

This list does not include numerous reviews in newspapers and periodicals, introductions to works by other authors, or paperback editions and reprints.

1935 *Strafford, 1593–1641*. London: Jonathan Cape. 366pp

1938 *The Thirty Years War*. London: Jonathan Cape. 544pp

1939 *Oliver Cromwell*. Great Lives series. London: Duckworth. 144pp
   The Emperor Charles V. Translated from the German of Karl Brandi. London: Jonathan Cape. 645pp

1944 *William the Silent*. London: Jonathan Cape. Also New Haven, Conn.: Yale University Press. 256pp
   Battlefields in Britain. Britain in Pictures series. London: Collins. 47pp

1946 *Velvet Studies: Essays on Historical and Other Subjects*. London: Jonathan Cape. 159pp
   Wilhelm den Tyste. Swedish translation of *William the Silent*. Stockholm: LUJS. 395pp
   Auto-da-Fé. Translation of *Die Blendung* by Elias Canetti. London: Jonathan Cape. 464pp

1947 *Willem de Zwijger*. Dutch translation of *William the Silent*. Amsterdam/Brussels: Elsevier. 285pp

1947   *Guillaume le Taciturne.* French translation of *William the Silent.* Paris: Editions Tallandier. 347pp

1949   *Richelieu and the French Monarchy.* Teach Yourself History series. London: Hodder and Stoughton for English University Press. 204pp
'King Charles I: The Case for the Execution'. In the Historical Association's *Charles I.* London: George Philip. 7pp

1950   *Seventeenth Century English Literature.* Home University Library series. London: Oxford University Press. 186pp
Reading History. A National Book League reader's guide. London: Cambridge University Press. 14pp

1951   *The Last of the Radicals: The Life of Josiah C. Wedgwood, MP.* London: Jonathan Cape. 252pp

1952   *Montrose.* Brief Lives series. London: Collins. 158pp

1953   'Some Contemporary Accounts of the Great Civil War' (a lecture given 1948). In *Transactions of the Royal Society of Literature.* London: Oxford University Press. 15pp

1954   *King Charles I and the Protestant Cause.* From *Proceedings of the Huguenot Society of London*, vol. 19, no. 2. London: Butler & Tanner. 27pp

1955   *The Great Rebellion: The King's Peace, 1637–1641.* London: Collins. 510pp. Also New York: Macmillan. 500pp
'Comedy in the Reign of Charles I'. In *Studies in Social History: A Tribute to G. M. Trevelyan.* London: Longmans Green. 28pp
Edward Gibbon. London: British Council. 36pp

1956 *Literature and the Historian*. Presidential address to the English Association. London: English Association. 15pp

1957 *The Common Man in the Great Civil War*. The Fairclough Lecture in the University of Leicester. Leicester: Leicester University Press. 23pp
The Sense of the Past. The Leslie Stephen Lecture. London: Cambridge University Press. 27pp

1958 *The Great Rebellion: The King's War, 1641–1647*. London: Collins. 703pp

1959 *The King's War*. New York: Macmillan. 701pp

1960 *Truth and Opinion: Historical Essays*. London: Collins. 254pp. Also New York: Macmillan. 250pp
Poetry and Politics under the Stuarts. The Clark Lectures of 1958. Cambridge: Cambridge University Press. 220pp
'The Covenanters in the First Civil War'. In *Scottish Historical Review*, vol. 39, no. 127. 15pp
'Good King Charles's Golden Days'. In *The Restoration of the Stuarts: Blessing or Disaster?* Washington, DC: Folger Shakespeare Library. 25pp

1961 *Thomas Wentworth, First Earl of Strafford, 1598–1641: A Revaluation*. London: Jonathan Cape. 415pp
The Thirty Years War. New York: Doubleday. 520pp
'The Scientists and the English Civil War'. In *The Logic of Personal Knowledge: Essays Presented to Michael Polanyi*. London: Routledge & Kegan Paul. 11pp

1963 *History and Hope: The Foundation Lecture, Birkbeck College*. London: Birkbeck College. 14pp
Thomas Wentworth, Earl of Strafford. New York: Macmillan. 400pp

1964 *The Trial of Charles I*. London: Collins. 253pp
A Coffin for King Charles. New York: Macmillan. 255pp

1964 'The Close of an Epoch'. In *Shakespeare's World*, ed. James Sutherland and Joel Hurstfield. London: Edward Arnold. 19pp
La Guerra dei Trent' Anni. Italian translation of *The Thirty Years War.* Varese: dall'Oglio. 537pp

1965 'The Divisions Harden'. In *The Reformation Crisis*, ed. Joel Hurstfield. London: Edward Arnold. 12pp

1966 'Shakespeare between Two Wars'. In *Shakespeare Celebrated*, lectures delivered at the Folger Shakespeare Library, Washington, DC. New York: Cornell University Press. 30pp

1967 *Der Dreissigjährige Krieg.* German translation of *The Thirty Years War.* Munich: Paul List Verlag. 517pp
Literature as Background Evidence. From *Mosaic: A Journal for the Comparative Study of Literature and Ideas.* Manitoba: University of Manitoba Press. 6pp
The World of Rubens, 1577–1640. New York: Time-Life. 192pp

1968 *Tod dem König: Der Prozess gegen Karl I.* German translation of *The Trial of Charles I.* Munich: Paul List Verlag. 276pp

1969 *Milton and His World.* London: Lutterworth Press. 48pp
A Sense of the Past. New York: Macmillan. 158pp

1970 *Wege der Mächtigen.* German translation of *William the Silent, Richelieu and the French Monarchy* and *Oliver Cromwell.* Munich: Paul List Verlag. 552pp
Oliver Cromwell and the Elizabethan Inheritance. The first J. E. Neale Lecture in English History. London: Jonathan Cape. 23pp

1973 *Oliver Cromwell.* Revised and augmented edition. London: Duckworth. 127pp

1975 *The Political Career of Peter Paul Rubens.* The Walter Neurath Memorial Lecture, Birkbeck College, London. London: Thames & Hudson. 63pp

1978 *The English Civil War in Perspective.* The first Sophia Lecture, University of Newcastle upon Tyne. Newcastle: University of Newcastle upon Tyne. 12pp

1984 *The Spoils of Time: A Short History of the World up to 1550.* London: Collins. 399pp

1985 *The Spoils of Time: A World History from the Dawn of Civilization through the Early Renaissance.* New York: Doubleday. 353pp